MATH GAMES & ACTIVITIES

Vol. 2, A Toolbox of Duplicating Designs for Middle and Upper Grade Elementary School Teachers

Paul Shoecraft

Math Games and Activities Vol. 2
ISBN 0-86651-331-0
(previously ISBN 0-941530-02-7)
DS01722

Math Games and Activities Vol. 1 and Vol. 2 Set
ISBN 0-86651-332-9
(previously ISBN 0-941530-00-0)
DS01723

9 10 11 12 13 14 - MA - 02 01 00 99 98

DALE
SEYMOUR
PUBLICATIONS
P.O. BOX 10888
PALO ALTO, CA 94303

Acknowledgments

For much of the contents of this book I am in debt to other people, some of whose names I have forgotten, some of whose names are mentioned in the bibliography, and some of whose names are given below.

Teachers:

Neil Cox and Lynne Messenger of the Western Australian schools for classroom testing the problem solving material associated with **Motley Crab Adder and mates.** Jonathan Knaupp of Arizona State University for **BT Numo** and **Colored Squares.** And Thomas Palumbo of the Philadelphia schools for the bulk of the material on math / language arts.

Publishers:

Addison-Wesley Publishing Company, Inc. for permission to reprint the small fraction cakes from the instructor's manual to **BASIC MATHEMATICS: A BLUEPRINT FOR SUCCESS.** The American National Metric Council for permission to reprint the metric table on page 073. The Arizona Silver Belt for the use of their typesetting equipment. The National Council of Teachers of Mathematics for permission to reprint **PMDAS** from **THE ARITHMETIC TEACHER** and **Tessellating with Quadrilaterals** and **Tessellating with Triangles** from **THE MATHEMATICS TEACHER.** And the publishers of **SCIENCE TEACHER** for permission to reprint **Metric Proverbs.**

Artists:

Joy Scott of Churchlands College of Advanced Education for her contributions to the non-technical art. Mike Quaintance of Bailey, Colorado for the cover photograph.

To my wife, Lynne, my one true love, who ignored the fact that I had to ignore her more than I wanted to to write this.

TABLE
OF
CONTENTS

RESOURCE PAGE DIRECTORY

Resource	Location		Description					
	Directions	Duplicating design(s)	Manipulative	Game	Activity	Worksheet	Instructional aid	General Supplies
Addition (Combining) Dominoes	01	61-63		●				
Algo Onslaught	01	42-53		●				
Algo Onslaught Cards (Operations)	02	44-49					●	
Algo Onslaught Scorecard	04	53					●	
Angles	04	252			●			
Angle Wedges	04	251	●					
Applying the Pythagorean Theorem	08	220				●		
Areas of Polygons	08	211-212				●		
Areas of Similar Figures on the Sides of Right Triangles	09	213-214				●		
Areas of Triangles	09	210				●		
Bank It or Clear It	010	107-108		●				

Resource	Location		Description					
	Directions	Duplicating design(s)	Manipulative	Game	Activity	Worksheet	Instructional aid	General Supplies
Beat the Clock	012	20-21		●				
Blank Cards	012	9-13						●
Blank Dominoes	013	14						●
Blank Gameboards	013	6-8						●
Bowl-a-Fact	013	28		●				
BT Numo	015	110-126		●				
Calcuprose	016	171			●			
Centimeter and Millimeter Rulers	016	224						●
Chain	016	35-36				●		
Circular Dot Paper	017	175-176					●	
Clap Your Hands	017	162				●		
Cliff Hanger	017	16-19		●				
Codes and Docs	018	26-27				●		
Colored Squares	018	105		●				
Compass Worksheet	020	253					●	
Congruent Squares	022	37-38			●			
Count the Diagonals	022	271				●		
Count the Dots	023	269				●		
Count the Intersection points	024	272				●		
Count the Regions	025	270				●		
Creating Creatures	026	168				●		
Cube Cutout	027	178			●			

Resource	Location		Description					
	Directions	Duplicating design(s)	Manipulative	Game	Activity	Worksheet	Instructional aid	General Supplies
Deci-Builder or Deci-Buster	027	109		●				
Decimal Rummy	028	127-133		●				
Discard	030	29-34		●				
Division (Separating Neatly) Rummy	031	74-80		●				
Diviso	032	22-24		●				
Dot Paper	033	209					●	
Elementary Statistics	033	267-268			●			
English Measurement Array Cards	034	222			●			
Equivalent Fraction Array Cards	035	106			●			
Equivalent Fraction Dominoes	036	95-97		●				
Equivalent Fraction Rummy	037	98-104		●				
Equivalent Square Roots	038	219				●		
Estimating Probabilities	038	261-266			●			
Experience Roster	039	1						●
Fast Fill-ins	040	166				●		
FDP Showdown	040	148-158		●				
FDP Showdown Cards (Operations)	041	150-154					●	
FDP Showdown Scorecard	043	158					●	

Resource	Location		Description					
	Directions	Duplicating design(s)	Manipulative	Game	Activity	Worksheet	Instructional aid	General Supplies
Figure-Four Rabbit Trap	043	172			●			
Food Find	044	169				●		
Fraction Cakes	045	83-94	●					
Fraction-Decimal-Percent Array Cards	055	137			●			
Fraction-Decimal-Percent Dominoes	056	134-136		●				
Fraction-Decimal-Percent Rummy	056	138-144		●				
Geo Pieces	056	173-174	●					
Geopolis	058	184-185		●				
Grid Paper	059	208					●	
Grids and Drigs	060	39-40				●		
Helicopter Cutouts	060	260					●	
Homonym Hunt	062	160				●		
Leapfrog	062	274			●			
Lengths of Curves	063	216				●		
Lengths of Edges of Squares	063	217				●		
Lengths of Segments	064	218				●		
Line Designs	064	190-197			●			
Make-a-Whole	067	82		●				
McDonald's Hamburgers Worksheet	067	81				●		

Resource	Location		Description					
	Direc-tions	Dupli-cating design(s)	Manip-ulative	Game	Acti-vity	Work-sheet	Instruc-tional aid	General Supplies
Metric Array Cards	068	227-228			●			
Metric Calipers	070	225						●
Metric Conversion Concentration	070	231-232		●				
Metric Mastery	071	240-250		●				
Metric Prefix Con-centration	071	229-230		●				
Metric Proverbs	072	235				●		
Metric Reference Sheet	073	223					●	
Metrics Makes for Tens	074	226			●			
Mirror Symmetry	074	188-189, 198-200			●			
Missing Letter Problem Solving	076	167				●		
Mixed Facts Array Cards	076	25			●			
Motley and Mates	077	60					●	
Motley Crab Adder	077	54					●	
Multiplication (Com-bining Neatly) Dominoes	080	64-66		●				
Perimeters of Polygons	081	221				●		
Place Value Words	081	159				●		
PMDAS	081	170			●			
Qwazy Qwilt	082	215			●			

Resource Page Directory, Continued

Resource	Location		Description					
	Directions	Duplicating design(s)	Manipulative	Game	Activity	Worksheet	Instructional aid	General Supplies
Regular Dodecahedron Cutout	082	180			●			
Regular Icosahedron Cutout	082	181			●			
Regular Octahedron Cutout	082	179			●			
Regular Tetrahedron Cutout	083	177			●			
Rotational Symmetry	083	202-203				●		
Rotational Symmetry Cutouts	084	201			●			
Sir Crab Multiplier	084	56					●	
Slide Symmetry	085	205				●		
Slide Symmetry Cutouts	086	204			●			
Space Race	086	236-239		●				
Spinners	087	2-5		●				●
Subtraction (Separating) Rummy	088	67-73		●				
Sum Vowels	088	161				●		
Tessellating with Quadrilaterals	088	207			●			
Tessellating with Triangles	089	206			●			
The Great Legalizer	089	58					●	
The Impeccable Twin Dividers	090	57					●	

Resource	Location		Description					
	Directions	Duplicating design(s)	Manipulative	Game	Activity	Worksheet	Instructional aid	General Supplies
The Magnificent Equalizer	091	59					●	
The Scruffy Twin Subtractors	093	55					●	
The Word for Today Is S.E.A.	094	164				●		
Three Vowels	095	163				●		
Tower Puzzle	095	273			●			
Traceable Houses	095	187				●		
Traceable Networks	096	186				●		
Trees	098	165				●		
Tunnel	098	145-146	●					
Verifying Probabilities	0100	254-259			●			
Vertices, Faces, and Edges	0101	182-183				●		
What Am I?	0102	233-234			●			

INTRODUCTION

Description

    MATH GAMES & ACTIVITIES is a two-volume resource for teaching mathematics in the elementary school. The first volume is for grades K-5, the second for grades 4-9. In that this is the second volume, what is said in what follows is about this volume in particular.

    MATH GAMES & ACTIVITIES is essentially two things: One, it is a resource for teachers who like to teach, who like to say to students things like "Do this or that," "Look at this or that," "Think about this or that," who like to say these sorts of things more than things like "Turn to page blah-blah-blah and do the 'odd' exercises." In this regard, it contains nearly 125 "ideas" on how to enhance one's teaching of mathematics. Two, it is a resource which attempts to account for the fact that however easily an idea might be communicated, and however much a teacher might want to implement it, that to implement it typically requires the production of materials, a time consuming and energy draining enterprise, particularly in relation to being responsible for 20 or more students in one's professional life and being responsive to friends and family in one's personal life. Thus in addition to the ideas, it contains well over 250 duplicating designs with which to easily and inexpensively implement the ideas.

Organization

    To obtain an overview of the resource provided by **MATH GAMES & ACTIVITIES**, begin by skimming through the **Resource Page Directory** beginning on page v I I. In doing so, note that the ideas listed there are listed in alphabetical order in both the directory and in the front matter immediately following the directory, that the ideas are categorized in terms of

        ✔ manipulatives

        ✔ games

        ✔ activities

        ✔ worksheets

✔ instructional aids

✔ general supplies

and that the ideas are located in the front matter and among the duplicating designs by two sets of page numbers, the first having to do with the whereabouts of the directions for the ideas, the second with the whereabouts of the duplicating designs for the ideas. (The page numbers for the directions are preceded with a zero to distinguish them from the page numbers for the duplicating designs.)

Then pick a topic from the **Table of Contents** and "browse" through the duplicating designs the topic directs you to. As you do so, think about how the duplicating designs are probably used. Then turn to the **Resource Page Directory** again and locate the page numbers of the directions for the duplicating designs and read some of the directions. Chances are that what you read will be very much like what you thought you would read.

Finally, turn to the **Index** beginning on page 317 and note the way it categorizes the duplicating designs and directs you to other material in **MATH GAMES & ACTIVITIES** which touches on the same topic.

Throughout, note the shading and the guides along the edges of some of the pages of the book to facilitate leafing through the book.

Use

In using **MATH GAMES & ACTIVITIES**, the key consideration is always what you want to make from the duplicating designs in it. This determines the sort of equipment you will need to bring to bear on them.

> If you want to make transparencies of them, simply adjoin them one at a time to a piece of transparency film and run them and the film through a Thermofax machine.

> If you want to make single copies of them, simply Xerox them.

> If you want to make single copies of them, but you want the copies colored, backed, and / or laminated, Xerox them and see to the coloring, backing, and / or laminating of the copies as you perhaps watch your favorite television program.

> If you want to make multiple copies of them, make ditto masters for them using a Thermofax machine and

make the copies from the ditto masters using a ditto machine.

If you want to make multiple copies of them, but you want the copies colored, backed, and / or laminated, make the copies as already mentioned and have your class or a parent group help with the coloring, backing, and / or laminating of them.

If you want to make multiple copies of them on poster board so as to not have to back them, cut stencils for them using a Thermofax machine and print from the stencils directly onto poster board using a Gestetner duplicator. (Some schools have reprographic centers which will do this for you and will even "cut along the solid or dotted lines" for you.)

Note that all that is ever done with the duplicating designs is copy them. Thus they should last indefinitely for any number of different uses.

Another thing to consider in using **MATH GAMES & ACTIVITIES** is the cost of the supplies involved, the paper, poster board*, paste, crayons, transparency film, and laminating film. Note, however, that the cost is easily reconciled by comparing it to what really costs in education, the buildings, buses, utilities, and most of all, the services of maintenance and custodial persons, teachers, counselors, and administrators, none of which or whom, in themselves, teach anyone anything. Thus the thing to keep in mind if worried about the cost of supplies is that they are part of the "delivery" system, that they, along with what we say to students and have them do or read, are what all the buildings, buses, utilities . . . are there for, to have students learn. This is not to mean that we should be wasteful of supplies, but rather that we should never be so watchful of them to where we reduce our effectiveness in the classroom to where what is spent on buildings, buses, utilities . . . is largely wasted.

*A cost-free alternative to poster board for backing purposes is empty cereal boxes, a resource students can supply in abundance.

A man unusually committed to life in all things observed a hill of ants in a farmer's field. Looking up, he saw the farmer headed toward the ants with his plow. The man thought, "If only I were an ant, I could tell the ants of their peril that they might move out of the way of the farmer's plow." So he became an ant.

CONTENTS

Manipulatives

MATH GAMES & ACTIVITIES contains duplicating designs for the following manipulative materials:

- ✔ angle wedges

- ✔ fraction cakes

- ✔ geo pieces

In addition, it contains games, worksheets, and suggestions with which to direct their use as given under the headings in the front matter for the manipulative materials.

If your classroom is not equipped with these manipulative materials, or is not equipped with them in sufficient amounts, you can make reasonable facsimilies of them from the duplicating designs for such. To this end, you would make suitable numbers of copies of the duplicating designs and have your class or a parent group color and back the copies and afterwards cut them out. If you have them laminate them before cutting them out, the manipulative materials you end up with will be nearly as attractive and long lasting as those made of wood or plastic.

If your classroom is already equipped with sufficient quantities of the above mentioned manipulative materials, then, instead of making more of them, you could make copies of the duplicating designs for them, and with the copies make task cards or flannel board materials with which to direct the use of the manipulative materials. You could also make transparencies of them, and with the transparencies make materials for directing the use of the manipulative materials with an overhead projector.

As to why we teach with manipulative materials, the reasons are many and varied:

They hold students' interest.

They allow for the development of a vocabulary

common to both teacher and students.

They provide for individual differences with respect to ways of approaching a problem.

They permit verification of results.

But the most important reason for teaching with manipulative materials is that they give meaning to mathematics in that they are the "something else" by which it is understood. To see this, note that nothing can be understood solely in terms of itself. To illustrate, if you were to look up **ancespitorian** in the dictionary and were to find the following, you still would not know what it meant.

an·ces·pi·tor·i·an (ăn-sĕs′ pĭ-tôr′ē-ən) **adj.** what is said about something which is ancespitorian

At best, all you would know about **ancespitorian** is how to spell and pronounce it. To know what it meant, you would have to know how it was like or unlike something else which you already knew about.

Incidentally, if you try to find **ancespitorian** in a dictionary, you will not find it. It is just a made-up word with which to make a point. Still, if you wanted to make it into a word, a good definition for it would be "anything which can be 'spelled' and pronounced but which is not understood." With this definition, one could then say that the objective of teaching with manipulative materials is to achieve in students' minds more than a mere ancespitorian knowledge of mathematics.

Games

MATH GAMES & ACTIVITIES contains instructions and duplicating designs for nearly 30 games -- card games, dominoe games, board games, and other types of games, the titles and locations of which are given in the **Resource Page Directory**. Some of them, like **Discard** or **Diviso**, are renderings of games you might already know. But some of them, notably, **Algo Onslaught** and **FDP Showdown**, are new to this publication. If copies of the duplicating designs for the games are colored, backed, and laminated, the result is educational materials with striking appeal and marked durability. In viewing the games, note that nearly all of them can be adapted to a variety of topics.

As to the purpose of the games in **MATH GAMES & ACTIVITIES**, they are used primarily to focus attention on key concepts such as base and place value and to motivate drill and practice on things like the basic facts which need to be committed to memory. In this regard, the games can be used to stock a math lab or an interest center, in which case only one or two copies of the games wanted would be needed. However, a more exciting use of the games is to use them to actually teach with, in which case 10 or more copies of the games wanted would be needed, enough for an entire class. To experiment with the feasibility of teaching with games, begin with a game like **Bowl-a-Fact** with a consumable gameboard. In this way your investment in the experiment in terms of supplies used and time spent will be negligible.

Some things to consider in using the games in **MATH GAMES & ACTIVITIES** are the following:

Before reading the directions for a game, have a good look at the duplicating designs for the game. In this way you will probably anticipate many of the directions for the game and will therefore be reading the directions more for confirmation than for understanding.

Note that there is no right or wrong way to play the games. Rather, there are effective ways to play them, ways in which to meet the educational objectives of the games. Thus the directions for the games can be altered to focus on other objectives or to make the games easier or harder for certain students.

Note that the directions for the board games with "finish" spaces on the gameboards do not specify how one gets to the finish spaces. Does one just have to get there? Or does one have to get there exactly? Thus a ruling needs to be made on this. One such rule is the "bounce back" rule, a rule that if a player moves into a finish space but still has some moves to go, the player must "bounce back" the number of moves to go. To illustrate, if a player were three moves away from the finish space and rolled a 5, the player would move 1, 2, 3 and into the finish space, and then 4, 5 and right back to where the player started from.

To facilitate the making of classroom quantities of a game, make multiple copies of the game on poster board as explained under **Use**. In this way you can even save on the coloring in by choosing a suitable color of poster board.

When making copies of the duplicating designs for a game, always make a few more copies than you intend to make up and store them in a folder. In this way you can easily replace a game which gets lost or destroyed.

To make one of the gameboards where the gameboard

is in two pieces, lay next to one another the edges of the gameboard which are to be joined and tape along the edges with a piece of clear tape as long as the gameboard is wide. (See Figure 1.)

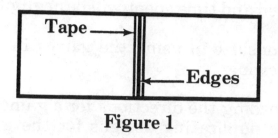

Figure 1

To strengthen the join on the gameboard, use two pieces of tape, one piece on top of the other. Note: Do **not** tape on both sides of the gameboard. If you do, the gameboard will not fold easily. Thus if you want the gameboard to fold in (so as to protect the playing surface of the gameboard while the gameboard is in storage), tape on the playing surface of the gameboard. If you want the gameboard to fold out (so as to draw attention to the gameboard while the gameboard is on display as in a clear plastic bag), tape on the back of the gameboard.

Keep the time which you personally invest in the making of games to a minimum. In this way, you won't mind so much if some of them get lost or scruffed up. What is wanted are games which are valued but not to the point of reluctance at letting students play them and perhaps take them home with them.

Always store the games flat rather than rolled. If you roll them, you can hardly ever get them to lie really flat again.

Make copies of the directions for the games as well and mount the copies on poster board or on the games themselves that they might be included with the games. (Note that the directions for the games are in boldface type to make them easy to read if copied.)

Make transparencies of the duplicating designs for a game that the rules for the game might be easily explained to an entire class with an overhead projector.

As a follow-up to the card games and dominoe games, use transparencies of the cards and dominoes with an overhead projector as flash cards for a class.

Involve students as much as possible in the making of the games. In doing so, you not only end up with lots of games, but with students who have a personal investment in them and therefore an interest in playing them.

As to why one should consider teaching with games, note the following: In addition to simulating real world uses of mathematics and making pleasurable the drill and practice necessary for mastery, they

✔ motivate

✔ build confidence

✔ improve attitudes

✔ encourage peer teaching

✔ allow for individual differences

The latter point is most apparent with games, because the deciding factor in who wins in games is typically luck, not ability. For this reason, games can even be used in tutoring situations without diminishing the interest value of the games, because the one being tutored is just as likely to win as the one doing the tutoring.

Activities

Activities refer to many things in education: students manipulating objects, working busily at their desks, or moving about the classroom or outdoors. The main ingredient is involvement -- involvement of the students in what they are doing. Another ingredient is the direction, either written or spoken, the students are given. Examples from **MATH GAMES & ACTIVITIES** of direction which leads to involvement would be the line designs, the probability experiments, the exercises on making symmetric figures, the activities on estimating and verifying probabilities, and the puzzles and array cards on various topics.

Worksheets

The worksheets in **MATH GAMES & ACTIVITIES** are on a variety of topics: the number facts, whole number arithmetic, square roots, symmetry, traceability, and others. They appear in forms known to be appealing to students: puzzles, word games, counting exercises, tracing exercises, pattern searches, and others. They are distinguished from the **activities** in **MATH GAMES & ACTIVITIES** in that they are self-contained.

A reason for using the worksheets in **MATH GAMES & ACTIVITIES** is to obtain a written record of what students know, a record which can be used for evaluation purposes. If duplicated as transparencies or in classroom quantities, they can be used to direct a lesson or series of lessons. They can also be used to stock an interest center or to make individual assignments.

Instructional Aids

In general, an instructional aid differs from an activity or a worksheet in that an instructional aid is something a teacher uses instead of something students use. It is used to get the attention of students or to give students something they can react to in response to teacher directives.

The instructional aids in **MATH GAMES & ACTIVITIES** are of the sort a teacher would use in presenting a lesson to an entire class or in diagnosing strengths and weaknesses in relation to whole numbers, fractions, decimals, and percents. An example of the former would be a lesson on the geometry of the circle with the circular dot paper. An example of the latter the use of the **Algo Onslaught cards** and **Algo Onslaught scorecard** or the **FDP Showdown cards** and **FDP Showdown scorecard** with the games of **Algo Onslaught** and **FDP Showdown**, respectively.

General Supplies

The general supplies in **MATH GAMES & ACTIVITIES** consist of things like rulers and spinners which have use in general, the **Experience Roster** which is for record keeping, and blank cards, dominoes, and gameboards which can be used to add to the games and activities in **MATH GAMES & ACTIVITIES**. Their location is given in the **Resource Page Directory**.

DIRECTIONS IN ALPHABETICAL ORDER

Addition (Combining) Dominoes

A game for two to four on addition as combining.

Materials:

One set of Addition (Combining) Dominoes (pp. 61-63) per group.

Directions:

The same as for Equivalent Fraction Dominoes.

Some examples of some matches for the Addition (Combining) Dominoes would be the "1 + 3" and "one plus three," the "3 + 5" and "five combined with three," and the "two combined with four" and the picture of two combined with four.

Algo Onslaught

A game for two to four on whole number arithmetic.

The significance of Algo Onslaught is twofold: First, it reviews the entire subject of whole number arithmetic. Second, it diagnoses deficiencies in the subject by subskill. The manner in which it diagnoses is explained under Algo Onslaught Cards and Algo Onslaught Scorecard.

Materials:

For each group, a die, an Algo Onslaught gameboard (pp. 42-43), a deck of Algo Onslaught cards (Operations, pp. 44-49, Chance, pp. 50-51), and an Algo Onslaught key (p. 52). For each player, a marker, an Algo Onslaught scorecard (p. 53), and a pen or pencil and some scrap paper.

Directions:

In preparation, the Algo Onslaught cards are shuffled and placed on the gameboard in the spaces provided.

To begin, the players put their markers on the Start square on the gameboard. Then each player rolls the die. The player rolling the highest number plays first. The play rotates clockwise.

To play, a player draws an Operations card and works one of the problems on the card. The player then checks his or her answer to the problem using the Algo Onslaught key. If incorrect, the player records a "miss" in the appropriate space on his or her Algo Onslaught scorecard, and the play goes to the next player. If correct, the player records a "hit" instead, rolls the die, and moves his or her marker around the gameboard as many squares as the number showing on the die. If the player lands on a Chance square, the player draws a Chance card and abides by its instructions. The play then goes to the next player.

The first player to reach the Finish square on the gameboard wins.

Note that the gameboard is self-instructional in that it illustrates the algorithms for working with whole numbers.

Algo Onslaught Cards (Operations: pp. 44-49)

Nearly 200 problems on whole number arithmetic. The key for the problems is on page 52.

The operations cards for **Algo Onslaught** are used to diagnose deficiencies in whole number arithmetic by subskill. To this end, the **Algo Onslaught scorecard** (p. 53) is scanned to note the cards with which a student is having difficulty, and Table 1 is referred to to note the subskills of whole number arithmetic which correspond to the cards. The rule of thumb for diagnosing is that three or more cards with a "miss" for a subskill indicate a weakness in the subskill.

For a ready source of prescriptions, see Shoecraft, P.J. **BASIC MATHEMATICS: A BLUEPRINT FOR SUCCESS**, Addison-Wesley Publishing Company, Inc., 1979. The whole number portion of the table of contents of same is nearly identical to the contents of Table 1!

Table 1. The Correspondence between the Operations Cards for Algo Onslaught and the Subskills of Whole Number Arithmetic

Algo Onslaught Cards	Subskills of Whole Number Arithmetic by Operation			
	Addition	Subtraction	Multiplication	Division
1-6	Addition facts	Subtraction facts	Multiplication facts	Division facts
7-12	Three single-digit addends	Exchanging facts	Single-digit multiplier without exchanging	Single-digit divisor, two-digit dividend
13-18	Addition without exchanging	Subtraction without exchanging	Single-digit muiltiplier with exchanging of ones	Single-digit divisor, three-digit dividend
19-24	Two addends with exchanging of ones	Subtraction with exchanging of tens	Single-digit multiplier with exchanging of tens	Single-digit divisor, no zeros in quotient
25-30	Two addends with exchanging of tens	Subtraction with exchanging of hundreds	Single-digit multiplier with exchanging of ones and tens	Single-digit divisor, zeros in quotient
31-36	Two addends with exchanging of ones and tens	Subtraction with exchanging of tens and hundreds	Single-digit multiplier with exchanging of ones, tens, hundreds, ...	Two-digit divisor, no zeros in quotient
37-39	Three addends with exchanging of ones and tens	Subtraction with exchanging of tens, hundreds, thousands, ...	Two-digit multiplier	Two-digit divisor, zeros in quotient
40-42	Three addends with exchanging of ones and tens	Subtraction with exchanging of tens, hundreds, thousands, ...	Multiplier with three or more digits	Divisor with three or more digits
43-45	Addition with exchanging of ones, tens, hundreds, ...	Exchanging across zeros	Multiplier with terminal zeros	Fractional remainder
46-48	Addition with exchangking of ones, tens, hundreds, ...	Exchanging across zeros	Multiplier with non-terminal zeros	Decimal remainder

Algo Onslaught Scorecard (p. 53)

A record keeping instrument for the problems on the Operations cards for Algo Onslaught.

The purpose of the **Algo Onslaught scorecard** is to assist with the diagnosis of deficiencies in whole number arithmetic as explained under **Algo Onslaught Cards**. To this end, have students use the same scorecard every time they play **Algo Onslaught**, and have them work each problem on the Operations cards for **Algo Onslaught** once only. The objective is to have them fill in the parts of the scorecard which pertain to the subskills of whole number arithmetic which they should know already or are learning about. A strategy for accomplishing this is to have them play the game for two or three class periods that they might fill in the bulk of what they are to fill in, and then to have them work from only the **Algo Onslaught cards** for an additional class period that they might fill in the rest of what they are to fill in.

Angles (p. 252)

Eight angles that can be measured with the Angle Wedges on page 251.

The measures of the angles are as follows:

a. 40^0

b. 135^0

c. 60^0

d. 90^0

e. 90^0

f. 20^0

g. 45^0

h. 130^0

Angle Wedges (p. 251)

A set of 10-, 15-, and 30-degree Angle Wedges. A classroom set of them would consist of the two circles worth of Angle Wedges per student.

The major uses of the **Angles Wedges** are to give meaning to degree measure and to direct the discovery of certain key theorems in geometry. For the former, have students measure the angles on page 252, first with the **Angle Wedges**, then with protractors. (See **Angles** for the measures of the angles.) For the latter, have students use the **Angle Wedges** with a circular geoboard or the circular dot paper on pages 175-176 along the lines suggested below.

"Show me a central angle (an angle whose vertex is at the center of a circle as in Figure 1).

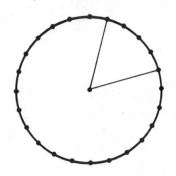

Figure 1

"Show me a central angle that subtends (cuts off) one 'fence rail' (the arc between two adjacent dots on the circumference of a circle as in Figure 2). Two fence rails. Three fence rails." And so on up to six fence rails.

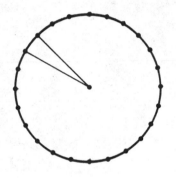

Figure 2

"What's the measure of a central angle that subtends six fence rails?" (90°)

"How do you know?" (It forms a right angle.)

"What's the measure of a central angle that subtends two fence rails?" (30°)

"Prove it with the **Angle Wedges**.

"What's the measure of a central angle that subtends one fence rail?" (15°)

"Prove it with the **Angle Wedges**.

"Show me an inscribed angle (an angle whose vertex is on the circumference of a circle as in Figure 3).

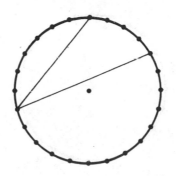

Figure 3

**Measuring angles with Angle Wedges
and protractors**

"Show me a central angle that subtends two fence
rails and an inscribed angle that subtends the same two
fence rails (as in Figure 4).

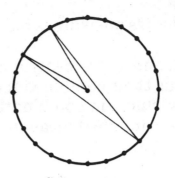

Figure 4

"What's the measure of each?" (30° for the central angle, 15° for the inscribed angle).

"Prove it with the **Angle Wedges.**

"Show me some more central angles and inscribed angles that subtend the same number of fence rails.

"What's the measure of each in each case?" (The measure of the central angle will always be twice that of the inscribed angle -- the first key theorem.)

"Prove it with the **Angle Wedges.**"

Using the theorem just discovered, it can be shown that the measure of an angle inscribed in a semicircle is 90°, and that the measure of the sum of the angles of an inscribed triangle is 180°. For the former, see Figure 5. For the latter, Figure 6.

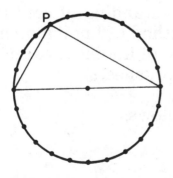

Figure 5

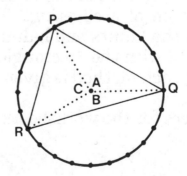

Figure 6

In Figure 5, the diameter is a central angle which subtends half the circle. Thus its measure is 180°. And angle P is an inscribed angle which subtends the same arc as the diameter. Thus its measure is half 180° or 90°.

In Figure 6, angles A, B, and C are central angles which, in combination, subtend the entire circle. Thus their combined measure is 360°. And angles P, Q, and R are inscribed angles which, in combination, subtend the same arcs as angles A, B, and C. Thus their combined measure is half 360° or 180°.

Applying the Pythagorean Theorem (p. 220)

An application of the Pythagorean theorem on finding the lengths of segments.

The answers are as follows:

a. $\sqrt{20}$ or $2\sqrt{5}$

b. $\sqrt{34}$

c. $\sqrt{10}$

d. $\sqrt{26}$

e. $\sqrt{5}$

f. $\sqrt{8}$ or $2\sqrt{2}$

g. $\sqrt{52}$ or $2\sqrt{13}$

Areas of Polygons

Two worksheets on the concept of area.

When we say that the area of a figure is, say, 10, what we mean is that to cover the figure would take 10 of some other figure. Thus the concept of area entails the notion of a covering. This understanding of area is exercised on page 211 with the "units and half-units" method of finding areas of polygons, and on page 212 with the "rectangle" method of finding areas of polygons. An explanation of each method is given on the worksheets.

The answers for the worksheets are as follows:

Page 211:

a. 4
b. 9
c. 28
d. 2
e. 8

f. 18
g. 23
h. 6
i. 10
j. 12

k. 4
l. 12
m. 8
n. 12
o. 40

a. 5	e. ½	i. 5	m. 6½
b. 10	f. ½	j. 5	n. 10
c. 17	g. ½	k. 5½	o. 10½
d. ½	h. 5	l. 6	p. 13½

Areas of Similar Figures on the Sides of Right Triangles (pp. 213-214)

Two worksheets on the Pythagorean "relationship" -- a generalization of the Pythagorean theorem.

The Pythagorean theorem is a statement about right triangles, that for a right triangle with legs of lengths a and b and hypotenuse of length c, $a^2 + b^2 = c^2$. But since a^2 is the area of the square that could be constructed on the leg of length a, b^2 the area of the square that could be constructed on the leg of length b, and c^2 the area of the square that could be constructed on the hypotenuse of length c, the theorem could be stated as follows, that the sum of the areas of the squares on the legs of a right triangle equals the area of the square on the hypotenuse of the right triangle. The significance of the worksheets, then, is that they illustrate that what the Pythagorean theorem asserts about squares on the sides of a right triangle can be generalized to all figures -- triangles, rectangles, and circles, to name only a few -- so long as the figures are **similar**, that is, of the same shape.

The answers for the worksheets are as follows:

Page 213:

a. 1, 4, 5
b. 1, 1, 2
c. 2, 8, 10
d. 2, 2, 4
e. 2, 8, 10
f. 2, 2, 4
g. 5, 20, 25
h. 1, 9, 10
i. 2, 2, 4

Page 214:

a. 2, 8, 10
b. 2, 8, 10
c. 3, 3, 6
d. 1, 4, 5
e. 2, 4½, 6½
f. 4, 4, 8
g. 6, 24, 30
h. 3, 12, 15

Areas of Triangles (p. 210)

A worksheet on the concept of area.

Areas of Triangles serves a dual purpose: One, it facilitates the learning of the "rectangle" method of finding area as referred to under **Areas of Polygons.** Two, it gives meaning to $A = \frac{1}{2}bh$, the formula for the area of a triangle in terms of its base **b** and height **h:** It shows the reason for the ½ -- the fact that the area of a triangle is always half that of a rectangle.

The answers for the worksheet are as follows:

a. 1	g. 3	m. 3	s. ½
b. 1½	h. 2	n. 12½	t. 1
c. 2	i. 9	o. 8	u. 3
d. 2½	j. 7½	p. 4½	v. 4
e. 5	k. 6	q. 2	w. 6
f. 4	l. 4½	r. ½	

Bank It or Clear It

BANK IT

A game for two to four on exchanging "up" (regrouping) that gives meaning to base ten numeration and addition of decimals.

Materials:

For each group, a Bank It spinner (p. 108) and a seven-color assortment of counters. (To construct the spinner, see SPINNERS.) For each player, a Bank It or Clear It gameboard (p. 107).

Directions:

In preparation, the players agree on a color coding scheme and color code their gameboards by putting a different colored counter in each of the circles at the top of their gameboards.

To begin, each player spins the spinner. The player spinning the highest power of ten plays first. The play rotates clockwise.

To play, a player spins the spinner and places the number of counters indicated on his or her gameboard in the column indicated. The .001 on the spinner signifies the column on the far right, the .01 on the spinner the second column in from the far right, the .1 on the spinner the third column in from the far right, and so on up to the 1000 on the spinner which signifies the column on the far left. Thus the decimal point on the spinner simply indicates that the column will be on the right side or dashed portion of the gameboard. Then the player "legalizes," that is, makes whatever exchanges are necessary to keep from breaking the "law of the land" in "ten land" and having to go to jail, and places the resultant on his or her gameboard in the appropriate columns. (As explained under The Great Legalizer, the law of the land in ten land is "Never,

never get caught with ten or more things alike else GO TO JAIL!" Thus the law necessitates the exchanging of ten counters of one color for one counter of another color, namely, of the color corresponding to the next higher power of ten.) The play then goes to the next player.

The first player to get at least one counter in each column without going to jail wins.

Variation:

To abstract the game to addition of decimals, have players play the game with only the spinner and paper and pen or pencil to keep track of what WOULD be on the gameboards if they and the counters WERE being used.

CLEAR IT

A game for two to four on exchanging "down" (regrouping) that gives meaning to base ten numeration and subtraction of decimals.

Materials:

For each group, a Clear It spinner (p. 108) and a seven-color assortment of counters. (To construct the spinner, see SPINNERS.) For each player, a Bank It or Clear It gameboard (p. 107).

Directions:

In preparation, the gameboards are color coded as for Bank It. Then each player puts a counter of each color on his or her gameboard in the column for that color.

To begin, each player spins the spinner. The player spinning the highest power of ten plays first. The play rotates clockwise.

To play, a player spins the spinner and REMOVES the number of counters indicated from his or her gameboard from the column indicated. This will often require a player to exchange a counter of one color for ten counters of another color, namely, of the color corresponding to the next lower power of ten. (Note that there is no going to jail here. As soon as a player gets too many of one thing alike, the player always gives enough of them away to keep from going to jail.) The play then goes to the next player.

The first player to clear his or her gameboard wins.

Variation:

The same as for Bank It except in terms of subtraction.

Beat the Clock

A game for two to four on the multiplication facts for five. With different numbers, as with the blank Beat the Clock gameboard on page 21, a game on any of the multiplication facts.

Materials:

Two dice for each group. Eleven markers and a Beat the Clock gameboard (p. 20) for each player.

Directions:

To begin, each player rolls the dice. The player rolling the highest total plays first. The play rotates clockwise.

To play, a player rolls the dice, multiplies the total on the dice by five, and indicates the answer by putting a marker on his or her gameboard on the circle of the same number as the answer. The play then goes to the next player.

The first player to cover all 11 circles on his or her gameboard wins.

Blank Cards

Blank cards for adding to the game and activity cards in this book.

The blank cards on page 9 are for adding to the money for **BT Numo** and the cards for

- Algo Onslaught

- Decimal Rummy

- Discard

- Division (Separating Neatly) Rummy

- Equivalent Fraction Rummy

- FDP Showdown

- Fraction-Decimal-Percent Rummy

- Metric Conversion Concentration

- Metric Mastery

- ✓ Metric Prefix Concentration

- ✓ Subtraction (Separating) Rummy

The blank cards on page 10 are for adding to the **BT Numo cards.** Those on page 11 for adding to the **Space Race cards.** And those on page 12 for making array cards additional to the

- ✓ **English Measurement array cards**

- ✓ **Equivalent Fraction array cards**

- ✓ **Fraction-Decimal-Percent array cards**

- ✓ **Metric array cards**

- ✓ **Mixed Facts array cards**

And the blank cards on page 13 are for adding to the **Diviso cards.**

Blank Dominoes (p. 14)

Blank dominoes for adding to the dominoe games in this book:

- ✓ **Addition (Combining) Dominoes**

- ✓ **Equivalent Fraction Dominoes**

- ✓ **Fraction-Decimal-Percent Dominoes**

- ✓ **Multiplication (Combining Neatly) Dominoes**

Blank Gameboards (pp. 6-8)

Blank gameboards for making gameboards for board games like Algo Onslaught, BT Numo, FDP Showdown, Geopolis, and Metric Mastery.

Bowl-a-Fact

A game for one to an entire class on the addition, subtraction, multiplication, and division facts. And in the scoring, a game on counting by tens and adding whole numbers.

Materials:

Three dice per group. One Bowl-a-Fact gameboard (p. 28) per player.

Directions:

Bowl-a-Fact is a take off on tenpin bowling. Each player gets 10 frames of 10 pins each on the gameboard. The objective each frame is to "knock down" all 10 pins with one or two throws of the dice.

To begin, each player rolls the dice. The player rolling the highest total plays first. The play rotates clockwise.

To play, a player rolls the dice, records the numbers showing on the dice in the spaces above the pins on the gameboard, and proceeds to combine the numbers IN AS MANY WAYS AS POSSIBLE using one or two of the four operations to make as many of the numbers on the pins as possible. The rule is to use each of the numbers on the dice once and only once.

For each whole number result of 10 or less, the player shades the pin for that result. The objective is to shade as many pins as possible. If the player shades all 10 pins, the play goes to the next player. If the player does not shade all 10 pins, the player rolls the dice again and proceeds as before, after which the play goes to the next player.

To illustrate, if on the first roll a player rolled a 1, 3, and 5, the player would shade the 1 $(5 - 3 - 1)$, 2 $(1 \times 5 - 3)$, 3 $(1 + 5 - 3)$, 7 $(3 + 5 - 1)$, 8 $(1 \times 3 + 5)$, 9 $(1 + 3 + 5)$ and 10 $((3 - 1) \times 5)$ pins. And if on the second roll, a 4, 5, and 6, the remaining pins: the 4 $(4 \times (6 - 5))$, 5 $(4 + 6 - 5)$, and 6 $(6 \times (5 - 4))$ pins -- a spare! And if the first roll had been a 1, 2, and 4, all 10 pins: the 1 $(4 - 2 - 1)$, 2 $(4 \div 2 \times 1)$, 3 $(1 + 4 - 2)$, 4 $(4 \times (2 - 1))$, 5 $(2 + 4 - 1)$, 6 $(1 \times (2 + 4))$, 7 $(1 + 2 + 4)$, 8 $(1 \times 2 \times 4)$, 9 $(2 \times 4 + 1)$, and 10 $(2 \times (1 + 4))$ pins -- a strike!!

To score, a player records the number of pins shaded for a frame in the scoring boxes on the gameboard for that frame and keeps a running total as in tenpin bowling by adding the sum of the pins if less than all 10, 10 plus the number of pins on the next roll if a spare, or 10 plus the number of pins on the next two rolls if a strike.

To illustrate, consider B.J.'s score for five frames of Bowl-a-Fact in Figure 7. The 5, 3, and 8 for Frame 1 correspond to 5 pins on the first roll, 3 pins on the second roll, and 8 pins for the total. The 6 and slash for Frame 2 correspond to 6 pins on the first roll and the remaining 4 pins on the second roll, the slash being the symbol for a spare. (The total for Frame 2 was figured once the score for the next roll was available: $25 = 8 + 10 + 7$.) And the crisscrossing slashes for Frame 4 correspond to all 10 pins on the first roll, the crisscrossing slashes being the symbol for a strike. (The total for Frame 4 was figured once the scores for the next two rolls were available: $50 = 33 + 10 + 4 + 3$.)

Name	Frame 1			Frame 2			Frame 3			Frame 4			Frame 5		
B.J.	5	3	8	6	/	25	7	1	33	X		50	4	3	57
Jess	X		20	6	/	35	5	2	42	6	3	51	4	/	
Lynne	9	/	20	X		39	4	5	48	7	2	57	X		
Paul	X		23	X		40	3	4	47	4	3	54	5	1	60

Figure 7

The high scorer for 10 frames wins. Since the highest possible score for a frame is 30 -- a strike followed by two strikes -- the highest possible score for 10 frames is 300: the score for 12 strikes in a row!

Variations:

To make for higher scores, allow combinations of any two of the three numbers for a roll along with combinations of all three numbers for the roll. Also, to identify students having difficulty with the basic facts, give a class a gameboard with a pre-recorded set of rolls for which the best possible total score is known.

BT Numo

A game for two to four on base ten numeration and addition and subtraction of decimals. (BT Numo stands for base ten numeration.)

Materials:

For each group, a BT Numo gameboard (pp. 110-111) and a deck of BT Numo cards (Go, pp. 112-118, Chance, pp. 119-121, and Deed, pp. 122-124). For each player, a marker, a BT Numo scorecard (p. 126), and $50 in BT Numo currency (p. 125). And for the bank, from $100 to $200 in BT Numo currency.

Directions:

In preparation, $10 from the bank is placed in each Escrow square on the gameboard, and the Go cards and Chance cards are shuffled and placed on the gameboard in the spaces provided.

To begin, the players put their markers on the Start square on the gameboard. Then each player draws a Deed (or Double Deed) card and KEEPS it. (Note: A player never has more Deed cards than the one drawn initially.) The player drawing the Deed card bearing the highest number plays first. The play rotates clockwise.

To play, a player, say, player A, draws a Go card and moves to the first square on the gameboard with the digit in the specified place. Then, if another player, say, player B, holds the Deed card for that square, player A pays player B $10. Also, if yet another player, say, player C, holds a Deed card with digits which correspond to some of the digits for that square, player A pays player C $1 for each such digit. The players then record the monies thus transferred on their scorecards, and the play goes to the next player.

To illustrate, if player A were on the Start square and drew "six in the one's place," he or she would move to square 276.591. Then, if player B held the Deed card for that square, player A would pay player B $10. Also, if player C held, say, the Deed card for 508.491, player A would pay player C $2 -- $1 for the nine in the hundredth's place and $1 for the one in the thousandth's place. Then the players would record the transactions on their scorecards: Player A would subtract $12, player B would add $10, and player C would add $2, after which the play would go to the next player.

If a player lands on a Chance square, the player draws a Chance card and does what it says. If a player lands on one of the four corners, the player collects whatever money is in the Escrow square for that corner. And every time a player lands on or passes the Start square, the player collects $10 from the bank.

The first player to accumulate $100 wins.

Calcuprose (p. 171)

An integration of math and language arts on writing arithmetic word problems.

Calcuprose is a pocket calculator activity on writing arithmetic word problems. It utilizes the fact that some numbers on a calculator look like letters when the calculator is turned upside down. Its major value is in motivating solution of arithmetic word problems.

Centimeter and Millimeter Rulers (p. 224)

Six Metric rulers.

Chain (p. 35)

A self-correcting exercise on whole number arithmetic. For different problems, use the blank Chain on page 36.

A student is to start with the link on the right of the chain and work his or her way around the chain link by link to the last link. The rule is to use the answer for one link in the problem for the next link. Thus the answers for the first three links would be 171, 57 (171 ÷ 3), and 38 (57 − 19).

If a student's answer for the last link does not agree with the answer given, the student is to start again and find the "weak" link.

Circular Dot Paper (pp. 175-176)

One page of large circular dot paper, one page of medium sized circular dot paper.

Circular dot paper is used to give meaning to degree measure and to direct the discovery of certain key theorems in geometry as explained under **Angle Wedges**.

Clap Your Hands (p. 162)

An integration of math and language arts on addition.

Clap Your Hands is implemented with a hand clapping activity. Relative to the groups of letters across the top of the worksheet, the first clapping gives the group, the second the letter within the group. To illustrate, a clap-clap followed by a clap-clap-clap, denoted 23, would mean second group (FGHIJ), third letter (H). Thus a clapped 23 (H) would be different from a clapped 32 (L), the same as the number 23 would be different from the number 32.

The answers for the worksheet are as follows:

1. a. Cat
   b. Strong
   c. Box
   d. Fig
   e. Bad
   f. Kick

2. a. 164
   b. 124
   c. 125
   d. 88

3. Answers will vary, but a word like **hover** is worth 168 points.

Cliff Hanger

A game for two to four on the addition and subtraction facts. With different numbers, as with the blank Cliff Hanger gameboard on pages 18-19, a game on any of the basic facts.

Materials:

One die and one Cliff Hanger gameboard (pp. 16-17) per group. One marker per player.

Directions:

To begin, the players put their markers on the edge of the cliff on the gameboard. Then each player rolls the die. The player rolling the highest number plays first. The play rotates clockwise.

To play, a player rolls the die and moves his or her marker down the cliff along the path he or she is on to the nearest ledge of the same number as the number showing on the die. If the player lands on a ledge with a rope on it, he or she slides down the rope to the ledge below. If on a ledge with a snake on it, he or she moves two ledges back up the cliff. The play then goes to the next player.

The first player down the cliff wins.

Codes and Docs (p. 26)

A worksheet on mixed facts. With different numbers, as with the blank Codes and Docs on page 27, a worksheet on any of the operations.

For **Codes and Docs**, a "code" is a straightforward application of one of the four operations, and a "doc" is a variation on a code. Thus problems 1-4 are codes, and problems 5 and 6 are docs. The answer to each problem is given below in terms of the rule it exhibits:

1. $A + B = C$
2. $A - B = C$
3. $A \times B = C$
4. $A \div B = C$
5. $A + B + 1 = C$
6. $2A + B = C$

Colored Squares

A game for two to four on equivalent fractions.

Materials:

Two dice and one set of colored rods per group. One Colored Squares gameboard (p. 105) per player.

Directions:

To begin, each player rolls the dice. The player rolling the highest total plays first. The play rotates clockwise.

To play, a player rolls the dice and selects any two rods which represent the fraction formed by the dice. To illustrate, if the player rolls a 2 and a 3, he or she might select a 2-rod and a 3-rod (for 2 / 3), a 4-rod and a 6-rod (for 2 / 3 = 4 / 6), or a 6-rod and a 9-rod (for 2 / 3 = 6 / 9). The player then places the rods on the gameboard with the objective of making as many squares of the same color as possible. The reason: Each square is worth its area in points. A one-by-one (white) square is worth 1 point, a two-by-two (red) square, 4 points, a three-by-three (light green) square, 9 points, and so on. The play then goes to the next player.

If a rod cannot be placed on the gameboard, it is stood on end next to the gameboard, and the number it represents with its length is subtracted from the points for the squares.

Playing colored squares

The game ends when either a player covers all of his or her gameboard or cannot play a rod. The points for any empty squares are then subtracted from the points for the squares. The player with the most points wins.

A sample gameboard showing the scoring is given below.

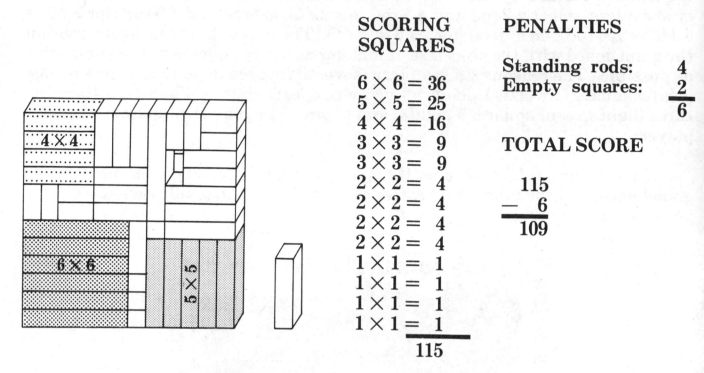

SCORING
SQUARES

$6 \times 6 = 36$
$5 \times 5 = 25$
$4 \times 4 = 16$
$3 \times 3 = 9$
$3 \times 3 = 9$
$2 \times 2 = 4$
$2 \times 2 = 4$
$2 \times 2 = 4$
$2 \times 2 = 4$
$1 \times 1 = 1$
$1 \times 1 = 1$
$1 \times 1 = 1$
$1 \times 1 = 1$

115

PENALTIES

Standing rods: 4
Empty squares: 2
6

TOTAL SCORE

115
$-$ 6
109

Compass Worksheet (p. 253)

A page of drawings of a compass.

The **Compass worksheet** is used to illustrate an application of degree measure. To begin, have students note that the outer ring of numbers or "azimuth ring" on a compass gives bearings in relation to north in terms of degrees or "azimuth numbers." (Azimuth is Arabic for "the way.") Then have them draw arrows on the compasses on the worksheet to indicate various bearings. An example of what they should draw for a bearing of 45° is given in Figure 8.

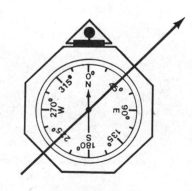

Figure 8

To add sophistication to the exercise, teach the names and bearings of the eight principle winds and the eight half-winds. The names and bearings of the former are given in Figure 9 and Table 2, respectively. Those of the latter in Figure 10 and Table 3, respectively.

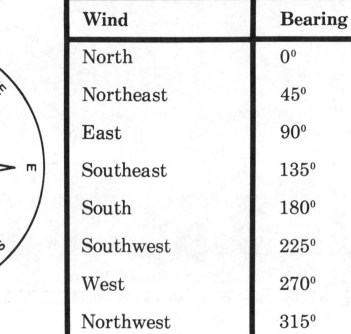

Table 2. **The Bearings of the Eight Principle Winds**

Wind	Bearing
North	$0°$
Northeast	$45°$
East	$90°$
Southeast	$135°$
South	$180°$
Southwest	$225°$
West	$270°$
Northwest	$315°$

Figure 9

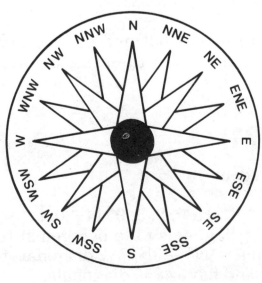

Table 3. **The Bearings of the Eight Half-Winds**

Wind	Bearing
North-northeast	$22\frac{1}{2}°$
East-northeast	$67\frac{1}{2}°$
East-southeast	$112\frac{1}{2}°$
South-southeast	$157\frac{1}{2}°$
South-southwest	$202\frac{1}{2}°$
West-southwest	$247\frac{1}{2}°$
West-northwest	$292\frac{1}{2}°$
North-northwest	$337\frac{1}{2}°$

Figure 10

As a follow-up, have students make treasure maps for one another to follow using real compasses.

Sighting along a compass

Congruent Squares (p. 37)

A puzzle on whole number arithmetic. With different numbers, as with the blank Congruent Squares on page 38, a puzzle on any topic.

The shapes on **Congruent Squares** are to be cut out and put together to make four squares all the same size. The shapes with the same answers go together.

Count the Diagonals (p. 271)

An investigation of the diagonals of polygons

Count the Diagonals yields the number pattern 0, 2, 5, 9, 14, 20, . . . which determines the rule for finding the number of diagonals for a polygon in terms of the number of sides of the polygon. The rule is $(N^2 - 3N) \div 2$ diagonals for N sides. Thus a polygon with, say, 100 sides would have 4850 diagonals.

To help students discover the rule, have them tabulate the number pattern in relation to **N**, the number of sides, as follows:

N	3N	N²	Number of Diagonals
3	9	9	0
4	12	16	2
5	15	25	5
6	18	36	9
7	21	49	14
8	24	64	20

As explained in advanced courses in algebra, the key to knowing that the rule would include an **N²** term was to note that it would take two successive differences to reduce the number pattern to a constant:

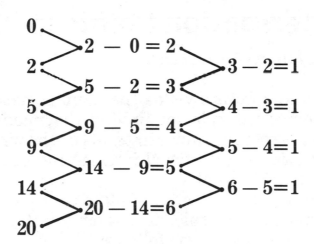

Count the Dots (p. 269)

An investigation of triangles made of dots.

Count the Dots yields the number pattern 1, 3, 6, 10, 15, 21, 28, . . . which determines the rule for finding the number of dots in a triangle made of dots in terms of the number of dots on an edge of the triangle. The rule is $(N^2 + N) \div 2$ dots all total for **N** dots on an edge. Thus a triangle made of dots with, say, 100 dots on an edge would consist of 5050 dots.

To help students discover the rule, have them tabulate the number pattern in relation to **N**, the number of sides, as follows:

N	N²	Number of dots
1	1	1
2	4	3
3	9	6
4	16	10
5	25	15
6	36	21
7	49	28

An alternate way to help students discover the rule is to direct their attention to the sum of the number of dots in each row of a triangle made of dots. To illustrate, for the triangle with 100 dots on an edge, the sum would be $1 + 2 + 3 + \ldots + 98 + 99 + 100$, and the numbers in the sum from the "outside in" total 101 fifty times: $1 + 100 = 101, 2 + 99 = 101, 3 + 98 = 101, \ldots, 50 + 51 = 101$.

Count the Intersection Points (p. 272)

An investigation of intersecting circles.

Count the Intersection Points yields the number pattern 2, 6, 12, 20, 30, 42, . . . which determines the rule for finding the maximum number of intersection points for intersecting circles in terms of the number of circles. The rule is $N^2 - N$ intersection points for N intersecting circles. Thus, say, 100 circles would intersect in 9900 points.

To help students discover the rule, have them tabulate the number pattern in relation to N, the number of sides, as follows:

N	N²	Number of intersection points
2	4	2
3	9	6
4	16	12
5	25	20
6	36	30
7	49	42

As explained in advanced courses in algebra, the key to knowing that the rule would include an N^2 term was to note that it would take two successive differences to reduce the number pattern to a constant:

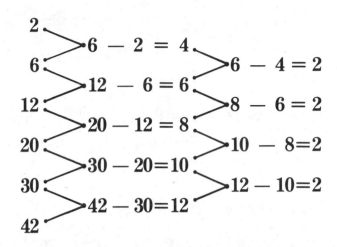

Count the Regions (p. 270)

An investigation of regions made by lines on a rectangle.

Count the Regions yields the number pattern 2, 4, 7, 11, 16, 22, . . . which determines the rule for finding the maximum number of regions made by lines on a rectangle in terms of the number of lines. The rule is $(N^2 + N + 2) \div 2$ regions for N lines. Thus, say, 100 lines on a rectangle would result in 5051 regions.

To help students discover the rule, have them tabulate the number pattern in relation to N, the number of sides, as follows:

N	N²	Number of regions
1	1	2
2	4	4
3	9	7
4	16	11
5	25	16
6	36	22

As explained in advanced courses in algebra, the key to knowing that the rule would include an N^2 term was to note that it would take two successive differences to reduce the number pattern to a constant:

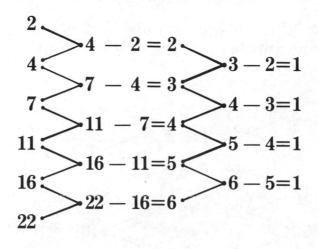

Creating Creatures (p. 168)

An integration of math and language arts on the multiplication facts.

The answers are as follows:

Clue	Word	Animal	Score
I am a yard cleaning tool.	Rake	Drake	20
What Bugs Bunny likes	Carrot	Parrot	36
"At present" is another meaning for me.	Now	Sow	9
I am the opposite of skinny.	Fat	Bat	9
I am the opposite of hate.	Love	Dove	16
I am a water crosser.	Boat	Goat	16
This is very close to jelly.	Jam	Ram	9
I am on the top of a person's head.	Hair	Hare	16
This word means not tight.	Loose	Goose	25
I lie on the grass in the morning.	Dew	Shrew	15
I am the opposite of far.	Near	Deer	16
The first name of Tatum O'Neal's father	Ryan	Lion	16
The biggest part of a tree	Trunk	Skunk	25
A wet baby often does this.	Scream	Bream	30
The back part of a shoe	Heel	Seal	16
This is the sound a dog makes.	Bark	Shark	20
		Total	294

Cube Cutout (p. 178)

A model of one of the five regular polyhedra.

The model focuses attention on vertices, faces, and edges with the cutting and pasting involved in making it.

Deci-Builder or Deci-Buster

DECI-BUILDER

A game for two to four similar to Bank It on exchanging "up" (regrouping) in base ten.

Materials:

For each group, two dice, a set of base ten blocks or a four-color assortment of counters, and a Deci-Builder or Deci-Buster gameboard (p. 109).

Directions:

In preparation, if using the blocks, the players make the unit the ".001 block," the long the ".01 block," the flat the ".1 block," and the cube the "1 block." If using the counters, the players color code the counters by making one of the colors the ".001 color," another of the colors the ".01 color," still another of the colors the ".1 color," and the remaining color the "1 color." Then each of the players selects a side of the gameboard and puts nine .1 blocks or colors on the gameboard in his or her .1 space.

To begin, each player rolls the dice. The player rolling the highest total plays first. The play rotates clockwise.

To play, a player rolls the dice and places as many .001 blocks or colors on the gameboard in his or her .001 space as the total on the dice. Then, as with Bank It, the player legalizes (by making whatever exchanges are necessary to keep from breaking the law of the land in ten land and having to go to jail) and places the resultant on the gameboard in the appropriate spaces. The play then goes to the next player.

The first player to build a 1 block or color without going to jail wins.

Variation:

To emphasize decimal notation, put, say, 20 numbers between .900 and .999 on the blackboard and make the winner the first player to build a 1 block or color or make one of the numbers on his or her side of the gameboard in the process.

DECI-BUSTER

A game for two to four similar to Clear It on exchanging "down" (regrouping) in base ten. (See BANK IT OR CLEAR IT.)

Materials:

The same as for Deci-Builder.

Directions:

In preparation, the values of the blocks or counters are decided on the same as for Deci-Builder. Then each of the players selects a side of the gameboard and puts one .001 block or color, one .01 block or color, one .1 block or color, and one 1 block or color on the gameboard in the spaces for such.

To begin, each player rolls the dice. The player rolling the highest total plays first. The play rotates clockwise.

To play, a player rolls the dice and REMOVES as many .001 blocks or colors as the dice indicate from his or her side of the gameboard. As with Clear It, this will often require a player to exchange a .1 block or color for ten .01 blocks or colors or a .01 block or color for ten .001 blocks or colors. The play then goes to the next player.

The first player to "bust their 1 block or color," that is, to have to exchange their 1 block or color for ten .1 blocks or colors, wins.

Variation:

The same as for Deci-Builder except with numbers between 1.000 and 1.111 on the blackboard.

Decimal Rummy

A game for two to four on the meaning of decimals.

Materials:

One deck of Decimal Rummy cards (pp. 127-133) per group.

Directions:

Decimal Rummy is played the same as regular rummy.

To begin, each player draws a card. The player drawing the highest card deals, and the player to the left of the person dealing plays first. The play rotates clockwise. The person dealing shuffles the deck, deals seven cards to each player, lays what is left of the deck face down, and turns the top card of the deck face up and lays it next to the deck to start the discard pile.

To play, a player takes either the top card of the deck or the top card of the discard pile. The object is to make "spreads," "books," and "runs." A spread is three of a kind such as the ".03," "point zero three," and "3 / 100." A book is four of a kind such as the picture of three-hundredths as well. The player then discards one card, and the play goes to the next player.

When a player makes a spread, book, or run, the player lays it face up. Also, when a player draws the fourth card to another player's spread or draws a card that would play on another player's run, the player may, at his or her option, lay the card face up.

The play stops when a player lays all of his or her cards face up. Each player then gets five points for each card face up minus five points for each card still in his or her hand.

The first player to get 100 points wins.

Note: A rummy deck can also be used to play other card games, notably, Fish, War, and Concentration. The rules for each of these games follow:

FISH

To begin, each player draws a card. The player drawing the highest card deals, and the player to the left of the person dealing plays first. The play rotates clockwise. The person dealing shuffles the deck, deals five cards to each player, and lays what is left of the deck face down.

To play, a player, say, player A, looks at his or her cards and asks any other player for a card like one of them. If the other player has the card, he or she must give it to player A who lays it face up with the card it is like to make a "pair." (An example of a pair for the Decimal Rummy cards would be the ".03" and "point zero three.") Player A then repeats the process until he or she asks for a card that another player does not have, in which case the player tells player A to "fish." Player A then draws the top card from the deck, and the play goes to the next player.

If a player runs out of cards before the deck is exhausted, the player draws the top three cards from the deck and resumes play as his or her turn would dictate.

The player with the most pairs after all the cards have been paired wins.

WAR

To begin, each player draws a card. The player drawing the highest card deals, and the player to the left of the person dealing plays first. The play rotates clockwise. The person dealing shuffles the deck and deals out ALL the cards to the players as the players stack their cards without looking at them.

To play, the players take turns putting the top cards from their stacks of cards face up on top of one another. Then, if a card so placed would make a pair with the card directly beneath it, the players race to put a hand on the pile thus formed. The first player to do so gets all the cards in the pile.

The player who ends up with everyone else's cards wins.

CONCENTRATION

To begin, the players select any eight pairs from the Decimal Rummy cards to make a "short" deck. The players then draw one card each from the short deck. The player drawing the highest card shuffles the short deck and spreads it out face down to make a four-by-four array. The player to the left of the player making the array plays first. The play rotates clockwise.

To play, a player draws two cards from the array. If the cards make a pair, the player keeps the cards and continues to draw cards two at a time until he or she draws two cards which do not make a pair, in which case he or she returns the cards which do not make a pair to the array exactly as they were, and the play goes to the next player.

The player with the most pairs after all the cards have been drawn wins.

Discard

A game for two to four on the addition, subtraction, multiplication, and division facts.

Materials:

One deck of Discard cards (pp. 29-34) per group.

Directions:

Discard is played along the lines of dominoes except with cards.

To begin, the players decide on a dealer. The dealer shuffles the deck, deals five cards to each player, lays what is left of the deck face down, and turns the top card of the deck face up and lays it next to the deck to start the discard pile. The player to the left of the dealer plays first. The play rotates clockwise.

To play, a player tries to make a match between the sum, difference, product, or quotient of the two numbers on one of his or her cards with the sum, difference, product, or quotient of the two numbers on the top card of the discard pile. To illustrate, if a player held the card $\boxed{\substack{9\\2}}$, and the top card of the discard pile were the $\boxed{\substack{4\\3}}$, the player could make a match because $9 - 2 = 4 + 3$. Other cards for which a match could be made would be the $\boxed{\substack{7\\1}}$ and $\boxed{\substack{4\\2}}$ (because $7 + 1 = 4 \times 2$), the $\boxed{\substack{2\\1}}$ and $\boxed{\substack{9\\3}}$ (because $2 + 1 = 9 \div 3$), and the $\boxed{\substack{8\\2}}$ and $\boxed{\substack{3\\2}}$ (because $8 - 2 = 3 \times 2$).

Once a player makes a match, the player "discards" the card with which the match was made by laying it face up on top of the discard pile, and the play goes to the next player. If a player cannot make a match, the player draws a card from the deck and tries to make a match with that card. And if the player cannot make a match with that card, the player keeps on drawing until he or she can and does make a match.

The objective is to discard all of one's cards. The first player to do so gets five points for each of the cards still in the other players' hands.

If a player cannot make a match, and all of the deck has been drawn, the play goes to the next player, and the object becomes to discard all of one's cards or to have as few cards as possible. If no one runs out of cards, the player with the least number of cards gets five points for each of the cards still in the other players' hands minus five points for each of the cards still in his or her hand.

The first player to get 100 points wins.

Division (Separating Neatly) Rummy

A game for two to four on division as separating "neatly" (into twos, threes, fours, and so on).

Materials:

One deck of Division (Separating Neatly) Rummy cards (pp. 74-80) per group.

Directions:

The same as for Decimal Rummy.

An example of a spread for the Division (Separating Neatly) Rummy cards would be the "4 ÷ 2," "four divided by two," and "four separated neatly into twos." An example of a book the picture of four separated neatly into twos as well.

Diviso

A game for two on the division facts.

Materials:

One Diviso gameboard (p. 22) and one set of Diviso cards (pp. 23-24) per group.

Directions:

To begin, the cards are laid face down and scrambled. Then the players take five cards each, examine their cards for the highest number, and compare highest numbers. The player with the card bearing the highest number plays first by laying the card face up on one of the squares on the gameboard.

To play, the players take turns laying cards next to one another face up on the squares on the gameboard. The rule is that the numbers on the adjacent edges of the cards must be multiples or exact divisors of one another. To illustrate, note the cards played in Figures 11, 12, and 13.

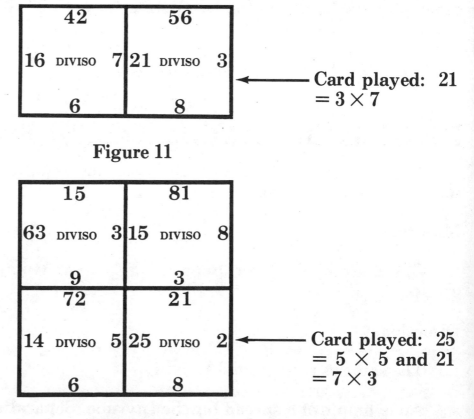

Card played: 21
= 3 × 7

Figure 11

Card played: 25
= 5 × 5 and 21
= 7 × 3

Figure 12

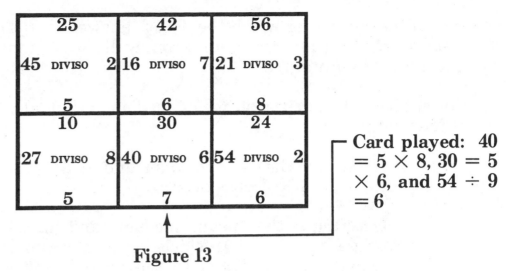

25	42	56
45 DIVISO 2	16 DIVISO 7	21 DIVISO 3
5	6	8
10	30	24
27 DIVISO 8	40 DIVISO 6	54 DIVISO 2
5	7	6

Card played: 40 = 5 × 8, 30 = 5 × 6, and 54 ÷ 9 = 6

Figure 13

To score, if a player plays a card that touches one edge as in Figure 11, the player gets one point. If two edges as in Figure 12, three points. And if three edges as in Figure 13, 10 points. If a player cannot play, the player draws a card and keeps on drawing until he or she can and does play.

The objective is to play all of one's cards. The first player to do so gets 10 points plus two points for each of the cards still in the other player's hand.

The winner is the first player to get 50 points.

In the event that the gameboard is entirely filled in or all the cards are drawn and neither player can play, all the cards are laid face down and scrambled, and the play continues as from the beginning.

Dot Paper (p. 209)

A page of 1-centimeter dot paper with which to make problems on area and perimeter as shown on pages 210-221.

Elementary Statistics (pp. 267-268)

Two exercises on mean, median, and mode.

For a set of numbers, the **mean** is the average, the **median** the "middle" number, and the **mode** the number which occurs most often. Thus for the numbers 3, 3, 4, 5, and 10, the mean is 5 ((3 + 3 + 4 + 5 + 10) ÷ 5), the median 4, and the mode 3.

To figure the mean, median, and mode for an item on the values survey on page 268 for which the "best" answer is on the "agree" side of the scale, score 5 for strongly agree, 4 for agree, and so on down to 1 for strongly disagree. For an item on the survey for which the "best" answer is on the "disagree" side of the scale, score in the reverse: 5 for strongly disagree, 4 for disagree, and so on down to 1 for strongly agree.

For additional exercises on mean, median, and mode, have students work on the following:

> Determine the mean, median, and mode for the **sum** of the digits on 50 license plates.

> Determine the mean, median, and mode for the average speed of 20 vehicles over a given distance. Compare your findings to the posted speed for that distance and describe your feelings at the comparison.

> Determine the mean, median, and mode for the "fright" distances of 10 birds. The fright distance of a bird is the distance between you and the bird when it flys away.

> Determine the mean, median, and mode for the average response time of 10 truckers to a honking signal.

> Determine an "average" person by comparing a person's height to his or her weight for 10 persons.

> Determine an "average" circle by comparing a circle's circumference to its diameter for 10 circles.

English Measurement Array Cards (p. 222)

A puzzle on the hodge podge of English measures.

The **English Measurement array cards** are used to show the confusing nature of the English system of measurement. Thus they can be used to emphasize the clarity of the metric system.

To use the **English Measurement array cards**, have students cut them out and place them next to one another to where the edges of the cards connect equivalent measurements. The key equivalences are the following:

> One ounce equals 16 drams.

> One dram equals $27\frac{11}{32}$ grains.

> One pint equals 4 gills.

$31\frac{1}{2}$ gallons equal 1 barrel.

When the cards are assembled properly, they should appear as follows:

1 quart	100 pounds / 1 short hundred-weight / 16 ounces / 16 drams / 1 ounce	1 pound / 1 hand / 4 inches
2 pints / 1 hogshead	$27\frac{11}{32}$ grains / 1 dram / 1 pint / $31\frac{1}{2}$ gallons	1 barrel / 1 gallon / 4 quarts
2 barrels	8 furlongs / 1 statute mile / 4 gills / 20 short hundred-weights	1 short ton

Equivalent Fraction Array Cards (p. 106)

A puzzle on equivalent fractions.

The **Equivalent Fraction array cards** are to be cut out and placed next to one another to where the edges of the cards connect equivalent fractions. When this is done, the cards should appear as follows:

Fraction dominoes grid (3 × 3):

$\dfrac{4}{5}$ $\dfrac{1}{2}$	$\dfrac{24}{30}$ $\dfrac{7}{10}$ $\dfrac{1}{5}$	$\dfrac{70}{100}$ $\dfrac{1}{3}$
$\dfrac{2}{4}$ $\dfrac{25}{100}$	$\dfrac{20}{100}$ $\dfrac{9}{12}$ $\dfrac{9}{4}$ $\dfrac{3}{8}$ $\dfrac{4}{3}$	$\dfrac{9}{3}$ $\dfrac{2}{3}$ $\dfrac{5}{8}$
$\dfrac{1}{4}$ $\dfrac{1}{10}$	$\dfrac{32}{32}$ $\dfrac{3}{30}$ $\dfrac{1}{10}$ $\dfrac{12}{12}$	$\dfrac{40}{40}$ $\dfrac{6}{5}$ $\dfrac{25}{6}$

Equivalent Fraction Dominoes

A game for two to four on equivalent fractions.

Materials:

One set of Equivalent Fraction Dominoes (pp. 95-97) per group.

Directions:

To begin, the dominoes are laid face down in what is called the bone yard and scrambled. Then the players take five dominoes each and examine them for doubles -- for dominoes with equivalent ends. The player with the highest double, or "spinner," lays it face up. This starts the game. The next player to play is the one to the left of the one playing the spinner. The play rotates clockwise. If no double is drawn, everything starts over until a double is drawn.

To play, a player matches the end of one of his or her dominoes with the end of a dominoe laying face up. If playing a double, the player matches the SIDE of the double with the end of the dominoe, that is, the player plays the double sideways. Conversely, if the dominoe laying face up is a double, the match is made with the side of the double. However, if the dominoe laying face up is the spinner, the match is made with the ends OR sides of the spinner. Thus there are never more than four possible plays: the plays off the ends or sides of the dominoes emanating from the ends and sides of the spinner. (See Figure 14.)

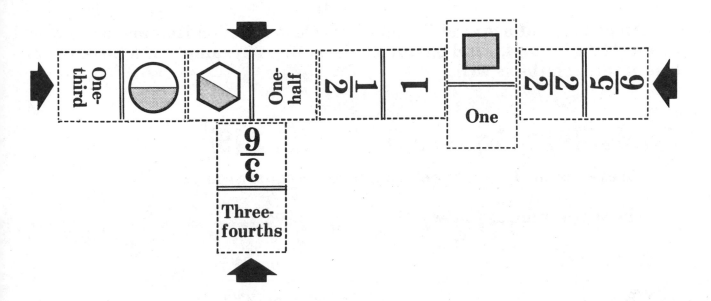

Figure 14. A double one-half for a spinner and, as indicated with arrows, four possible plays: anything equivalent to 1 / 2, 5 / 6, 3 / 4, or 1 / 3.

Once a match has been made, the play goes to the next player. If a player cannot make a match, the player draws from the bone yard until he or she can and does make a match.

The objective is to run out of dominoes. The first player to do so gets five points for each of the dominoes still with the other players.

If a player cannot make a match, and the bone yard is depleted, the play goes to the next player, and the object becomes to run out of dominoes or to have as few dominoes as possible. If no one runs out of dominoes, the player with the least number of dominoes gets five points for each dominoe still with the other players minus five points for each dominoe still in his or her hand.

The first player to get 100 points wins.

Equivalent Fraction Rummy

A game for two to four on equivalent fractions.

Materials:

One deck of Equivalent Fraction Rummy cards (pp. 98-104) per group.

Directions:

The same as for Decimal Rummy.

An example of a spread for the Equivalent Fraction Rummy cards would be the "1 / 2," "2 / 4," and picture of one-half. An example of a book the picture of three-sixths as well.

Equivalent Square Roots (p. 219)

An exercise on literally seeing equivalent square roots.

The answers are as follows:

a. $\sqrt{18}$ or $3\sqrt{2}$

b. $\sqrt{16}$ or 4

c. $\sqrt{4}$ or 2

d. $\sqrt{9}$ or 3

e. $\sqrt{45}$ or $3\sqrt{5}$

f. $\sqrt{32}$ or $4\sqrt{2}$

g. $\sqrt{40}$ or $2\sqrt{10}$

Estimating Probabilities (pp. 261-265)

Five exercises on estimating probabilities for outcomes whose relative frequencies cannot be predicted before hand. For more exercises like them, use the blank table on page 266.

Two things should become apparent in the exercises on pages 261-265. One, that it is very easy to introduce bias in estimating probabilities. Two, that to get really good estimates of the probabilities for some outcomes, one probably needs to observe the outcomes in relation to a very large number of trials. As for the first, it is easily shown that how one presents a cartoon, for example, effects whether or not people laugh at it. And as for the second, it should be noted that insurance companies, for example, study the "fate" of many, many millions of people before estimating the probability of (and thereby determining the premium for) a person of a particular sex and age, say, crashing their car or living one more year.

The answer to the code breaking exercise on page 263 is given below.

A good glass in the bishops hostel in the devils seat

forty one degrees and thirteen minutes north east and by north main branch seventh limb east side shoot from the left eye of the deaths head a bee line from the tree through the shot fifty feet out

Experience Roster (p. 1)

An instrument for keeping track of the mathematics students experience.

An "experience roster" is of major value in an activity-oriented curriculum that allows for some option on what students work on. It lends order to a curriculum based on the familiar:

I hear and I forget.

I see and I remember.

I do and I understand.

An example of its use is given below. One or more check marks in a given column and row mean the experience in that column for the student in that row the number of times indicated.

Name	Experience	Cliff Hanger	Beat the Clock	Diviso	Bowl-a-Fact	Discard	Algo Onslaught															
Willard					✓✓✓		✓✓															
Ruth		✓✓✓			✓																	
Ken			✓			✓✓	✓✓															
Jackie		✓	✓✓			✓	✓															

Fast Fill-ins (p. 166)

An integration of math and language arts on addition.

The answers are as follows:

Clue	Number of letters	Two of the letters	Word	Score
A honey eater	4	A.B.	Bear	27
A president	7	L.L.	Lincoln	83
A part of a boat	4	M.T.	Mast	31
A number	5	E.T.	Eight	73
A month	5	I.L.	April	62
A part of your body	3	E.Y.	Eye	45
A snake	5	A.R.	Cobra	28
A bird	5	N.R.	Robin	41
A city	7	E.K.	New York	97
A state	5	A.O.	Idaho	49
A river	11	P.P.	Mississippi	139
			Total	675

FDP Showdown

A game for two to four on fractions, decimals, and percents.

The significance of FDP Showdown is twofold: First, it reviews nearly all of the subjects of fractions, decimals, and percents. Second, it diagnoses deficiencies in the subjects by subskill. The manner in which it diagnoses is explained under FDP Showdown Cards and FDP Showdown Scorecard.

Materials:

For each group, a die, an FDP Showdown gameboard (pp. 148-149), a deck of FDP Showdown cards (Operations, pp. 150-154, Chance, pp. 155-156), and an FDP Showdown key (p. 157). For each player, an FDP Showdown scorecard (p. 158) and a pen or pencil and some scrap paper.

Directions:

In preparation, the FDP Showdown cards are shuffled and placed on the gameboard in the spaces provided.

To begin, the players put their markers on the Start space on the gameboard. Then each player rolls the die. The player rolling the highest number plays first. The play rotates clockwise.

To play, a player draws an Operations card and works one of the problems on the card. The player then checks his or her answer to the problem using the FDP Showdown key. If incorrect, the player records a "miss" in the appropriate space on his or her FDP Showdown scorecard, and the play goes to the next player. If correct, the player records a "hit" instead, rolls the die, and moves his or her marker around the gameboard as many spaces as the number showing on the die. If the player lands on a Chance space, the player draws a Chance card and does what it says. The play then goes to the next player.

The first player to reach the Finish space on the gameboard wins.

Note that the gameboard is self-instructional in that it illustrates the procedures for working with fractions, decimals, and percents.

FDP Showdown Cards (Operations: pp. 150-154)

Nearly 150 problems on fractions, decimals, and percents. The key for the problems is on page 157.

The **Operations cards** for **FDP Showdown** are used to diagnose deficiencies in working with fractions, decimals, and percents by subskill. To this end, the **FDP Showdown scorecard** (p. 158) is scanned to note the cards with which a student is having difficulty, and Table 4 is referred to to note the subskills of fractions, decimals, and percents which correspond to the cards. The rule of thumb for diagnosing is that two or more cards with a "miss" for a subskill indicate a weakness in the subskill.

For a ready source of prescriptions, see Shoecraft, P.J. **BASIC MATHEMATICS: A BLUEPRINT FOR SUCCESS**, Addison-Wesley Publishing Company, Inc., 1979. The fraction, decimal, percent portion of the table of contents of same is nearly identical to the contents of Table 4!

Table 4. The Correspondence between the Operations Cards for FDP Showdown and the Subskills of Fractions, Decimals, and Percents

FDP Show-down Cards	Subskills of Fractions, Decimals, and Percents by Problem			
	a	**b**	**c**	**d**
1-4	Addition of fractions with equal denominators	Subtraction of fractions with equal denominators	Multiplication of fractions	Division of fractions
5-8	Addition of fractions with unequal denominators	Subtraction of fractions with unequal denominators	Multiplication of fractions and whole numbers	Division of fractions and whole numbers
9-12	Addition of fractions, whole numbers, and mixed numbers without exchanging	Subtraction of fractions, whole numbers, and mixed numbers without exchanging	Multiplication of fractions and mixed numbers	Division of fractions and mixed numbers
13-16	Addition of fractions, whole numbers, and mixed numbers with exchanging	Subtraction of fractions, whole numbers, and mixed numbers with exchanging	Multiplication of mixed and whole numbers	Division of mixed and whole numbers
17-20	Meaning of decimal	Meaning of percent	Multiplication of mixed numbers	Division of mixed numbers
21-24	Converting decimals to fractions and mixed numbers	Rounding decimals	Converting decimals to percents	Converting fractions and mixed numbers to percents
25-28	Converting fractions and mixed numbers to decimals	Adding decimals	Converting percents to decimals	Converting percents to fractions and mixed numbers
29-32	Subtracting decimals	Multiplying decimals	Finding a percent of a number	Finding the percent one number is of another
33-36	Dividing decimals	Multiplying or dividing decimals by powers of ten	Converting fractions to repeating decimals	Finding a number given a percent of the number

FDP Showdown Scorecard (p. 158)

A record keeping instrument for the problems on the Operations cards for FDP Showdown.

The purpose of the **FDP Showdown scorecard** is to assist with the diagnosis of deficiencies in working with fractions, decimals, and percents as explained under **FDP Showdown Cards**. To this end, have students use the same scorecard every time they play **FDP Showdown,** and have them work each problem on the **Operations cards** for **FDP Showdown** once only. The objective is to have them fill in the parts of the scorecard which pertain to the subskills of fractions, decimals, and percents which they should know already or are learning about. A strategy for accomplishing this is to have them play the game for two or three class periods that they might fill in the bulk of what they are to fill in, and then to have them work from only the **FDP Showdown cards** for an additional class period that they might fill in the rest of what they are to fill in.

Figure-Four Rabbit Trap (p. 172)

An exercise on measuring and working from a scale drawing. Also, an application of the fact that the triangle is the only rigid polygon.

Materials:

A ruler, three sticks 20, 25, and 40 centimeters long, a knife with which to notch the stricks, and a box large enough and strong enough to hold a rabbit. A good source for the sticks is kite struts.

Comments:

The motivation for building a **figure-four rabbit trap** is that it works. It actually catches rabbits, and anything else hungry enough to take the bait. When built and set, it should look like the trap in the photograph below. The bait is attached to the end of the horizontal stick that is under the box.

Figure-four rabbit trap

Regarding the construction of the "figure four," note that it involves the construction of a 30°-60°-90° triangle -- the only right triangle for which the hypotenuse is twice the length of the shorter leg. And when the figure four is assembled, note that it illustrates the strengthening use triangles are put to in construction as in bracing walls, trussing bridges, and supporting towers.

Food Find (p. 169)

An integration of math and language arts on the multiplication facts.

The answers are as follows:

1. a. Nut, 6   f. Apple, 15
    b. Corn, 8   g. Tart, 12
    c. Egg, 12   h. Crab, 16
    d. Pear, 8   i. Pie, 9
    e. Bun, 9   j. Curd, 8

2. Answers will vary, but something like:

    a. Figure, 36   d. Hamburger, 54
    b. Meatball, 48   e. Nice, 24
    c. Tease, 30   f. Saucer, 36

3. Answers will vary, but something like:

    a. Appeal, 54   b. Beanball, 72
       Appear, 54   Beanie, 54
       Appease, 63   Beano, 45

Fraction Cakes

Pictures in terms of a circular unit of halves, thirds, fourths, and so on up through twelfths, excluding sevenths and elevenths.

The large pictures (pp. 83-92) are for making paper models or flannel board replicas of fraction cakes, the small ones (pp. 93-94) for making task cards or overhead transparencies for fraction cakes. A classroom set of the large ones would consist of one each of the ten of them per student with the understanding that some of them would have to be shared for some problems.

Fraction cakes are used to develop the concept of equivalent fractions and give meaning to addition, subtraction, multiplication, and division of fractions. In using them for equivalent fractions and addition and subtraction of fractions, always insist that only "pieces of cake" of the same color be combined or separated. In this way, the connection between what is done with the fraction cakes and what is done with paper and pen or pencil on these topics is easily made.

Some examples of how the fraction cakes are used are given below. For motivational reasons, some of the examples are in terms of **The Magnificent Equalizer, Motley Crab Adder,** and **The Scruffy Twin Subtractors.**

EQUIVALENT FRACTIONS

In way of introduction, do two things: One, instruct students on how **The Magnificent Equalizer** is driven to make things different yet the same: different in appearance, yet the same in quantity. Two, instruct them on a peculiarity of **The Magnificent Equalizer,** that with fractions he is sometimes "generous," sometimes "parsimonious" -- stingy in the extreme -- but that in either case, he never mixes "colors" (denominators). (As explained below, the generous nature of **The Magnificent Equalizer** is called upon when we want him to make fractions have the same denominator, the parsimonious nature when we want him to simplify a fraction.)

Then, as illustrated below, have students do the following with the fraction cakes, first for fractions like 1 / 2 which are simplified to begin with, then for fractions like 9 / 12 which are **not** simplified to begin with:

Using fraction cakes with fractions already simplified:

"Show me a half. Show me some things **The Magnificent Equalizer** would do with it if he were asked to be 'generous.'" (He would turn it into 2 fourths, 3 sixths, 4 eighths, and the like where in each case it would be possible to share the cake with more people than to begin with.)

Intersperse with questions like the following:

"How would you describe what you have?" ("Two fourths, 3 sixths, 4 eighths, or whichever")

"How would you write it?" (2 / 4, 3 / 6, 4 / 8, or whichever)

"What can you say about a half and (whichever)?" ("That a half is the same amount as 2 fourths, 3 sixths, 4 eighths, or whichever")

"How would you write that?" (1 / 2 = 2 / 4, 1 / 2 = 3 / 6, 1 / 2 = 4 / 8, or whichever)

Using fraction cakes with fractions NOT already simplified:

"Show me 9 twelfths. Show me what **The Magnificent Equalizer** would do with them if he were asked to be 'parsimonious.'" (He would turn them into 3 fourths where the number of pieces of cake that could be shared would be as few as possible.)

Intersperse with questions like the following:

"How would you describe what you ended up with?" ("Three fourths")

"How would you write it?" (3 / 4)

"What can you say about 9 twelfths and 3 fourths?" ("That they are the same amount")

"How would you write that?" (9 / 12 = 3 / 4)

Later -- perhaps days later -- and as illustrated below, have students switch to the symbolics of converting fractions to equivalent fractions, first for fractions like 1 / 2 which are simplified to begin with, then for fractions like 9 / 12 which are **not** simplified to begin with:

Working with paper and pen or pencil with fractions already simplified:

"Write 1 / 2. Write some things **The Magnificent Equalizer** would do to it if he were asked to be generous." (In symbolic form, **The Magnificent Equalizer** is a tall, slender one with a superimposed 2 / 2, 3 / 3, 4 / 4, or the like as illustrated in Figure 15. If asked to be generous, he responds with the fraction aspect of his character. If asked to be parsimonious, with the unit aspect of his character. Thus some of the things he would do to 1 / 2 if asked to be generous is multiply it by 2 / 2 to change it to 2 / 4, multiply it by 3 / 3 to change it to 3 / 6, multiply it by 4 / 4 to change it to 4 / 8, or the like as illustrated in Figure 16.)

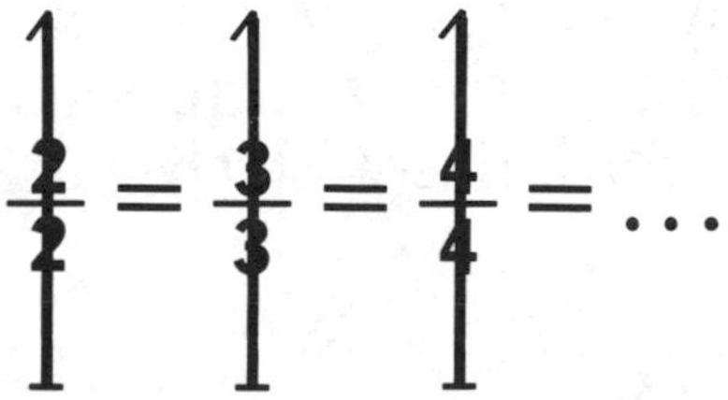

$$\frac{\frac{1}{2}}{1} = \frac{\frac{1}{3}}{1} = \frac{\frac{1}{4}}{1} = \dots$$

Figure 15.

$$\frac{1}{2} \times \frac{\frac{1}{2}}{1} = \frac{2}{4} \text{ or } \frac{1}{2} \times \frac{\frac{1}{3}}{1} = \frac{3}{6} \text{ or } \frac{1}{2} \times \frac{\frac{1}{4}}{1} = \frac{4}{8} \dots$$

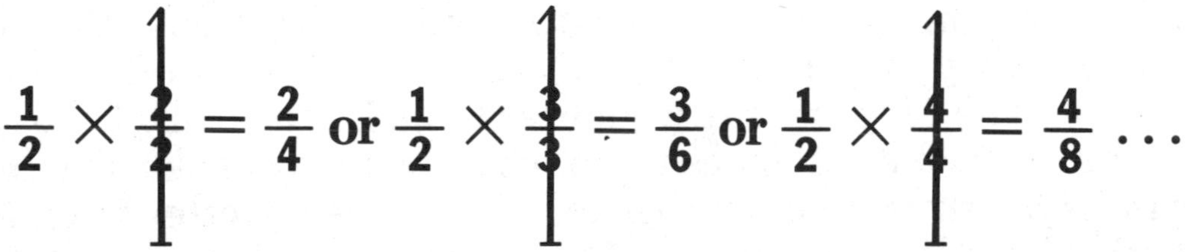

Figure 16

Working with paper and pen or pencil with fractions which are NOT already simplified:

"Write 9 / 12. Write what **The Magnificent Equalizer** would do to it if he were asked to be 'parsimonious.'" (He would regard himself as a one disguised as 3 / 3 and "remove" himself from the fraction as illustrated in Figure 17.)

$$\frac{9}{12} = \frac{3}{4} \times \frac{\cancel{3}}{\cancel{3}} = \frac{3}{4}$$

Figure 17

Note that whether being "generous" or "parsimonious," students always make the fractions different yet the same: different in appearance, yet the same in quantity. And note as well that even if they have never multiplied fractions before, they can do so here because of the ease with which it can be accomplished: Just multiply across. (Or "unmultiply" across if simplifying.) Later, when they know more about fractions, they can be shown that "multiplying across" is in accordance with the rules for multiplying them.

ADDITION OF FRACTIONS

To begin, remind students of the dual nature of **The Magnificent Equalizer**, that with fractions he is sometimes generous, sometimes parsimonious. Then advise them on two peculiarities of **Motley Crab Adder** in relation to fractions: One, that however much he is driven to combine fractions, that he will not combine them if they are of different colors, but rather will first appeal to the generous side of **The Magnificent Equalizer** to make them all of the same color. Two, that right after he combines them, that he always asks **The Magnificent Equalizer** to be parsimonious with them. (Thus when **Motley Crab Adder** runs into fractions, he relies heavily on **The Magnificent Equalizer**.) Then have students add with the fraction cakes as illustrated below:

Using fraction cakes to add fractions with like denominators:

> "Show me an eighth. Show me three more eighths. Show me what **Motley Crab Adder** would do with them." (Since they are of the same color, he would combine them. Then he would appeal to the parsimonious side of **The Magnificent Equalizer** who would turn them into a half.)

> Then, "How would you record what he would do with them?"

$$\frac{1}{8} + \frac{3}{8} = \frac{4}{8} = \frac{1}{2} \times \frac{4}{4} = \frac{1}{2}$$

Using fraction cakes to add fractions for which the least common denominator is one of the denominators of the fractions:

"Show me an eighth. Show me a fourth. Show me what **Motley Crab Adder** would do with them." (He would first appeal to the generous side of **The Magnificent Equalizer** to make them the same color. Then he would combine them. Afterwards, he would ask **The Magnificent Equalizer** to be parsimonious with them, but to no avail.)

Then, "How would you record what he would do with them?"

$$\frac{1}{8} + \frac{1}{4} = \frac{1}{8} + \left(\frac{1}{4} \times \frac{2}{2}\right) = \frac{1}{8} + \frac{2}{8} = \frac{3}{8}$$

Using fraction cakes to add fractions with unlike denominators:

"Show me a third. Show me a fourth. Show me what **Motley Crab Adder** would do with them." (He would proceed as before.)

Then, "How would you record what he would do with them?"

$$\frac{1}{3} + \frac{1}{4} = \left(\frac{1}{3} \times \frac{4}{4}\right) + \left(\frac{1}{4} \times \frac{3}{3}\right) = \frac{4}{12} + \frac{3}{12} = \frac{7}{12}$$

SUBTRACTION OF FRACTIONS

The procedure for teaching subtraction of fractions with fraction cakes is essentially the same as that for teaching addition of fractions with fraction cakes. To begin, remind students of the generous / parsimonious nature of **The Magnificent Equalizer** as given under **EQUIVALENT FRACTIONS**. Then advise them on how **The Scruffy Twin Subtractors** are just as peculiar with fractions as **Motley Crab Adder**, that however much they are driven to separate them, that they will not do so if they are of different colors, but rather will first appeal to the generous side of **The Magnificent Equalizer** to make them the same color, and that right after they separate them, that they always ask **The Magnificent Equalizer** to be parsimonious with what they leave. (Thus when they run into fractions, they, too, rely heavily on **The Magnificent Equalizer**.) Then have students work with the fraction cakes, first in relation to fractions with like denominators, then in relation to fractions for which the least common denominator is one of the denominators of the fractions, and finally in relation to fractions with unlike denominators. The language in each case is "Show me (whatever). Show me what **The Scruffy Twin Subtractors** would do with it if they wanted (whatever)." And, "How would you record what they would do with it?"

MULTIPLICATION OF FRACTIONS

To begin, advise students on the relaxed nature of things when we multiply with fraction cakes, that when we do so, that we do not worry about things being of the same color. Then have them multiply with the fraction cakes as illustrated below:

Using fraction cakes to multiply a fraction times a fraction

"Show me 2 thirds. Show me half of them. Record what you did."

$$\frac{2}{3} \times \frac{1}{2} = \frac{1}{3}$$

"Show me 3 fifths. Show me two-thirds of them. Record what you did."

$$\frac{3}{5} \times \frac{2}{3} = \frac{2}{5}$$

And so on.

Using fraction cakes to multiply a fraction times a whole number

"Show me a fourth. Show me that much three times. Record what you did."

$$\frac{1}{4} \times 3 = \frac{3}{4}$$

"Show me a half. Show me that much five times. Show me the simplest form of what you have. Record what you did."

$$\frac{1}{2} \times 5 = \frac{5}{2} = 2\frac{1}{2}$$

And so on.

Using fraction cakes to multiply a fraction times a mixed number

"Show me 4 fifths. Show me that much 1½ times. Show me the simplest form of what you have. Record what you did."

$$\frac{4}{5} \times 1\frac{1}{2} = \frac{6}{5} = 1\frac{1}{5}$$

"Show me 9 tenths. Show me that much 1⅔ times. Show me the simplest form of what you have. Record what you did."

$$\frac{9}{10} \times 1\frac{2}{3} = \frac{15}{10} = 1\frac{1}{2}$$

And so on.

Using fraction cakes to multiply a mixed number times a mixed number

"Show me a one and a third together. Show me that

much 1½ times. Show me the simplest form of what you have. Record what you did."

$$1\frac{1}{3} \times 1\frac{1}{2} = 1 + \frac{1}{3} + \frac{1}{2} + \frac{1}{6} = 2$$

"Show me 3 ones and 3 fourths together. Show me that much 1⅔ times. Show me the simplest form of what you have. Record what you did."

$$3\frac{3}{4} \times 1\frac{2}{3} = 5\frac{5}{4} = 6\frac{1}{4}$$

And so on.

Note that what students record each time is only part of the solution process for multiplying fractions, whole numbers, and mixed numbers. Thus once they get everything recorded, the strategy is to have them look for patterns in what they have recorded that they might discover how to work with only the numbers themselves to get the same answers. The objective is to have them arrive at the following three generalizations:

✔ To multiply fractions, simply multiply across.

✔ To multiply a fraction and a whole number, think of the whole number as a fraction over 1 and multiply across.

✔ To multiply with a mixed number, change the mixed number to a fraction and multiply across.

DIVISION OF FRACTIONS

To begin, advise students that as with multiplying with fraction cakes, that we do not worry about things being of the same color when we divide with fraction cakes. Next, remind them of the fact that a division problem can be thought of in either of two ways: as a statement about something being separated into groups of a certain size, or as a statement about something being separated into a certain number of groups in equal amounts, that, for example, 12 ÷ 3 can be thought of as a statement about 12 being separated into groups of three, in which case there would be four groups, or as a statement about 12 being separated into three groups in equal amounts, in which case there would be three groups of four each. Then have them divide with the fraction cakes as illustrated below:

Using fraction cakes to divide a fraction by a fraction

"Show me a half. Show me that much separated into fourths. How many fourths did you get?" ("Two") "Record what you did."

$$\frac{1}{2} \div \frac{1}{4} = 2$$

"Show me 2 thirds. Show me that much separated into sixths. How many sixths did you get?" ("Four") "Record what you did."

$$\frac{2}{3} \div \frac{1}{6} = 4$$

And so on.

Using fraction cakes to divide a fraction by a whole number

"Show me a third. Show me that much separated into two groups in equal amounts. How much did you end up with in each group?" ("A sixth") "Record what you did."

$$\frac{1}{3} \div 2 = \frac{1}{6}$$

"Show me 3 fourths. Show me that much separated into six groups in equal amounts. How much did you end up with in each group?" ("An eighth") "Record what you did."

$$\frac{3}{4} \div 6 = \frac{1}{8}$$

And so on. (The case of a mixed number divided by a whole number is dealt with similarly.)

Using fraction cakes to divide a mixed number by a fraction

"Show me a one and a half together. Show me that much separated into fourths. How many fourths did you get?" ("Six") "Record what you did."

$$1\tfrac{1}{2} \div \tfrac{1}{4} = 6$$

"Show me 2 ones and a fourth together. Show me that much separated into eighths. How many eighths did you get?" ("Eighteen") "Record what you did."

$$2\tfrac{1}{4} \div \tfrac{1}{8} = 18$$

And so on. (The case of a whole number divided by a fraction is dealt with similarly.)

Using fraction cakes to divide a mixed number by a mixed number

"Show me 2 ones and a third together. Show me that much separated into groups the size of a one and a sixth together. How many groups did you get?" ("Two") "Record what you did."

$$2\tfrac{1}{3} \div 1\tfrac{1}{6} = 2$$

"Show me 3 ones and a half together. Show me that much separated into groups the size of 2 ones and a third together. How many groups did you get?" ("One and a half") "Record what you did."

$$3\tfrac{1}{2} \div 2\tfrac{1}{3} = 1\tfrac{1}{2}$$

And so on. (The cases of a fraction or a whole number divided by a mixed number is dealt with similarly.)

Note that what students record each time is only part of the solution process for dividing fractions, whole numbers, and mixed numbers. Thus once they get everything recorded, the strategy is the same as before with multiplying fractions, to have them look for patterns in what they have recorded that they might discover how to work with only the numbers themselves to get the same answers. The objective is to have them arrive at the following generalization:

> ✔ To divide when fractions are involved, DON'T DIVIDE. Rather, flip the divisor (written as a fraction) upside down and multiply in keeping with the rules for multiplying fractions.

Fraction-Decimal-Percent Array Cards (p. 137)

A puzzle on fraction-decimal-percent equivalences.

The **Fraction-Decimal-Percent array cards** are to be cut out and placed next to one another to where the edges of the cards connect equivalent fractions, decimals, and percents. When this is done, the cards should appear as follows:

Fraction-Decimal-Percent Dominoes

A game for two to four on fraction-decimal-percent equivalences.

Materials:

One set of Fraction-Decimal-Percent Dominoes (pp. 134-136) per group.

Directions:

The same as for Equivalent Fraction Dominoes.

Some examples of some matches for the Fraction-Decimal-Percent Dominoes would be the "3 / 10" and ".3," the ".5" and "50%," and the "point seven five" and the three-fourths shaded square.

Fraction-Decimal-Percent Rummy

A game for two to four on fraction-decimal-percent equivalences.

Materials:

One deck of Fraction-Decimal-Percent Rummy cards (pp. 138-144) per group.

Directions:

The same as for Decimal Rummy.

An example of a spread for the Fraction-Decimal-Percent Rummy cards would be the "0.1," "1 / 10," and "2 / 20." An example of a book the "10%" as well.

To increase the complexity of the game, allow "runs" and "ones." A run is a sequence of three or more cards that increases by tenths such as the "1 / 2," "0.6," and "70%." A one is three or more cards that sum to one such as the "1 / 4," "1 / 5," "0.25," and "30%."

Geo Pieces (pp. 173-174)

A set of manipulatives for exercising geometric vocabulary and illustrating certain geometric principles. A classroom set of them would consist of one set per student.

The things one can have students do with the Geo Pieces are many and varied as illustrated below. The last two are of particular importance in that they illustrate that the sum of the measures of the angles of a polygon is determined by the number of sides of the polygon. Thus the last two can be used to draw attention to the fact that the sum of the measures of the angles of a triangle is always 180°.

Find the piece(s) with the longest side. (H)   The shortest side. (A, B, D, E, I, K) The most sides. (A)

Use B and E to make a shape with three sides. Four sides.

Game for two: Close your eyes and take five pieces. Open your eyes and count the sides of the pieces. Score one for the most sides. Repeat. The first player to three wins.

Game for two: Close your eyes and take two pieces. Open your eyes and use the pieces to make a shape with as few sides as possible. Score one for the least number of sides. Repeat. The first player to three wins.

If B costs 1 cent, how much would A cost? (6 cents) E cost? (3 cents) F cost? (8 cents) J cost? (4 cents)

If the perimeter of B is three, what is the perimeter of A? (6) E? (5) F? (8) I? (4) J? (6) K? (6) L? (8)

If the perimeter of B is 12 centimeters, make a shape with a perimeter of 20 centimeters. 40 centimeters. 60 centimeters. 80 centimeters. One meter.

Complete the pattern: B, G, D, . . . (3 sides, 4 sides, 3 sides, . . .)

Find 10 pairs of pieces for which the area of one is half the area of the other. Now find one more. (A and E, C and G, C and K, D and J, F and J, G and H, G and I, G and L, H and K, I and K, K and L, and perhaps some others)

How tall a tower can you make if each piece of the tower must lie entirely within the piece it is on? (A five-piece tower is the tallest tower possible.)

Which pieces are mirror symmetric along a diagonal? (A, F, I, and L)

What's the rule?
a. B, C, D, H, and J (Triangle)
b. C, D, H, I, K, and L (Right angle)
c. A, B, D, E, I, and K (Short edge)

Use B and E to make a parallelogram.

Use B, D, E, and F to make a six-sided shape with two and only two pairs of parallel sides.

Using only four pieces, make a shape with no parallel sides.

Game for two: Mark a point on a piece of paper. Then close your eyes and take five shapes. Open your eyes and take turns placing a corner of your pieces on the point. Do **not** overlap the pieces. Score one for playing the last piece. Repeat. The first player to three wins.

If the smallest angle in D is one, what is the sum of the angles for B? (6) C? (6) H? (6) J? (6) E? (12) F? (12) G? (12) I? (12) K? (12) L? (12) A? (24)

Make a shape with five sides. If the smallest angle in D is one, what is the sum of the shape's angles? (18)

Geopolis

A game for two on three-dimensional solids.

Materials:

For each group, a Geopolis gameboard (pp. 184-185) and two dice. For each player, a marker and eight counters of a particular color.

Directions:

For best results, precede with the worksheets on vertices, faces, and edges on pages 182-183.

To begin, the players put their markers on the Start arrow on the gameboard. Then each player rolls the dice. The player rolling the higher total plays first.

To play, the players take turns rolling the dice and moving their markers along the gameboard as many spaces as the total on the dice. Then, in keeping with what is written on the space a player lands on, the player puts a counter in the center of the gameboard on a shape which satisfies what is written on the space. To illustrate, if a player were to land on the space with E = 12 (edges equal 12) written on it, the player would put a counter on shape B, G, M, or Q.

Once a player puts a counter on a shape, the other player cannot put a counter on the shape. The first player to put counters on eight shapes wins.

To make the game self-instructional, provide students with a handout giving the following "technical" information:

CONE: The pointy one you put ice cream on

CONGRUENT: Same size, same shape

CUBE: A square box

CYLINDER: Most tin cans are cylinders.

HEMISPHERE: Half a ball

POLYHEDRON: Three-dimensional and flat everywhere

PRISM: Describing one is harder than identifying one: A prism is a polyhedron having parallelograms as sides and parallel, congruent polygons as bases. A good place to look for prisms is on chandeliers.

PYRAMID: Not just a tourist attraction in Egypt, but any shape with a flat base and triangular sides, the latter of which come to a point

SPHERE: A ball

SPHEROID: A football

Grid Paper (p. 208)

A page of 1-centimeter grid paper.

A major use of grid paper is to find the areas of non-polygonal shapes such as circles, hands, and feet. The shapes are drawn or traced on the grid paper, and the areas of the shapes are found by counting the squares and bits of squares they encompass.

Grids and Drigs (p. 39)

A worksheet on whole number arithmetic. With different numbers, as with the blank Grids and Drigs on page 40, a worksheet on fractions, decimals, and percents.

For **Grids and Drigs**, a "grid" is a straightforward statement of an arithmetic problem, a "drig" a variation of a grid. Thus for **Grids and Drigs**, problems 1, 3, and 5 are grids, problems 2, 4, and 6 drigs. The answer to each problem is given below.

1.

	6	15	48	102
+ 7	13	22	55	109
− 5	1	10	43	97
× 2	12	30	96	204
÷ 3	2	5	16	34

2.

	8	24	88	212
+ 9	17	33	97	221
− 6	2	18	82	206
× 3	24	72	264	636
÷ 4	2	6	22	53

3.

	35	80	215	1760
+ 28	63	108	243	1788
− 23	12	57	192	1737
× 4	140	320	860	7040
÷ 5	7	16	43	352

4.

	28	63	105	2114
+ 35	63	98	140	2149
− 14	14	49	91	2100
× 5	140	315	525	10570
÷ 7	4	9	15	302

5.

	60	96	204	4272
+ 44	104	140	248	4316
− 54	6	42	150	4218
× 23	1380	2208	4692	98256
÷ 12	5	8	17	356

6.

	50	75	325	4000
+ 16	66	91	341	4016
− 42	8	33	283	3958
× 16	800	1200	5200	64000
÷ 25	2	3	13	160

Helicopter Cutouts (p. 260)

A pattern for making 10 helicopters.

The helicopters are used with the blank **Verifying Probabilities** table on page 259 to verify the extent to which helicopters fall within a predetermined area the expected number of times. To this end, have students lay out some tiles, mark off a certain number of them, and drop a great many helicopters on them to see if each of them gets its "fair share" of helicopters. To illustrate, in the photographs below the objective was to see how nearly four out of 64 helicopters would land on a particular four of the 64 tiles.

Dropping helicopters onto an eight-by-eight array of tiles

Missing twice in a row, a probability of $(60 / 64)^2 = (15 / 16)^2 = 225 / 256$

Homonym Hunt (p. 160)

An integration of math and language arts on addition.

The answers are as follows:

1.

Clue	Word	Homonym	Score
One twenty-fourth of a day	Hour	Our	10
One............street sign	Way	Weigh	10
The opposite of day	Night	Knight	20
Sixteen divided by 8	Two	Too	12
The window .... was broken	Pane	Pain	4
A father's boy	Son	Sun	9
A deaf person can't do this	Hear	Here	14
Ships sail in this body of water	Sea	See	13
A cub's mother	Bear	Bare	14
A fruit	Pear	Pare	14
A vegetable	Carrot	Karat	17
		Total	137

2. Answers will vary, but words like:

Buy -by - bye
Cite - sight - site
Ewe - yew - you
For - fore - four

Hi - hie - high
Oar - or - ore
Right - rite - write
Sew - so - sow

Leapfrog (p. 274)

An investigation of the "famous" Leapfrog puzzle.

The **Leapfrog puzzle** yields the number pattern 3, 8, 15, 24, 35, 48, 63, 80, 99, 120, . . . which determines the rule for figuring the minimum number of jumps to reverse the tees about the center hole in the puzzle in terms of the number of tees on either side of the center hole. For **N** such tees, the rule is $N^2 + 2N$ jumps.

As explained in advanced courses in algebra, the key to knowing that the rule would include an N^2 term was to note that it would take two successive differences to reduce the number pattern to a constant:

```
3
  \ 8 − 3 = 5
8 /              \ 7 − 5 = 2
  \ 15 − 8 = 7   /
15 \            \ 9 − 7 = 2
  \ 24 − 15 = 9 /
24 \            \ 11 − 9 = 2
  \ 35 − 24 = 11/
35 \            \ 13 − 11 = 2
  \ 48 − 35 = 13/
48 \            \ 15 − 13 = 2
  \ 63 − 48 = 15/
63 \            \ 17 − 15 = 2
  \ 80 − 63 = 17/
80 \            \ 19 − 17 = 2
  \ 99 − 80 = 19/
99 \            \ 21 − 19 = 2
  \ 120 − 99 = 21/
120
```

The answers to the questions for the **Leapfrog puzzle** are as follows:

1. Yes, but only 168 jumps are needed.
2. 255
3. $N^2 + 2N$

Lengths of Curves (p. 216)

A counting exercise on determining lengths.

The answers are as follows:

a. 13
b. 15
c. 16
d. 39
e. 16

f. 15
g. 87
h. 32
i. 31

Lengths of Edges of Squares (p. 217)

An exercise on literally seeing square roots.

The exercise relies on two major points: One, the square root of, say, N is the number which times itself is N. Two, a number times itself is the area of a square. Thus the square root of N can be visualized as the length of an edge of a square of area N.

The answers for the exercise are as follows:

a. $\sqrt{8}$ g. $\sqrt{26}$

b. $\sqrt{18}$ h. $\sqrt{4}$

c. $\sqrt{32}$ i. $\sqrt{9}$

d. $\sqrt{5}$ j. $\sqrt{25}$

e. $\sqrt{10}$ k. $\sqrt{16}$

f. $\sqrt{17}$

Lengths of Segments (p. 218)

The reverse of Lengths of Edges of Squares.

Line Designs (pp. 190-197)

Eight patterns for making line designs.

A **line design** is a design made by connecting points made to correspond to one another with lines to where the lines appear to be curved. The basis for such a design is a right angle whose sides meet two conditions: One, they are the same in length. Two, they exhibit the same number of equidistant dots. An example of such an angle and how it is made into a line design is given in Figure 18.

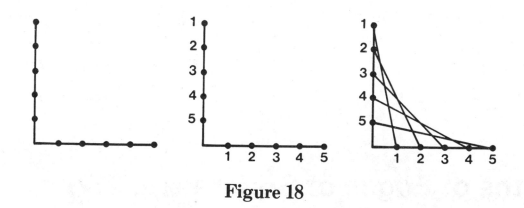

Figure 18

To alter the basic design, one varies on the relative lengths of the sides, the number of dots, and the size of the angle as illustrated in Figure 19.

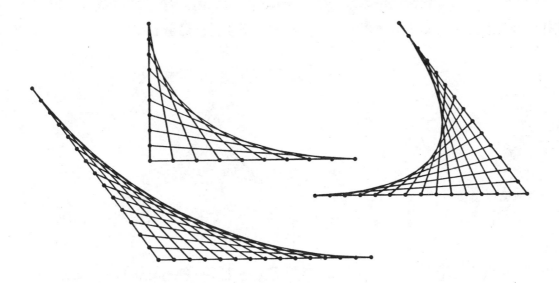

Figure 19

And to elaborate on the basic design, one combines angles as in Figure 20.

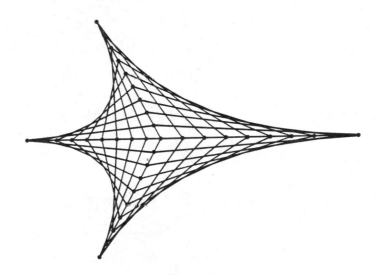

Figure 20

Note than an endless variety of line designs is possible.

The line designs for the eight patterns for making line designs are as follows:

Page 190: Shield

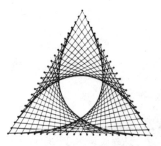

Page 191: Dart

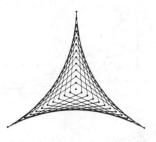

Page 192: Black Hole

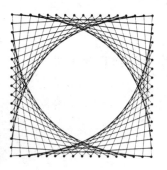

Page 193: Frosty Window

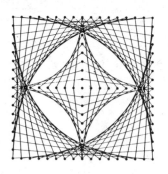

Page 194: Flying Saucer

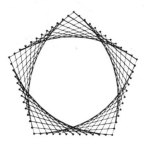

Page 195: Web

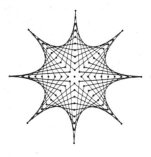

Page 196: Whirlpool

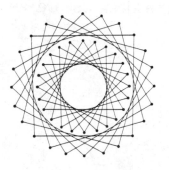

Page 197: Kaleidoscope

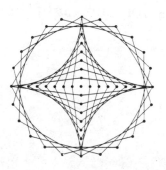

Make-a-Whole

A game for two to four on addition and subtraction of fractions in terms of fraction cakes.

Materials:

One Make-a-Whole spinner (p. 82) per group. (To construct the spinner, see SPINNERS.) One set of large fraction cakes (pp. 83-92) per player.

Directions:

To begin, each player puts a unit fraction cake, the one on page 83, face up in front of him or her to serve as his or her gameboard. Then each player spins the spinner. The player spinning the highest fraction plays first. The play rotates clockwise.

To play, a player spins the spinner and, if space permits, puts on his or her gameboard a fraction cake the size of the fraction showing on the spinner. If space does not permit, the player removes from his or her gameboard a fraction cake the size of the fraction showing on the spinner.

The first player to "make a whole," that is, to exactly cover the unit comprising his or her gameboard, wins.

Variation:

To emphasize addition and subtraction of fractions in symbolic form, have players play the game with only the spinner and paper and pen or pencil to keep track of what WOULD be on the gameboards if they and the fraction cakes WERE being used.

McDonald's Hamburgers Worksheet (p. 81)

A problem solving activity involving numbers in the billions, namely, the billions of hamburgers McDonald's Hamburgers has sold. To ease the burden of the computation involved, have students use a pocket calculator for the computation.

The thrust of the activity is to arrive at visualizations of numbers in the billions that students might better appreciate the enormity of such numbers.

The answers for the activity in terms of 10 billion hamburgers are as follows:

1. a. $[(10\,000\,000\,000 \times 2) \div 12] \div 5280 = 315{,}656.55$ miles high

   b. A stack of 10 billion hamburgers would reach the moon $315\,656.55 \div 238\,857 = 1.3215294$ times.

2. a. $[(6 \times 12 + 2 \times 10) \times 12] \div 4 = 276$ hamburgers per 4-inch strip of highway

   $\{[(10\,000\,000\,000 \div 276) \times 4] \div 12\} \div 5280 = 2287.3662$ miles long

   b. Little Rock, Arkansas and Seattle, Washington (2277 miles), New Orleans, Louisiana and San Francisco, California (2262 miles), or Portland, Oregon and Houston, Texas (2233 miles)

3. a. $[(10\,000\,000\,000 \times 3.7) \div 16] \div 2000 = 1{,}156{,}250$ tons

   b. Ten billion hamburgers would weigh a little more than 192,708 elephants. $(1\,156\,250 \div 6 = 192\,708.33)$

4. a. $10\,000\,000\,000 \div 2400 = 4{,}166{,}666.6$ gallons (of mustard)

   b. The mustard used in making 10 billion hamburgers would fill more than 160 railroad tank cars. $(4\,166\,666.6 \div 26\,000 = 160.2564)$

5. a. $10\,000\,000\,000 \div 300 = 33{,}333{,}333$ gallons (of ketchup)

   b. The ketchup used in making 10 billion hamburgers would be enough to paint the District of Columbia more than 11 times. $[(33\,333\,333 \times 650) \div (5280^2 \times 69.245) = 11.223693]$

6. a. $10\,000\,000\,000 \div 350 = 28{,}571{,}428$ gallons (of pickles)

   b. The jars of pickles used in making 10 billion hamburgers would be enough to go around Long Island, New York $\{[(28\,571\,428 \times 6.5) \div 12] \div 5280\} \div 300 = 9.7703216$ times.

Metric Array Cards

Two puzzles on the structure of the metric system. The one on page 227 is on the arithmetic meaning of kilo- (k), centi- (c), and milli- (m): 1000, 0.01, and 0.001, respectively. And the one on page 228 is on the metric conversions as listed under **Metric Conversion Concentration**.

The cards in each set of **Metric Array cards** are to be cut out and placed next to one another to where the edges of the cards connect equivalent measurements. When this is done, the cards should appear as follows:

Page 227:

1 km 1000 m 1 L 1000 mL	1200 m 10 mm 1 cm	1.2 km 1.2 m 120 cm
0.75 m 75 cm 25 cm .25 m	10 cm 100 mm 1 m 100 cm	1 mg 0.001 g
2.5 cm	25 mm	0.5 km 500 m

Page 228:

The weight of 100 mL of water 10 g	100 g 1 kg	The weight of 500 mL of water 500 g The weight of 1000 L of water
The weight of 10 mL of water 1 m³	The weight of 1 L of water 1 L 1 dm³	1 t The weight of 1 mL of water 1 g 100 kg
1000 L	1 mL The weight of 0.001 mL of water 1 mg	The weight of 100 L of water The weight of 10 L of water 10 kg

Metric Calipers (p. 225)

Three metric calipers, each of which should look like the following when assembled:

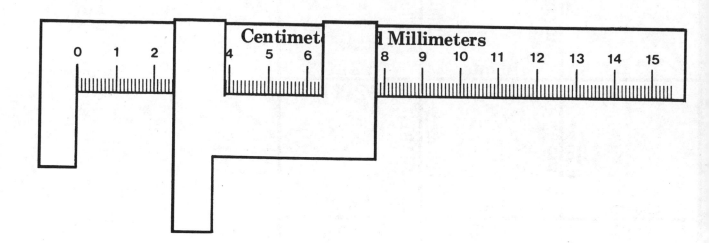

A metric caliper is used to measure round things like coins, fingers, and pencils.

Metric Conversion Concentration

A game for two to four on metric conversions.

Materials:

One set of Metric Conversion Concentration cards (pp. 231-232) per group.

Directions:

The same as for Metric Prefix Concentration.

The key conversions for the Metric Conversion Concentration cards are the following:

One cubic centimeter (cm^3) occupies 1 milliliter (mL).

One cubic decimeter (dm^3) occupies 1 liter (L).

One cubic meter (m^3) occupies 1000 liters (L).

One milliliter (mL) of water weighs 1 gram (g).

One liter (L) of water weighs 1 kilogram (kg).

One thousand liters (L) of water weighs 1000 kilograms (kg) or 1 metric ton (t).

To make the game self-instructional, have students play it with a copy of the Metric Reference Sheet on page 223 on hand.

Metric Mastery

A game for two to four on the metric system.

Materials:

For each group, a die, a ruler graduated in centimeters and millimeters (p. 224), a Metric Mastery gameboard (pp. 240-241), a deck of Metric Mastery cards (Questions, pp. 242-247, Chance, pp. 248-249), and a Metric Mastery key (p. 250). For each player, a marker.

Directions:

In preparation, the Metric Mastery cards are shuffled and placed on the gameboard in the spaces provided.

To begin, the players put their markers on the Start square on the gameboard. Then each player rolls the die. The player rolling the highest number plays first. The play rotates clockwise.

To play, a player draws a Question card and answers the question on the card. Then the player checks his or her answer to the question using the Metric Mastery key. If incorrect, the play goes to the next player. If correct, the player rolls the die and moves his or her marker around the gameboard as many squares as the number showing on the die. If the player lands on a Chance square, the player draws a Chance card and does what it says. The play then goes to the next player.

The first player to reach the Finish square on the gameboard wins.

Note that the gameboard is self-instructional in that it illustrates the terminology and key equivalences of the metric system.

Metric Prefix Concentration

A game for two to four on metric prefixes.

Materials:

One set of Metric Prefix Concentration cards (pp. 229-230) per group.

Directions:

To begin, the players decide on a "dealer." The dealer shuffles the cards and spreads them out face down to make a four-by-four array. The player to the left of the dealer plays first. The play rotates clockwise.

To play, a player draws two cards from the array. If the cards exhibit equivalent measurements, the player keeps the cards and continues to draw cards two at a time until he or she draws two cards which do not exhibit equivalent measurements, in which case he or she returns the cards which do not exhibit equivalent measurements to the array exactly as they were, and the play goes to the next player.

The key to determining equivalent measurements is knowing that kilo- means 1000, centi- 0.01, and milli- 0.001. Then for the cards,

$$1 \text{ mg (milligram)} = 0.001 \text{ g (grams)}$$

$$1 \text{ cm (centimeter)} = 0.01 \text{ m (meters)}$$

$$1 \text{ L (liter)} = 1000 \text{ mL (milliliters)}$$

$$1 \text{ m (meter)} = 0.001 \text{ km (kilometers)}$$

$$3.5 \text{ cm (centimeters)} = 35 \text{ mm (millimeters)}$$

$$3.5 \text{ m (meters)} = 350 \text{ cm (centimeters)}$$

$$1 \text{ kg (kilogram)} = 1000 \text{ g (grams)}$$

$$3.5 \text{ km (kilometers)} = 3500 \text{ m (meters)}$$

The player with the most cards after all the cards have been paired wins.

To make the game self-instructional, have students play it with a copy of the Metric Reference Sheet on page 223 on hand.

Metric Proverbs (p. 235)

A language arts activity on the metric units.

The answers for **Metric Proverbs** in terms of the most commonly used metric units are given below:

1. Mile (kilometer)
2. Peck (liter)
3. Inch (centimeter), mile (kilometer)
4. Nine feet (3 meters)
5. Mile (kilometer)
6. Ounce (gram), pound (kilogram)
7. Ten-foot (3-meter)
8. Mile (kilometer)
9. Ten gallon (33 liter)
10. Pound (kilogram)
11. Bushel (liter)
12. Ton (metric ton or 1000 kilograms)
13. Mile (kilometer)
14. Bushel (liter), peck (liter)
15. Pound (kilogram)

Metric Reference Sheet (p. 223)

A list of the most commonly used metric units.

The **Metric Reference Sheet** is used with **Metric Conversion Concentration** and **Metric Prefix Concentration** for self-instructional purposes. It was prepared in keeping with the following table from the **METRIC GUIDE FOR EDUCATIONAL MATERIALS,** a publication of the American National Metric Council, as were all of the metric materials in **MATH GAMES & ACTIVITIES.**

SI Unit Prefixes

Multiplication Factor	Prefix	Symbol	Pronunciation (USA)*	Term (USA)	Term (Other Countries)
$1\,000\,000\,000\,000\,000\,000 = 10^{18}$	exa	E	ex'a (a as in about)	one quintillion✔	one trillion
$1\,000\,000\,000\,000\,000 = 10^{15}$	peta	P	as in petal	one quadrillion✔	one thousand billion
$1\,000\,000\,000\,000 = 10^{12}$	tera	T	as in terrace	one trillion✔	one billion
$1\,000\,000\,000 = 10^{9}$	giga	G	jig'a (a as in about)	one billion✔	one milliard
$1\,000\,000 = 10^{6}$	mega	M	as in megaphone	one million	
$1\,000 = 10^{3}$	kilo	k	as in kilowatt	one thousand	
$100 = 10^{2}$	hecto	h★	heck'toe	one hundred	
$10 = 10$	deka	da★	deck'a (a as in about)	ten	
$0.1 = 10^{-1}$	deci	d★	as in decimal	one tenth	
$0.01 = 10^{-2}$	centi	c★	as in sentiment	one hundredth	
$0.001 = 10^{-3}$	milli	m	as in military	one thousandth	
$0.000\,001 = 10^{-6}$	micro		as in microphone	one millionth	
$0.000\,000\,001 = 10^{-9}$	nano	n	nan'oh (an as in ant)	one billionth✔	one milliardth
$0.000\,000\,000\,001 = 10^{-12}$	pico	p	peek'oh	one trillionth✔	one billionth
$0.000\,000\,000\,000\,001 = 10^{-15}$	femto	f	fem'toe (fem as in feminine)	one quadrillionth✔	one thousand billionth
$0.000\,000\,000\,000\,000\,001 = 10^{-18}$	atto	a	as in anatomy	one quintillionth✔	one trillionth

* The first syllable of every prefix is accented to assure that the prefix will retain its identity. Therefore, the preferred pronunciation of kilometer places the accent on the first syllable, not the second.

★ These prefixes have limited usage.

✔ These terms should be avoided in technical writing because the names for denominations above one million and below one millionth are different in most other countries, as indicated in the last column.

As for the limited usage of hecto-, deka-, deci-, and centi- referred to in the table, the primary use of hecto- and deka- is in illustrating the decimal nature of the metric systrem, that of deci- in defining the liter and in providing young children with a convenient measure, and that of centi- with meter. In general, the only prefixes used are kilo-, centi-, and milli-, but even they are restricted in use: Although all three of them are used with meter, only milli- is used with liter, and only kilo- and milli- are used with gram.

Metrics Makes for Tens (p. 226)

A measuring activity on the base ten structure of the metric system.

The lengths of the segments on **Metrics Makes for Tens** from top to bottom are as follows: 17cm, 16 cm, 15 cm, 14 cm, 12 cm, 11 cm, 9 cm, and 6 cm. Thus when the lengths are added, they illustrate that **1000 mm = 100 cm = 10 dm (= 1 m)**, that is, that the metric prefixes are related by powers of tens.

Mirror Symmetry (pp. 188-189, 198-200)

Two self-correcting worksheets on mirror symmetry and three worksheets on drawing mirror images.

A **mirror symmetric figure** is a figure with a "line of symmetry," a line along which a figure can be folded so as to make the figure coincide with itself or along which a mirror can be placed so as to reproduce in the mirror the half of the figure blocked out by the mirror. Two examples of mirror symmetric figures are given below. As indicated with dotted lines, the figure on the left has one line of symmetry, the figure on the right,   four lines of symmetry.

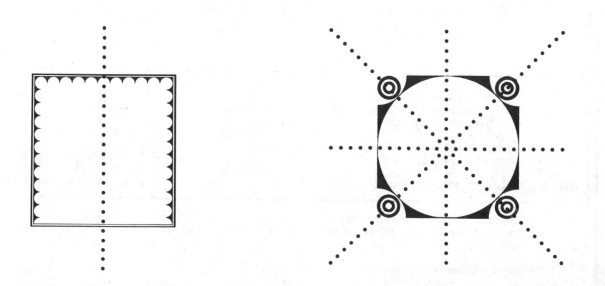

A **mirror image** is the reflection, real or imaginary, of a figure about a line.

To illustrate, the mirror image of segment AB about line ℓ below is segment A'B', and vice versa.

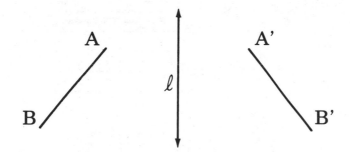

The answers for the worksheets are as follows:

Page 188:

Figures a, b, c, d, e, g, and h are mirror symmetric.

Page 189:

3. a. 90⁰

   b. 60⁰

   c. 45⁰

   d. 36⁰

   e. 30⁰

   f. 22½⁰

Page 198:

1. a. Four units
   b. Two units
   c. (2,4)
   d. (2,-4)

2. a. Five units
   b. Four units
   c. (5,4)
   d. (-5,4)

Page 199:

a.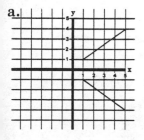

b.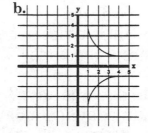

c.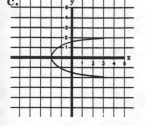

d.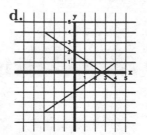

a.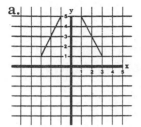

b.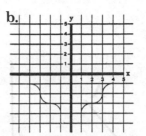

c.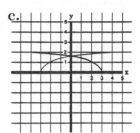

d.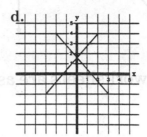

Missing Letter Problem Solving (p. 167)

An integration of math and language arts on problem solving.

Missing Letter Problem Solving is presented as follows: Find the question; find the answer. The objective is to motivate problem solving. A variation on the exercise is to have students use the same format to write questions for one another to work out.

The questions and answers for the worksheet are as follows:

1. How many days in two weeks? (14)
2. Two days are the same as how many hours? (48)
3. What is 6 times 9? (54)
4. Counting by tens, what comes after 34? (40)
5. How many eggs in three dozen eggs? (36)
6. If Mary is seven, and Bill is twice her age, how old is Bill? (14)
7. Which is larger, 5 times 4 or 8 times 2? (Five times 4)
8. How many pints in 3 quarts? (6)
9. How many sides do 10 squares have? (40)
10. Leap year has how many days? (366)
11. What is the difference between 20 and 7? (13)
12. Sixty is how much more than 42? (18)

Mixed Facts Array Cards (p. 25)

A puzzle on mixed facts.

The **Mixed Facts array cards** are to be cut out and placed next to one another to where the edges of the cards connect basic facts. When this is done, the cards should appear as follows:

$7 + 8$ $12 - 8$ 4	$18 \div 6$ 9	$2 + 4$ 42
15	3 2×5 10	9×7 $14 - 7$ 7
8	6×8	9
$17 - 9$ $30 \div 6$	72 $9 + 6$	$72 \div 8$ 18
	5	

Motley and Mates (p. 60)

Miniatures of Motley Crab Adder, The Scruffy Twin Subtractors, Sir Crab Multiplier, The Impeccable Twin Dividers, The Great Legalizer, and The Magnificent Equalizer.

The major use of **Motley and Mates** is in making transparencies and task cards for arithmetic word problems.

Motley Crab Adder (pp. 54)

The personification of addition as combining.

Motley Crab Adder is used to help students understand arithmetic word problems as explained below and illustrated in the appendix. If colored, he makes an attractive item for the bulletin board. If enlarged, as with an overhead projector, and colored, he makes an attractive poster. And since he is independent of computational skill, he can be talked about to even the lowest of achievers to help them see the mathematics implicit in the world around them.

An introduction to Motley would go something like this:

"Meet **Motley Crab Adder**, a strange character indeed. He always combines things. That's just the way he is. No one knows why.

"People have talked to him about this and have told him that he is strange because of it. They have even suggested that he see a psychiatrist. But he just smiles and goes on combining things.

"Also, when he combines things, he combines them in just any old way. This shows in his sloppy appearance and is why his first name is Motley.

"And look at all the things he can do!" (Mime some of the following:

> Raking grass or leaves
>
> Saving money in a piggy bank
>
> Putting letters in a mail box
>
> Putting on make-up
>
> Making a sandwich

"Can you show me these things he can do?" (Have students mime some of the following:

> Putting a puzzle together
>
> Putting toys in a toy box
>
> Building a rock wall
>
> Assembling something like a kite
> or a train set
>
> Packing a suitcase

Explaining Motley Crab Adder

To see how **Motley Crab Adder** helps students solve arithmetic word problems, consider him in relation to **The Scruffy Twin Subtractors** (p. 55), **Sir Crab Multiplier** (p. 56), and **The Impeccable Twin Dividers** (p. 57). Motley, the Scruffy Twins, Sir Crab, and the Impeccable Twins are personifications of the actions of combining, separating, combining "neatly" (by twos, threes, fours, and so on), and separating "neatly" (into twos, threes, fours, and so on), respectively -- of the kinds of actions taken with real things in the real world that can be interpreted mathematically: combining corresponds to addition, separating to subtraction, combining neatly to multiplication, and separating neatly to division.

The importance of Motley and mates is then seen in relation to the following four-step problem solving process for arithmetic word problems:

1. Understand the problem.

2. Decide what to do -- to add, subtract, multiply, or divide.

3. Do it.

4. Check the reasonableness of results.

Motley and mates help get things started. They help with Steps 1 and 2 in the problem solving process that whatever Step 3, paper-and-pencil or pocket calculator skills are known might be put to use.

To illustrate, suppose students were taught about addition as combining, subtraction as separating, multiplication as combining neatly, and division as separating neatly. Then to solve an arithmetic word problem, all they would have to do to get started is ask two questions:

1. What's happening, combining or separating?

2. How's it happening, just happening or happening neatly?

In so doing, they will come to see, for example, that throwing groceries into a shopping basket is combining, that making change is separating, that building a brick wall is combining neatly, and that sharing equitably with friends is separating neatly. In other words, that in related problems they should add, subtract, multiply, and divide, respectively.

The thing to keep in mind when helping children solve arithmetic word problems is that every combining action involves a separating action, and vice versa, just as every addition problem involves a subtraction problem, and vice versa. To illustrate, the action of combining groceries in a shopping basket presupposes the action of separating groceries from a shelf. Thus the key to helping students solve arithmetic word problems is to have them focus on the **pertinent** action.

To better appreciate Motley, the Scruffy Twins, Sir Crab, and the Impeccable Twins, they, in combination with **The Great Legalizer** (p. 58) and **The Magnificent Equalizer** (p. 59), illustrate the sum total of the ideas that are fundamental to the processes that are used over and over again in basic mathematics. (**The Great Legalizer** is the personification of the need in computing with whole numbers to regroup. **The Magnificent Equalizer** that of the need in working with fractions to make things "different yet the same" -- different in appearance, yet the same in quantity.)

Multiplication (Combining Neatly) Dominoes

A game for two to four on multiplication as combining "neatly" (by twos, threes, fours, and so on).

Materials:

One set of Multiplication (Combining Neatly) Dominoes (pp. 64-66) per group.

Directions:

The same as for Equivalent Fraction Dominoes.

Some examples of some matches for the Multiplication (Combining Neatly) Dominoes would be the "2 × 3" and "two times three," the "2 × 4" and "four combined neatly two times," and the "three combined neatly four times" and the three-by-four arrangement of squares.

Perimeters of Polygons (p. 221)

An extension of Applying the Pythagorean Theorem.

The answers are as follows:

a. $3 + 2\sqrt{2} + \sqrt{5}$

b. $2 + 2\sqrt{10}$

c. $7 + 3\sqrt{2} + \sqrt{5}$

d. $3\sqrt{2} + \sqrt{5} + \sqrt{17}$

e. $1 + \sqrt{2} + \sqrt{5} + 2\sqrt{13}$

Place Value Words (p. 159)

An integration of math and language arts on place value.

The answers are as follows:

1. Words like **blow, dirt, chow, blot, clot,** and **time**

2. a. 31
   b. 40
   c. 1111
   d. 2011
   e. 220
   f. 2110
   g. 2021
   h. 1102
   i. 3001

3. A word like **lint**
4. Answers will vary.
5. Wednesday
6. Answers will vary.

PMDAS (p. 170)

An integration of math and language arts on the order of operations.

PMDAS is a pocket calculator activity on the order of operations, that unless specified otherwise with parentheses, brackets, and braces, the order is multiplication or division, whichever comes first (reading from left to right), then addition or subtraction, whichever comes first (again, reading from left to right).

The answers for the worksheet are as follows:

1. 807 - LOB
2. 637 - LEg
3. 5604 - hOgS
4. 771 - ILL
5. 3045 - ShOE
6. 461375 - SLEIgh
7. 514 - hIS
8. 35336 - gEESE
9. 5507 - LOSS
10. 7738 - BELL
11. 7716 - gILL
12. 638 - BEg
13. 338 - BEE
14. 607 - LOg
15. 3507 - LOSE
16. 57718 - BILLS
17. 77345 - ShELL
18. 3705 - SOLE
19. 3504 - hOSE
20. 3704 - hOLE

Qwazy Qwilt (p. 215)

A mind boggler on area.

Qwazy Qwilt is used to draw attention to area as a covering instead of simply a multiplication problem. As is, the area of the 8-by-8 square on **Qwazy Qwilt** is 64. However, when the square is cut into the four pieces specified by the dotted lines on the square and made into a 5-by-13 rectangle, its area is 65! The reason: The pieces do not actually form a rectangle. Rather, if they are squared at the corners as they would be for a rectangle, they leave uncovered a very thin parallelogram of area one in the center.

Regular Dodecahedron Cutout (p. 180)

See CUBE CUTOUT.

Regular Icosahedron Cutout (p. 181)

See CUBE CUTOUT.

Regular Octahedron Cutout (p. 179)

See CUBE CUTOUT.

Regular Tetrahedron Cutout (p. 177)

See CUBE CUTOUT.

Rotational Symmetry (pp. 202-203)

Two worksheets on rotational symmetry, the first of which is self-correcting.

A **rotationally symmetric figure** is a figure with a "point of symmetry," a point about which a figure can be rotated and made to coincide with itself more than once in one complete revolution. The "degree of rotational symmetry" of the figure is then the minimum number of degrees in which the figure can be made to coincide with itself. An example of a rotationally symmetric figure is given below.

In that the "flower" in the example can be made to coincide with itself six times in one complete revolution, its degree of rotational symmetry is 60°, one-sixth of 360°.

The answers for the worksheets are as follows:

Page 202:

Figures a, b, d, e, f, g, h, i, and k are rotationally symmetric.

Page 203:

1. a. 90°
   b. 90°
   c. 30°
   d. 45°
   e. 15°
   f. 72°
   g. 60°
   h. 90°
   i. Almost 28°
   j. 180°
   k. 90°

2. I, O, S, X, Z

As a follow-up to the worksheets, consider having some flowers on hand for students to examine for rotational symmetry.

Rotational Symmetry Cutouts

The makings for a "hands on" experience with rotational symmetry.

The two renditions of the figure on page 201 are to be cut out and placed one on top of the other, and the one on top is to be rotated while the one beneath is held stationary. The object is to make the two coincide more than once in one complete revolution. In that they can be made to coincide four times in one complete revolution, the degree of rotational symmetry of the figure is 90°, one-fourth of 360°.

Sir Crab Multiplier (p. 56)

The personification of multiplication as combining "neatly" (by twos, threes, fours, and so on).

Sir Crab Multiplier is used to help students understand arithmetic word problems as explained under **Motley Crab Adder** and illustrated in the appendix. Like Motley, he can be made into an attractive item for the bulletin board or into an attractive poster. And also like Motley, he is independent of computational skill and can therefore be talked about to even the lowest of achievers to help them see the mathematics implicit in the world around them.

An introduction to Sir Crab would go something like this:

"Meet **Sir Crab Multiplier**, a strange character indeed. He always combines things 'neatly' (by twos, threes, fours, and so on). That's just the way he is. No one knows why.

"People have talked to him about this and have told him that regardless of all the 'neat' brick walls and things he's made, he's driving them crazy with the way he always combines things neatly. They have even suggested that the next time he wants to combine some things neatly, he stick his head in a bucket instead. But he just blows them a kiss and goes on combining things neatly.

"And marvel at how neatly he's dressed, just what you'd expect from someone who combines things neatly. No wonder he's addressed as 'Sir.'

"And look at all the things he can do!" (Mime some of the following:

Making a rug or a beaded belt

Picking four leaf clovers

Freezing water in ice cube trays

Stacking wood or timber

Exchanging dollars for pennies, nickels, dimes, or quarters a dollar at a time

"Can you show me these things he can do?" (Have students mime some of the following:

Soaking up water with a sponge

Blowing up a balloon

Buying cartons of eggs

Collecting animals for Noah's ark

Laying floor or roof tiles

Slide Symmetry (p. 205)

A self-correcting worksheet on slide symmetry.

A **slide symmetric figure** is a figure which can be made to coincide with itself by shifting it a particular distance in a particular direction. An example of a slide symmetric figure is given below.

The arrow in the example is to indicate the distance and direction of a slide which would make the figure coincide with itself. Note that many other slides which would make the figure coincide with itself are possible.

The answers for the worksheet are as follows: a, b, e, f, g, and h.

As a follow-up to the worksheet, have students examine such things as brick walls, tiled floors, and decorative borders for slide symmetry.

Slide Symmetry Cutouts

The makings for a "hands on" experience with slide symmetry.

The two renditions of the figure on page 204 are to be cut out and placed one on top of the other, and the one on top is to be slid across the one beneath it. The object is to make the two coincide in more than one way.

Space Race

A game for two to four on measuring in centimeters.

Materials:

One set of Space Race cards (pp. 237-239) per group. One Space Race gameboard (p. 236) and one centimeter / millimeter ruler (p. 224) per player.

Directions:

To begin, each player draws a card. The player drawing the card with the longest measurement on it plays first. The play rotates clockwise.

To play, a player draws a card and KEEPS it. If it is a card with instructions on it, the player does what it says. If it is a card with a measurement on it, the player constructs a segment the length of the measurement on his or her gameboard and labels the segment with its length. If it is the first segment constructed, it must start from the tip of the nose of the rocket on the gameboard. Otherwise, it must start from where the last segment left off. In either case, it may point in any direction so long as it does not pass COMPLETELY through any of the planets on the gameboard. Also, it may intersect another segment. The play then goes to the next player.

The objective is to visit all the planets on the gameboard. To visit a planet, a player must construct a segment which ends somewhere within the planet. Thus a visit to planet Cube from the tip of the rocket's nose might look like the following:

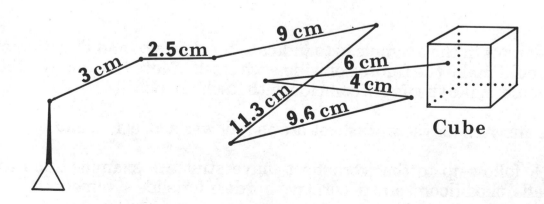

Note: The planets may be visited in any order.

The first player to visit all the planets wins.

In the event that all the cards are drawn, the cards are collected and shuffled, and the play resumes as before.

Spinners (pp. 2-3)

Twelve spinners divided into thirds, fourths, fifths, sixths, eighths, and tenths. For different numbers on the spinners, use the blank spinners on pages 4 and 5.

The first use of the spinners is as a substitute for a die or dice in a game. The second is as the makings of a game in their own right as will be explained after the following paragraph.

To make the spinners, pin them to boards or pencils with thumbtacks as in Figures 21 and 22, respectively.

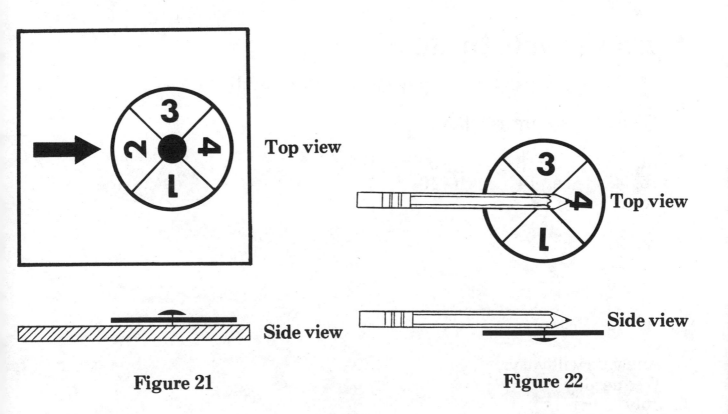

Figure 21   Figure 22

Note that in either case it is the face of the spinner that spins, and that in the first case the indicator arrow is drawn on the board, whereas in the second case the pencil itself is the indicator. To lessen the tendency of the pencil or "wand" model to yield the same number, hold the pencil horizontally.

To make a game out of the spinners, set a goal such as 21 and have students try to reach the goal by spinning two or three spinners and adding, subtracting, multiplying, or dividing the numbers indicated in any way possible. Have them record their results and keep a running total, and make the winner the first one to reach the goal.

Subtraction (Separating) Rummy

A game for two to four on subtraction as separating.

Materials:

One deck of Subtraction (Separating) Rummy cards (pp. 67-73) per group.

Directions:

The same as for Decimal Rummy except without runs.

An example of a spread for the Subtraction (Separating) Rummy cards would be the "3 — 2," "three minus two," and "two separated from three." An example of a book the picture of two separated from three as well.

Sum Vowels (p. 161)

An integration of math and language arts on addition.

The answers are as follows:

1. a. 7   d. 13   g. 5
    b. 4   e. 14   h. 10
    c. 6   f. 4   i. 7

2. a. 21
    b. 20
    c. 30
    d. 17
    e. 22

3. Answers will vary.
4. Wednesday
5. July
6. Names like Tom, Ron, and Lulu with no vowels other than an O or a U

Tessellating with Quadrilaterals (p. 207)

A variation of Tessellating with Triangles.

Tessellating with Triangles (p. 206)

A tessellation exercise.

A **tessellation** is a "tiling" or covering of a plane with non-overlapping figures as in a mosaic.

The Great Legalizer (p. 58)

The personification of the need in computing with whole numbers to regroup.

The Great Legalizer is used to help students regroup properly as explained below and illustrated for **Bank It** and **Deci-Builder**. In that **The Great Legalizer** represents one of the six processes fundamental to basic mathematics (as explained under **Motley Crab Adder**), he is worthy of display as on a bulletin board or classroom wall and is worth talking about to students. Since he is independent of computational skill, he can be displayed and talked about to even the lowest of achievers.

An introduction to **The Great Legalizer** would go something like this:

"Meet **The Great Legalizer**, the keeper of the law in the different lands. He always blows his whistle to remind someone with too many of one thing alike to exchange them for one of the next larger thing. You see, the law in two land is 'Never, never get caught with two or more things alike else GO TO JAIL!' The law in three land is 'Never, never get caught with three or more things alike else GO TO JAIL!' The law in four land is 'Never, never get caught with four or more things alike else GO TO JAIL!'" And so on.

"So what would **The Great Legalizer** do if he saw someone with, say, two things alike in two land?" (Blow his whistle to remind them to exchange them for one of the next larger thing.) "Three things alike in three land?" (Blow his whistle to remind them to exchange them for one of the next larger thing.) "Fifteen things alike in ten land?" (Blow his whistle to remind them to exchange ten of them for one of the next larger thing.) And so on.

"So you see, **The Great Legalizer** is a big help to **Motley Crab Adder** and **Sir Crab Multiplier** who are always ending up with too many of one thing alike. He can also be a big help to you!"

The introduction is greatly enhanced by having students use multi-base blocks or different colored counters to actually make the above exchanges (and additional exchanges).

The Impeccable Twin Dividers (p. 57)

The personification of division as separating "neatly" (into twos, threes, fours, and so on).

The Impeccable Twin Dividers are used to help students understand arithmetic word problems as explained under **Motley Crab Adder** and illustrated in the appendix. Like Motley, they can be made into an attractive item for the bulletin board or into an attractive poster. And also like Motley, they are independent of computational skill and can therefore be talked about to even the lowest of achievers to help them see the mathematics implicit in the world around them.

An introduction to the Impeccable Twins would go something like this:

> "Meet **The Impeccable Twin Dividers,** strange characters indeed. They always separate things 'neatly' (into twos, threes, fours, and so on). That's just the way they are. No one knows why.
>
> "People have talked to them about their style and have tried to get them to relax and stop all this separating neatly. They have even gone so far as to suggest that if they do it just one more time, they will have them committed. But **The Impeccable Twin Dividers** just smooth their clothes and go on separating things neatly.
>
> "And speaking of their clothes, look at how neatly they wear them, just what you'd expect of a twosome who separate neatly. Small wonder that part of their name is 'impeccable.'
>
> "And look at all the things they can do!" (Mime some of the following:
>
> > Unraveling knitting
> >
> > Mowing a lawn in strips
> >
> > Picking teams
> >
> > Sharing money equitably

Tearing down a brick wall a row
at a time

"Can you show me these things they can do?" (Have
children mime some of the following:

Folding socks

Cleaning venetian blinds

Bailing out a boat

Dealing out a deck of cards

Taking handfuls of things from a
container like nuts from a bowl or
chocolates from a box

Separating a ten "neatly" into fives

The Magnificent Equalizer (p. 59)

The personification of the need in working with fractions to make things
"different yet the same" – different in appearance, yet the same in quantity.

The Magnificent Equalizer is used to help students understand equivalent fractions as explained below and under **Fraction Cakes**. As a representative of one of the six processes fundamental to basic mathematics as listed under **Motley Crab Adder,** he is worthy of display (as on a bulletin board or classroom wall) and is worth talking about to students. Since he is independent of computational skill, he can be displayed and talked about to even the lowest of achievers.

An introduction to **The Magnificent Equalizer** would go something like this:

"Meet **The Magnificent Equalizer,** a truly wonderous person. He always makes things 'different yet the same' -- different in appearance, yet the same in quantity. That's just the way he is. No one knows why.

"People have talked to him about this and have told him that he is weird because of it. And many of them, believing that some things are better left alone, have taken to hiding things from him. But he, believing that everything can stand a little change, just goes on making things different yet the same. This shows in the equal sign on his chest and the equal weights, however sectioned, on the ends of his barbell.

"You see, he knows that most of the people criticizing him are just jealous, that they wish that they too could make things different yet the same. And small wonder. If they could, just imagine some of the things they could do.

"With only a click of their fingers, they could get the lawn mowed without all the mowing (that is, a different looking lawn even though the same lawn). They could get the garbage carried out without all the carrying (that is, a different location for the garbage even though the same garbage). They could even get rid of some of their bad habits without all the self-discipline (that is, a different set of behaviors even though the same persons).

"But enough of the wishful thinking. Let me show you some of the more down-to-earth things he can make different yet the same, things which you, too, can make different yet the same.

"He can take a simple piece of paper and use it to turn 1 / 2 into 2 / 4. And watch! You can do it too." (Have each student take a rectangular piece of paper, fold it in half, open it up, and color half of it. Then have all the students fold their papers back as they were, fold them in half again, and open them up. Each of them will see $1/2 = 2/4$, that is, a different way of viewing the same coloring.)

"And using the same piece of paper, he can turn $3/4$ into $6/8$, but, then, so can you." (Have each student color some more of his or her paper to where $3/4$ of it is colored. Then have all the students fold their papers back as they were after the last folding, fold them in half again, and open them up. Each of them will see $3/4 = 6/8$, thus, once again, a different way of viewing the same coloring.)

"And that's not all. He can even use this piece of paper to change $7/8$ into $14/16$. Can you show me what he would do?" (Have the students proceed as before.)

"What do you think he would turn $15/16$ into? How could you prove your answer?"

The Scruffy Twin Subtractors (p. 55)

The personification of subtraction as separating.

The Scruffy Twin Subtractors are used to help children understand arithmetic word problems as explained under **Motley Crab Adder** and illustrated in the appendix. Like Motley, they can be made into an attractive item for the bulletin board or into an attractive poster. And also like Motley, they are independent of computational skill and can therefore be talked about to even the lowest of achievers to help them see the mathematics implicit in the world around them.

An introduction to the Scruffy Twins would go something like this:

"Meet **The Scruffy Twin Subtractors**, strange characters indeed. They always separate things. That's just the way they are. No one knows why.

"People have talked to them about this and have tried to get them to change and stop all this separating. They have even said that they'll put them in straight jackets if they separate anything again. But **The Scruffy Twin**

Subtractors just shrug their shoulders and go on separating.

"Also, when they separate things, they separate them in just any old way. This shows in their tattered clothes and is why part of their name is 'scruffy.'

"And look at all the things they can do!" (Mime some of the following:

> Trimming fat off a steak
>
> Whittling a stick
>
> Mowing the lawn
>
> Robbing a piggy bank
>
> Taking a bite out of something like a pear or an apple

"Can you show me these things they can do?" (Have students mime some of the following:

> Scaling a fish
>
> Peeling a banana, orange, potato, or the like
>
> Spending part of a dollar
>
> Clipping or filing a toenail or a fingernail
>
> Ripping a page out of a phone book

The Word for Today is S.E.A. (p. 164)

An integration of math and language arts on addition.

The answers are as follows:

1. a. Steam, 67
    b. Seat, 59
    c. Spread, 83
    d. Baseball, 138
    e. Stream, 91

    f. Seal, 58
    g. Spear, 67
    h. Southeast, 107
    i. Seattle, 101
    j. Seam, 49

2. Some words that contain **May**: **mangey**, **many**, and **maybe**. Their values are 52, 41, and 59, respectively, for a score of 152.

Some words that contain **Sue**: **issue**, **sudden**, and **sure**. Their values are 66, 74, and 55, respectively, for a score of 195.

Some words that contain **Tom**: **atom**, **bottom**, and **tomato**. Their values are 50, 76, and 73, respectively, for a score of 199.

The total score for all the above would be 546.

Three Vowels (p. 163)

An integration of math and language arts on addition of fractions.

The answers are as follows:

1. Answers will vary, but something like:

   a. Easter, 1
   b. Orange, $1\frac{1}{4}$
   c. Hamburger, 1
   d. Chevrolet, 1
   e. Gillian, $\frac{3}{4}$

   f. Elephant, 1
   g. Abraham, $1\frac{1}{2}$
   h. Jupiter, $\frac{5}{8}$
   i. Phoenix, $\frac{7}{8}$
   j. Alaska, $1\frac{1}{2}$

2. Words like **level** (½), **radar** (1), and **keep** (½)

Tower Puzzle (p. 273)

An investigation of the "famous" Tower puzzle.

The **Tower puzzle** yields the number pattern 1, 3, 7, 15, 31, 63, 127, 255, 511, 1023, . . . which determines the rule for figuring the minimum number of moves needed to move a tower of rings a ring at a time in terms of the number of rings. For an N-ring tower, the rule is $2^N - 1$ moves.

The answers to the questions for the **Tower puzzle** are as follows:

1. Sloppy! They could have done it in 4096 moves.
2. $2^N - 1$
3. Working eight hours a day, five days a week, 48 weeks a year, it would take more than 155 years!

Traceable Houses (p. 187)

A corollary and follow-up to Traceable Networks.

A house can be walked through by walking through each of its doorways exactly once if all or all but two of its rooms have an even number of doorways. If all of its rooms have an even number of doorways, it can be walked through as described by starting in any of its rooms by being careful to finish in the same room. If all but two of its rooms have an even number of doorways, it can be walked through as described by starting in one of the rooms with an odd number of doorways by being careful to finish in the other room with an odd number of doorways. Thus for **Traceable Houses,** houses a, c, f, g, and i can be walked through as described.

To note the connection between houses that can be walked through by walking through each of their doorways exactly once and traceable networks, view the houses as networks by making the rooms points and the doorways segments such that two rooms with a common doorway appear as the end-points of a segment. Make the outside a point as well. An example of how this is done is given below.

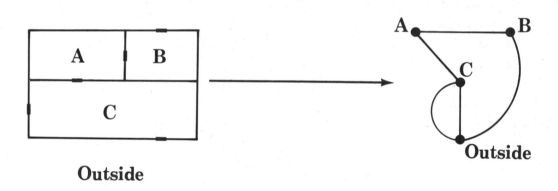

And when this is done, a house with all or all but two rooms with an even number of doorways would appear as a network with all or all but two even vertices, that is, as a traceable network. And walking through a doorway would correspond to tracing part of the network.

Traceable Networks (p. 186)

A tracing activity that leads to the discovery of the rule for determining if a network is traceable.

A network is **traceable,** that is, can be drawn without lifting the drawing instrument or drawing the same line twice, if all or all but two of its vertices are "even." (An even vertex is a vertex with an even number of edges emanating from it as in Figure 23.)

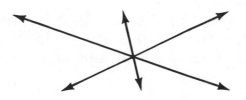

Figure 23

If all its vertices are even, it can be traced by starting at any one of them by being careful to finish at the same one. If all but two of its vertices are even, it can be traced by starting at one of the "odd" vertices by being careful to finish at the other odd vertex. (An odd vertex is a vertex with an odd number of edges emanating from it as in Figure 24.)

Figure 24

Thus for **Traceable Networks**, networks a, b, c, d, f, h, i, k, and m are traceable as shown in the following table:

Network	Number of even vertices	Number of odd vertices	Traceable
a	3	2	Yes
b	1	0	Yes
c	0	2	Yes
d	2	0	Yes
e	0	4	No
f	3	0	Yes
g	1	4	No
h	5	2	Yes
i	8	0	Yes
j	2	6	No
k	9	0	Yes
l	1	8	No
m	1	2	Yes

To give meaning to the rule for determining if a network is traceable, have students note that an even vertex is "safe," that is, that it provides an exit for every entry as shown in Figure 25, and that an odd vertex is "unsafe," that is, that it eventually runs out of exits for all possible entries as shown in Figure 26.

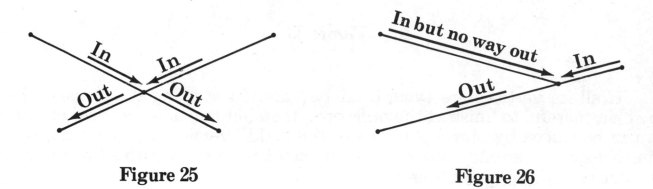

Figure 25   Figure 26

Trees (p. 165)

An integration of math and language arts on the multiplication facts.

The answers are as follows:

Clue	Tree	Score
The seashore	Beech	10
The hand	Palm	20
An inlet of the sea	Bay	12
Sadness	Pine	24
A country bumpkin	Hickory	21
The dead part of a fire	Ash	21
A winter coat	Fur	3
Neat appearance	Spruce	36
Gracefully tall and slender	Willow	54
A kind of grasshopper	Locust	48
	Total	265

Tunnel

A game for two to four on fractions, decimals, and percents. For different problems, use the blank Tunnel gameboard on page 146.

Materials:

For each group, two dice and a Tunnel gameboard (p. 145). For each player, a marker and a pen or pencil and some scrap paper.

Directions:

To begin, the players put their markers on the entrance to the tunnel on the gameboard. Then each player rolls the dice. The player rolling the highest total plays first. The play rotates clockwise.

To play, a player rolls the dice and moves his or her marker along the numbered spaces on the gameboard as many spaces as the total on the dice. The player then works the problem in the space he or she lands on and moves to the space of the same number as the answer to the problem. To illustrate, if a player is at the entrance to the tunnel and rolls a 9, the player moves 9 spaces to space 9, works the problem there, namely, $31.9 + 18.1$, and then moves to space 50 in keeping with the answer to the problem. The play then goes to the next player.

The first player to reach the end of the tunnel wins.

The answers to the problems for Tunnel are as follows:

1. Blank	21. 12	41. 60	61. 75	81. 96
2. 1	22. 36	42. 45	62. 70	82. 90
3. 6	23. 25	43. 62	63. 75	83. 50
4. 3	24. 15	44. 41	64. 60	84. 70
5. 1	25. 39	45. 52	65. 50	85. 99
6. 8	26. 16	46. 53	66. 71	86. 94
7. 15	27. 30	47. 60	67. 81	87. 91
8. 16	28. 40	48. 55	68. 75	88. 81
9. 50	29. 50	49. 50	69. 45	89. 96
10. 2	30. 42	50. 39	70. 90	90. 90
11. 9	31. 38	51. 60	71. 40	91. 72
12. 18	32. 50	52. 80	72. 80	92. 92
13. 2	33. 25	53. 25	73. 90	93. 99
14. 5	34. 31	54. 61	74. 56	94. 98
15. 27	35. 27	55. 64	75. 60	95. 95
16. 21	36. 54	56. 24	76. 90	96. 98
17. 40	37. 14	57. 66	77. 85	97. 90
18. 27	38. 48	58. 71	78. 90	98. 100
19. 16	39. 48	59. 68	79. 81	99. 100
20. 30	40. 32	60. 72	80. 68	100. Blank

Verifying Probabilities (pp. 254-258)

Five experiments for ruling on the predictive value of probabilities for relatively small numbers of trials. For more experiments like them, use the blank table on page 259.

An **outcome** is any of the ways something can occur, and if each of the ways is equally likely to occur, the **probability** of any one of the outcomes occurring is 1 / N for N the number of outcomes. Thus for tossing a coin, the probability of getting a head is ½, because there are two equally likely outcomes: getting a head or getting a tail.

The value in a probability is that it gives us a peek into the future. It tells us how something which has not yet happened will probably happen. To illustrate, a probability of ½ for tossing a coin and getting a head tells us that if we toss a coin, say, 100 times, we should get a head half or 50 of those times. In actual fact, however, and for sample sizes of less than several thousand or even a million or a billion, what a probability says ought to happen rarely happens, and, in many cases, does not even come close to happening, a point most likely brought out in the experiments on pages 254-258.

The shortcoming of a probability relative to its predictive value is that it never tells us the number of trials it takes for everything to work out like it is supposed to. Thus if what is supposed to happen does not happen after, say, 100 trials, the understanding is always that the number of trials was not "large" enough, where large could mean very large indeed. So in actuality, a probability gives us only a very rough look into the future. Still, a probability is of value in predicting a "trend," of telling us what to look for in the event of ever increasing numbers of trials.

The answers to some of the questions for some of the experiments are as follows:

Page 255:

3. The game is not fair. One way to see this is to consider what could happen in any two tosses of the coin:

> A head and a head, house wins $2
> A head and a tail, house wins $1
> A tail and a head, gambler wins $2
> A tail and a tail, house wins $1

Since each of the four outcomes is equally likely to occur, the house can expect to win $4 for every $2 the gambler wins.

3. That the die was loaded.

Vertices, Faces, and Edges (pp. 182-183)

Two exercises on the vertices, faces, and edges of polyhedra.

The exercises on the vertices, faces, and edges of polyhedra are of special interest in that they integrate arithmetic, algebra, and geometry: arithmetic in the computing of the sums and differences involved, algebra in the use of the variables V = number of vertices, F = number of faces, and E = number of edges, and geometry in the rules that surface, that for polyhedra without "holes," like the polyhedra on page 182, $V + F - E = 2$, and that for polyhedra with one hole, like the polyhedra on page 183, $V + F - E = 0$.

The answers for the worksheets are as follows:

Page 182:

Figure	V	F	E	V + F − E
a	4	4	6	2
b	8	6	12	2
c	5	5	8	2
d	6	8	12	2
e	9	9	16	2
f	5	6	9	2
g	6	6	10	2
h	7	7	12	2
i	6	5	9	2
j	8	12	18	2

1. Flat everywhere
2. 998
3. 5002
4. 19,849,581
5. $V + F - E = 2$

Page 183:

a. $V = 16$
   $F = 16$
   $E = 32$
   $V + F - E = 0$

b. $V = 9$
   $F = 9$
   $E = 18$
   $V + F - E = 0$

c. $V = 16$
   $F = 19$
   $E = 35$
   $V + F - E = 0$

d. $V = 10$
   $F = 11$
   $E = 21$
   $V + F - E = 0$

What Am I?

Two connect-a-dots on the structure of the metric system. The one on page 233 is on the arithmetic meaning of kilo- (k), centi- (c), and milli- (m): 1000, 0.01, and 0.001, respectively. And the one on page 234 is on the metric conversions as listed under Metric Conversion Concentration.

The dots on each **What Am I?** which correspond to equivalent measurements are to be connected with lines. When this is done, they should yield the following drawings:

Page 233:   **Page 234:**

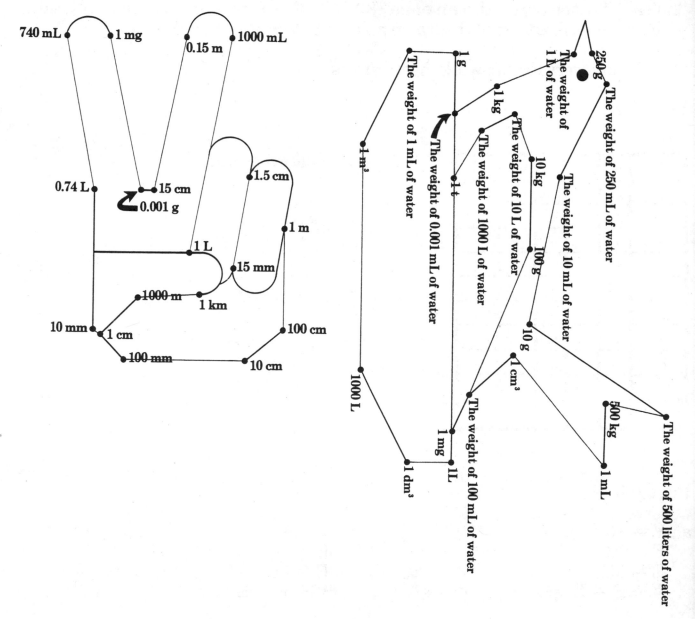

Note: The lines already on the drawings do **not** connect equivalent measurements.

Experience Roster

																						Name Experience

Spinner Cutouts
(3-, 4-, and 5-division)
Color, back, and laminate.
Pin to boards or pencils with thumbtacks.

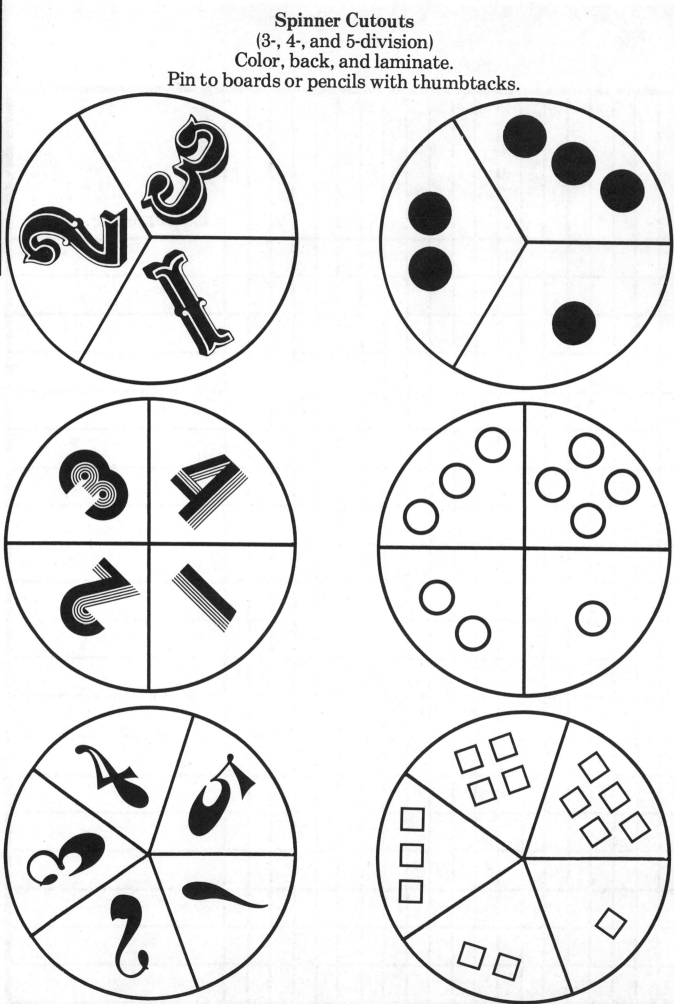

Spinner Cutouts
(6-, 8-, and 10-division)
Color, back, and laminate.
Pin to boards or pencils with thumbtacks.

Spinner Cutouts
(Blank)
3-, 4-, and 5-division

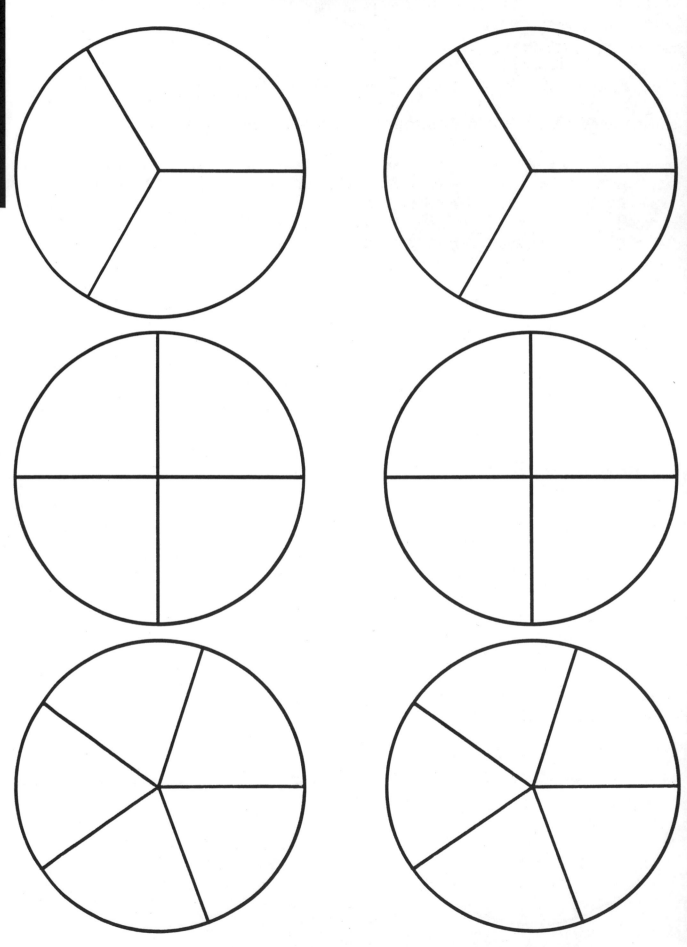

Spinner Cutouts
(Blank)
6-, 8-, and 10-division

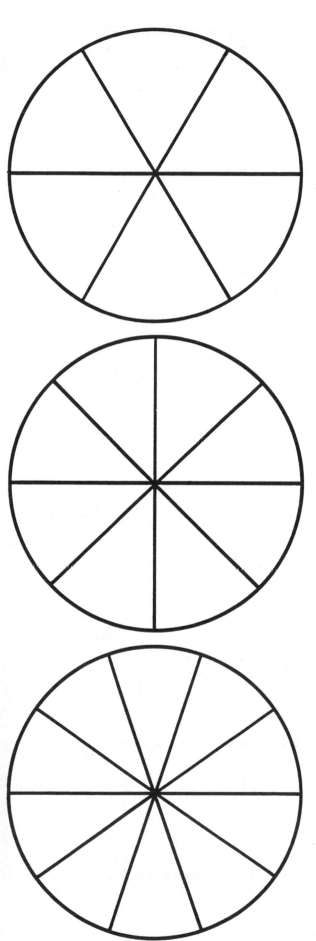
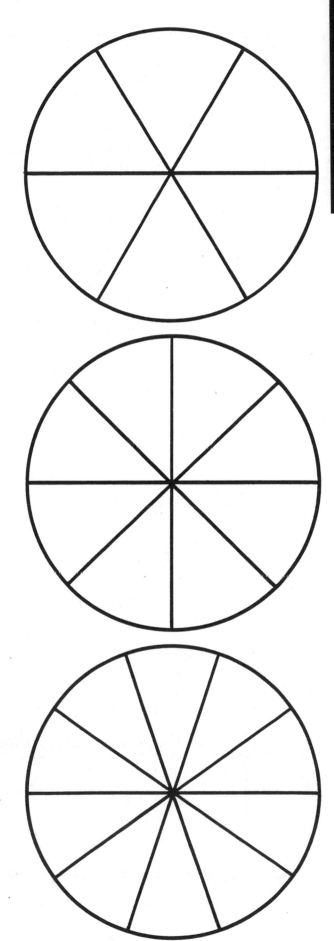

Blank Gameboard
(Either side of a 7 by 11)

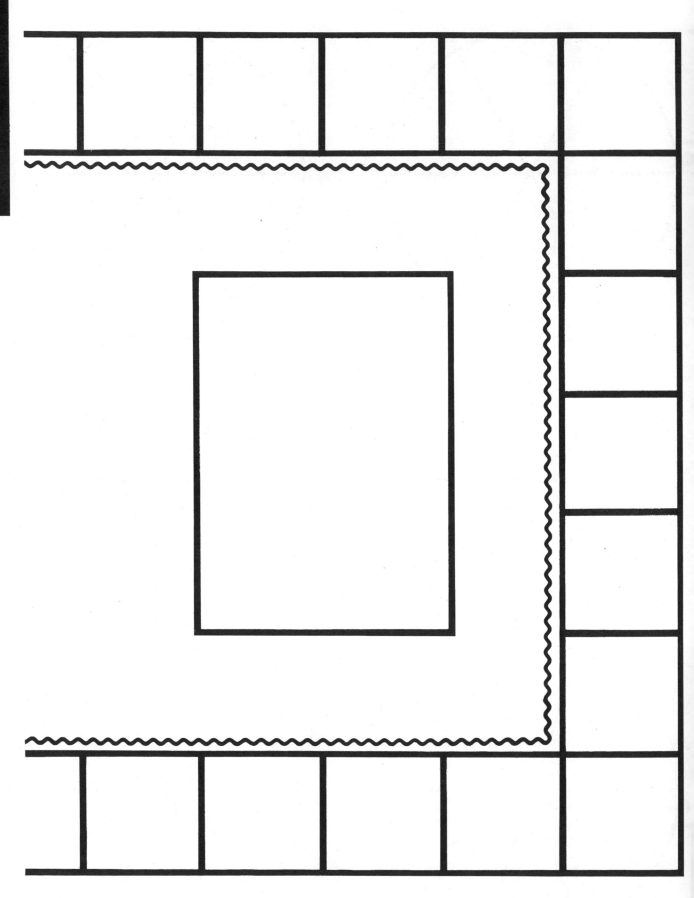

Blank Gameboard
(Either side of an 8 by 12)

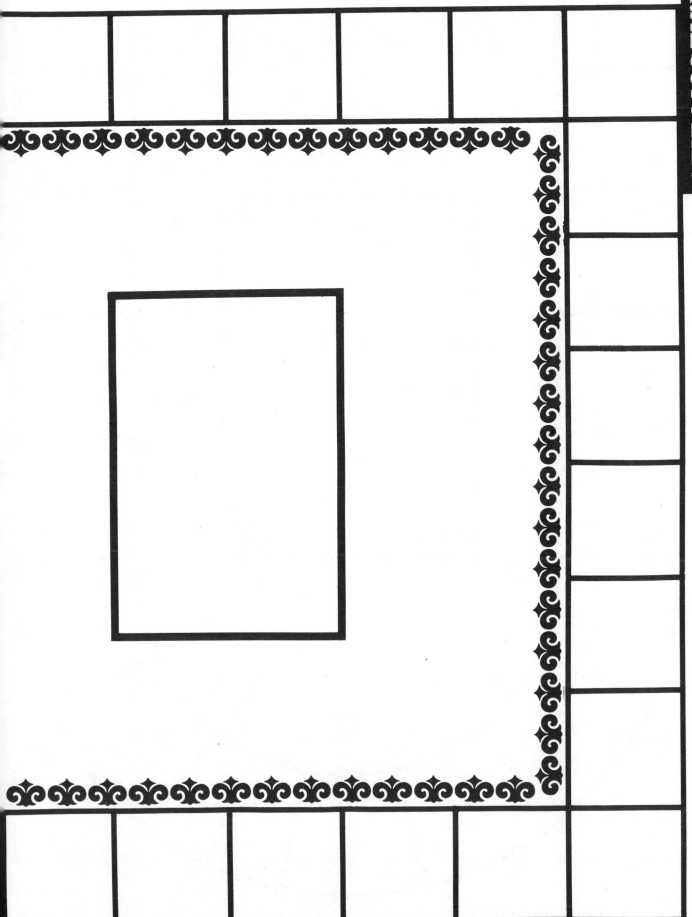

Blank Gameboard
(Either side of an oval)

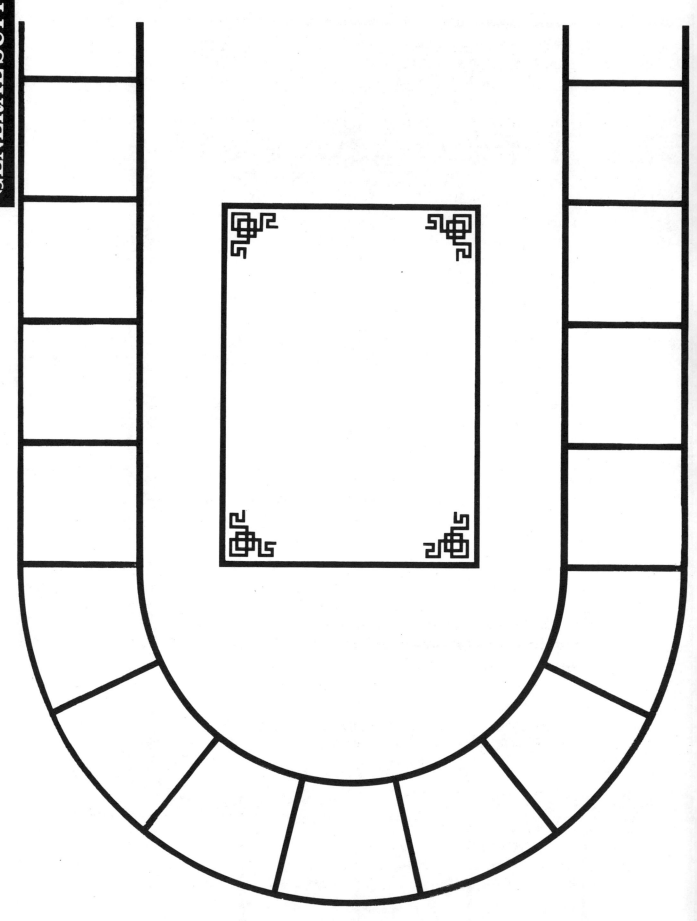

Blank Cards
(6 cm by 9 cm)

Blank Cards
(5 cm by 9 cm)

Blank Cards
(5 cm by 6 cm)

Blank Cards
(3 by 3 array cards)

Blank Cards
(4.5 cm by 4.5 cm)

Blank Dominoes

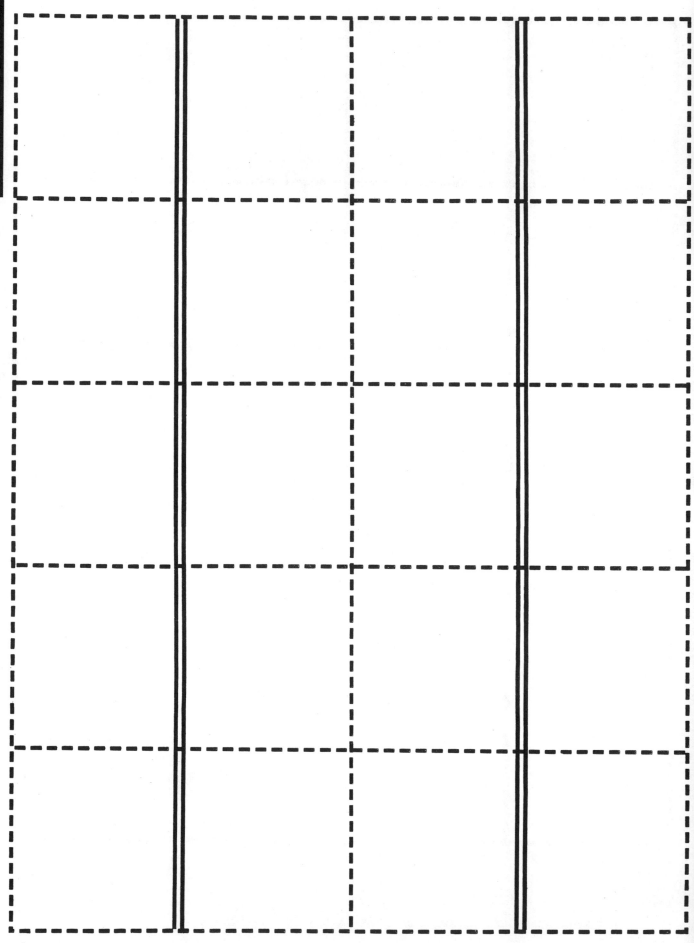

Hi! My name is Ima Blank-page. Turn the page and BEHOLD!

Cliff Hanger Gameboard
(Addition and subtraction facts)
Top
Color, back, and laminate.

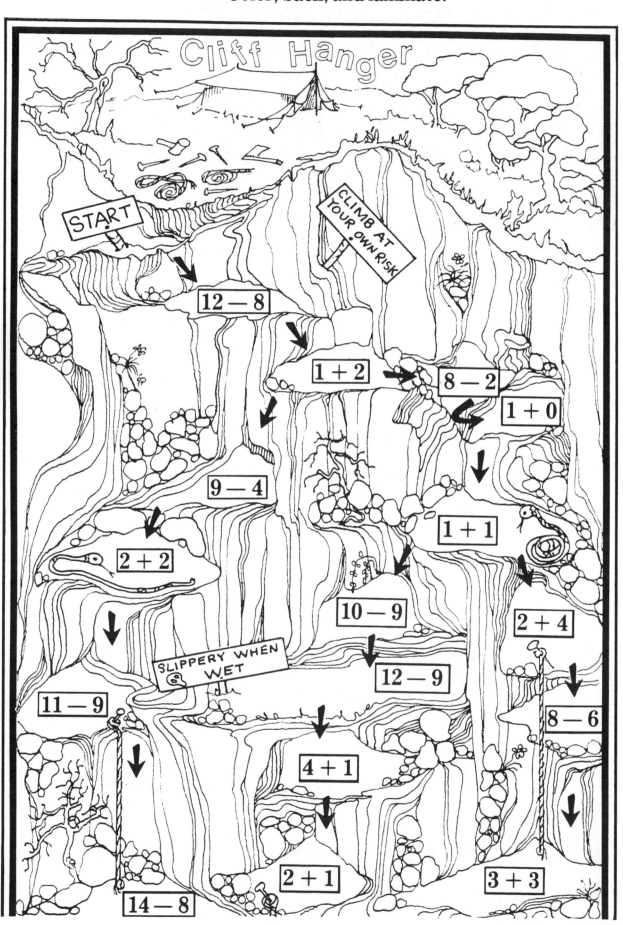

BASIC FACTS

Cliff Hanger

START

CLIMB AT YOUR OWN RISK

12 − 8

1 + 2

8 − 2

1 + 0

9 − 4

1 + 1

2 + 2

10 − 9

2 + 4

SLIPPERY WHEN WET

11 − 9

12 − 9

8 − 6

4 + 1

14 − 8

2 + 1

3 + 3

Cliff Hanger Gameboard
(Addition and subtraction facts)
Bottom
Color, back, and laminate.

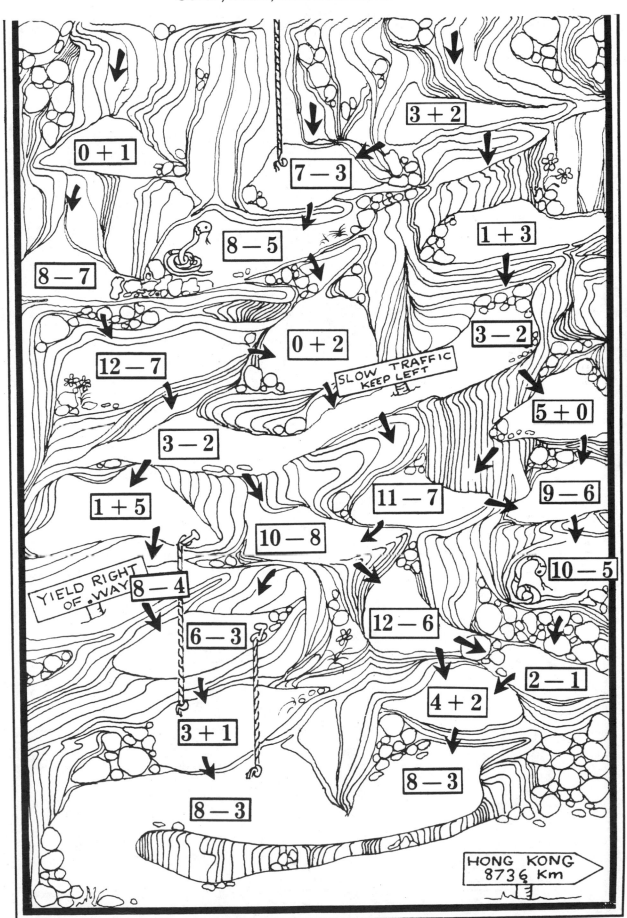

BASIC FACTS

Cliff Hanger

START

CLIMB AT YOUR OWN RISK

SLIPPERY WHEN WET

BASIC FACTS

SLOW TRAFFIC KEEP LEFT

YIELD RIGHT OF WAY

HONG KONG 8736 Km

BASIC FACTS

BASIC FACTS

BEAT THE CLOCK

BEAT THE CLOCK

2 3 4 5 6 7 8 9

Diviso Gameboard
Color, back, and laminate.

D I V I Z O

Diviso Cards
(Page 1 of two pages)
Back, laminate, and cut along solid lines.

25	42	56	12
45 DIVISO 2	16 DIVISO 7	21 DIVISO 3	24 DIVISO 9
5	6	8	4
10	30	24	12
27 DIVISO 8	40 DIVISO 6	54 DIVISO 2	18 DIVISO 3
5	7	6	8
20	42	48	32
16 DIVISO 9	81 DIVISO 7	56 DIVISO 5	35 DIVISO 4
4	3	9	2
28	15	81	14
16 DIVISO 9	63 DIVISO 3	15 DIVISO 8	64 DIVISO 4
7	9	3	2
49	72	21	10
36 DIVISO 7	14 DIVISO 5	25 DIVISO 2	18 DIVISO 6
5	6	8	4

Diviso Cards
(Page 2 of two pages)
Back, laminate, and cut along solid lines.

BASIC FACTS

16 **10** DIVISO **4** **2**	**10** **20** DIVISO **3** **8**	**42** **12** DIVISO **3** **9**	**30** **18** DIVISO **2** **3**
18 **63** DIVISO **5** **7**	**64** **45** DIVISO **4** **6**	**81** **32** DIVISO **7** **5**	**15** **56** DIVISO **9** **8**
63 **40** DIVISO **5** **4**	**36** **30** DIVISO **9** **3**	**25** **45** DIVISO **2** **4**	**32** **14** DIVISO **5** **3**
12 **36** DIVISO **6** **8**	**27** **48** DIVISO **8** **2**	**28** **64** DIVISO **7** **9**	**24** **35** DIVISO **6** **8**
72 **25** DIVISO **9** **4**	**14** **72** DIVISO **7** **2**	**54** **49** DIVISO **7** **6**	**16** **28** DIVISO **5** **6**

42

$2 + 4$

6

$18 \div 9$

$12 - 8$

3

10

$14 - 7$

9×8

6

$30 \div 6$

9

$17 - 9$

15

2×5

8

18

$72 \div 8$

6×7

7

9

5

72

$9 + 6$

4

$8 + 7$

BASIC FACTS

Name. . . . .

Fill in the tables.

1.

A	B	C
3	5	8
9	3	12
4	8	
7	7	
4	2	
6	8	

2.

A	B	C
16	9	7
7	4	3
	8	5
8		2
15	6	
	4	7

3.

A	B	C
2	3	6
8	9	72
4	6	
5	7	
1	8	
8	6	

4.

A	B	C
63	9	7
12	3	4
21	7	
36		6
42		7
	9	9

5.

A	B	C
2	3	6
4	7	12
3	4	
9	6	
7	8	
1	5	

6.

A	B	C
3	5	11
4	9	17
2	1	
7	6	
8	4	
3	8	

Name.............................

Fill in the tables.

1.

A	B	C

2.

A	B	C

3.

A	B	C

4.

A	B	C

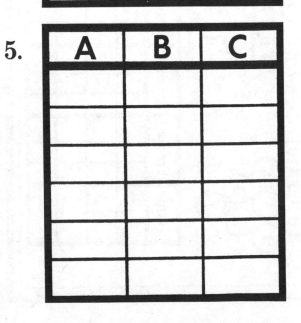

5.

A	B	C

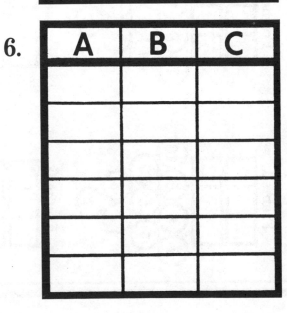

6.

A	B	C

BASIC FACTS

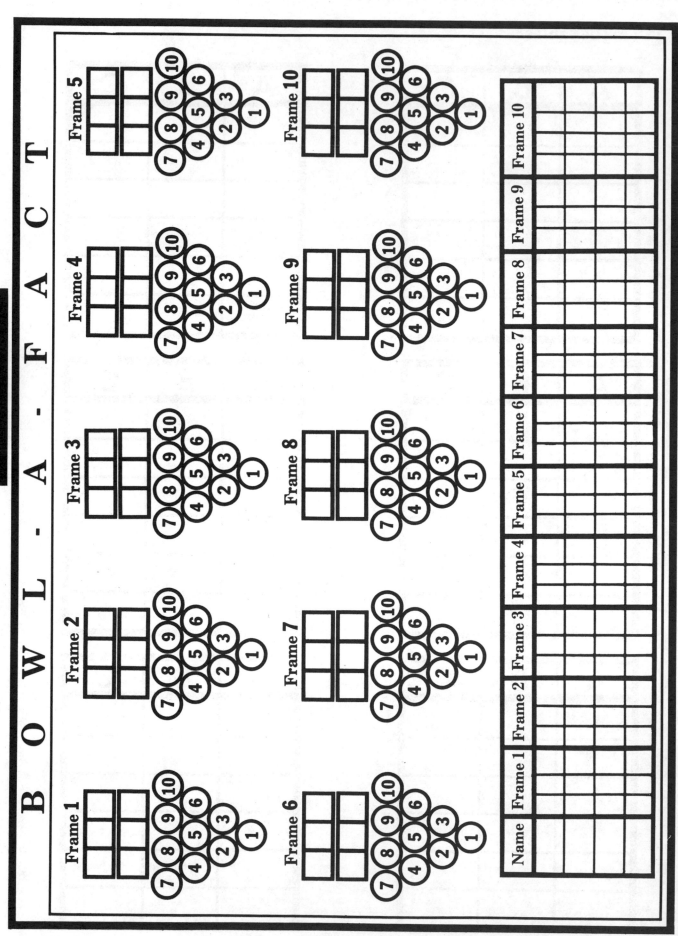

BASIC FACTS

B O W L - A - F A C T

Frame 5 · Frame 4 · Frame 3 · Frame 2 · Frame 1
Frame 10 · Frame 9 · Frame 8 · Frame 7 · Frame 6

Name · Frame 1 · Frame 2 · Frame 3 · Frame 4 · Frame 5 · Frame 6 · Frame 7 · Frame 8 · Frame 9 · Frame 10

Discard
(Page 1 of six pages)
Back, laminate, and cut along solid lines.

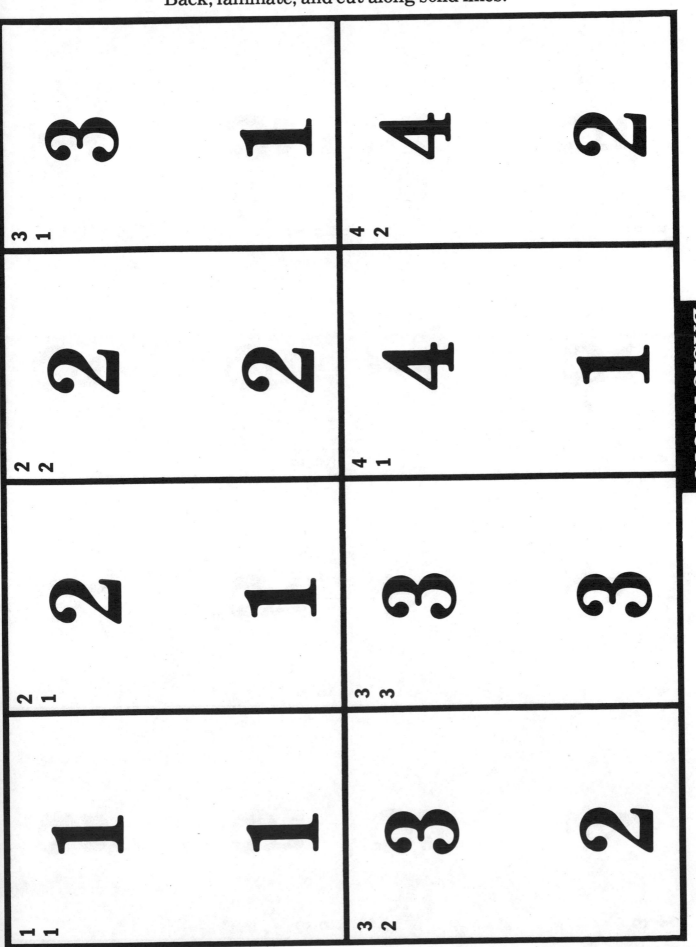

BASIC FACTS

Discard
(Page 2 of six pages)
Back, laminate, and cut along solid lines.

BASIC FACTS

5   2

6   1

5   1

5   5

4   4

5   4

4   3

5   3

5

2

6

1

5

1

5

5

4

4

5

4

4

3

5

3

Discard
(Page 3 of six pages)
Back, laminate, and cut along solid lines.

6	5	7	3
6	4	7	2
6	3	7	1
6	2	6̶	6̶

BASIC FACTS

Discard
(Page 4 of six pages)
Back, laminate, and cut along solid lines.

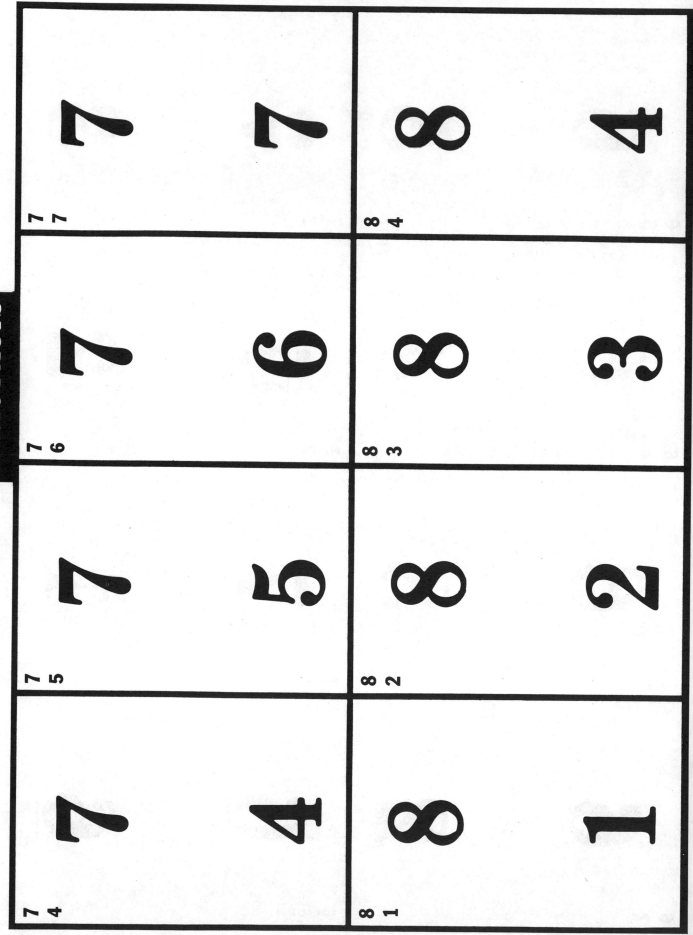

BASIC FACTS

Discard
(Page 5 of six pages)
Back, laminate, and cut along solid lines.

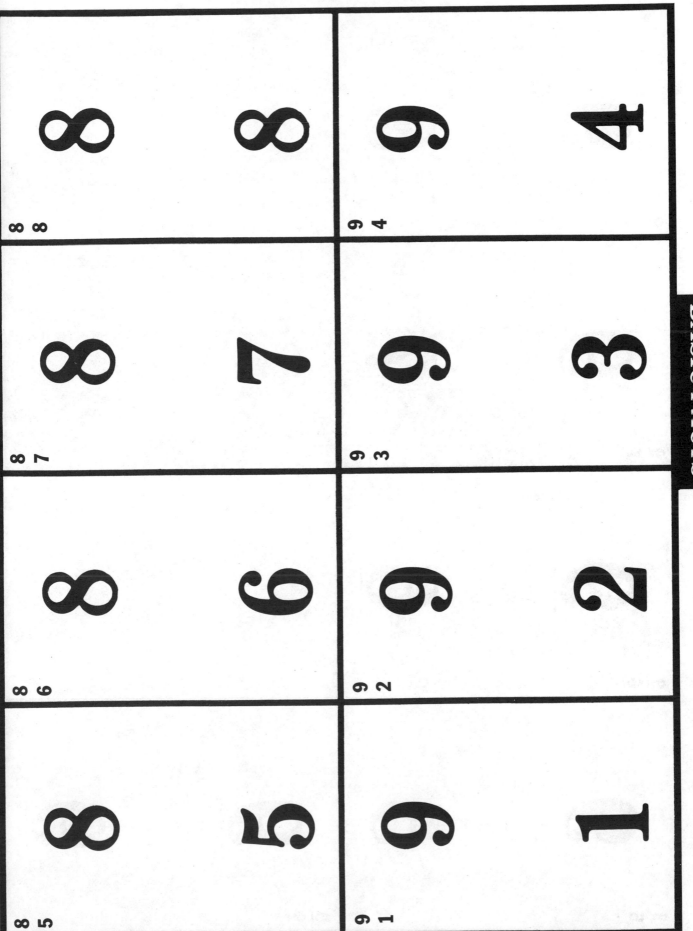

Discard
(Page 6 of six pages)
Back, laminate, and cut along solid lines.

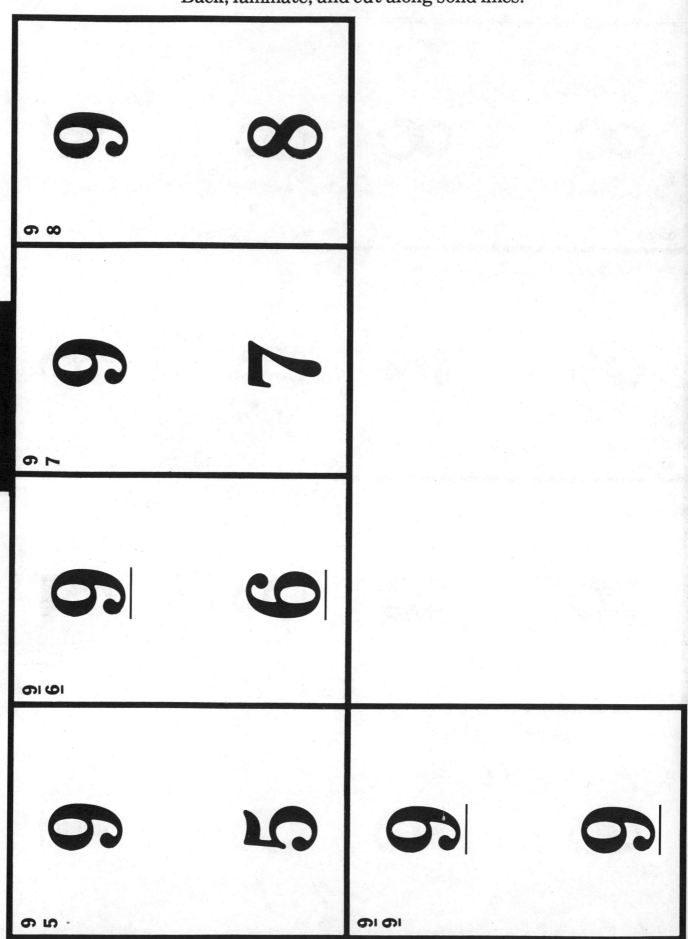

BASIC FACTS

Chain
(Mixed Operations)

Name ....

START

Make a chain with the answers. Avoid weak links.

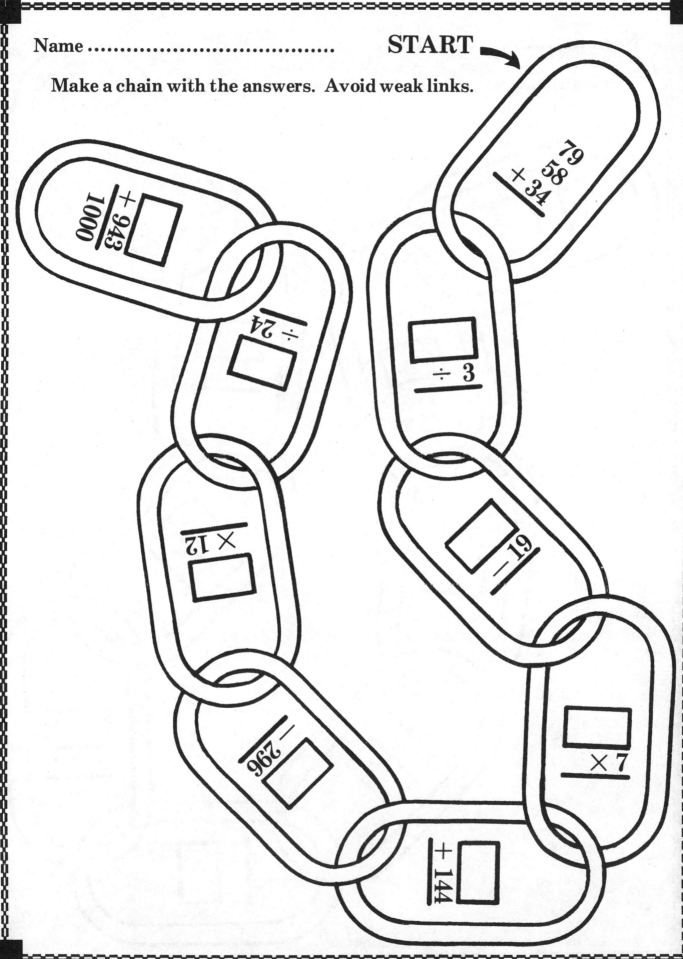

Chain
(Blank)

Name ....

START

Make a chain with the answers. Avoid weak links.

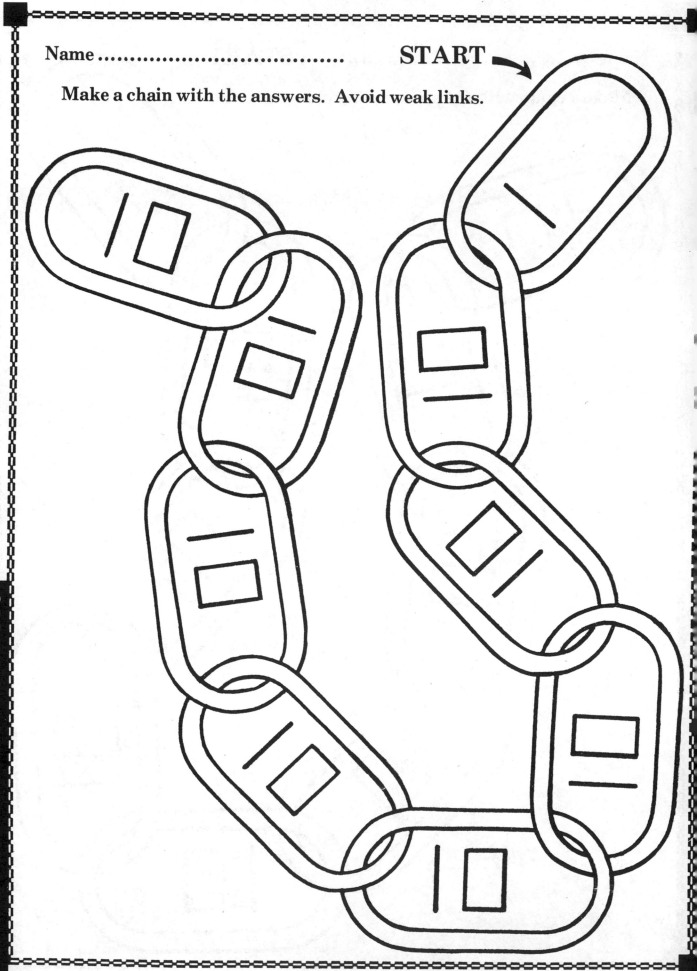

Four broken congruent squares. Cut them out and mend them. Use the numbers to help you.

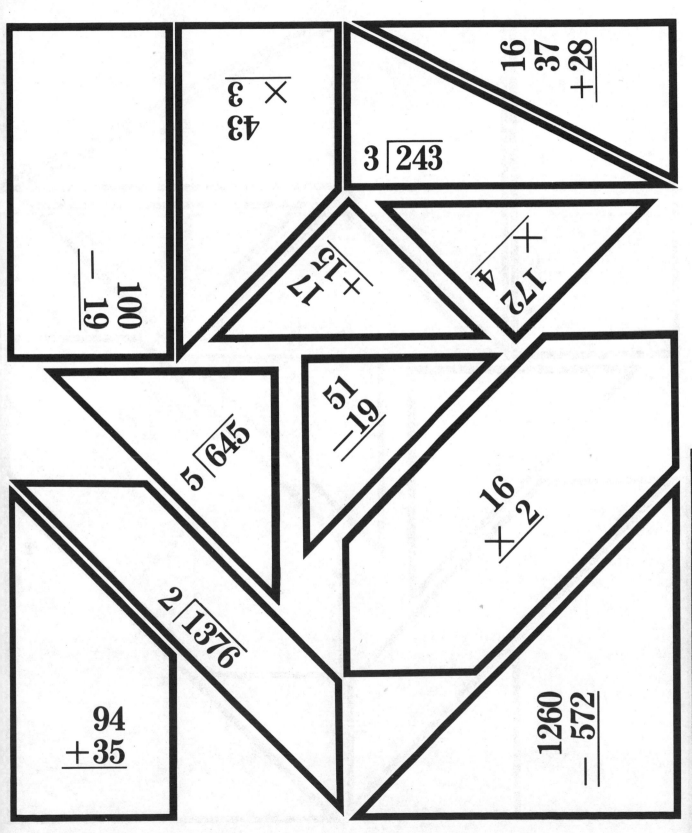

$$\frac{100}{-19}$$

$$43 \times 3$$

$$16 \\ 37 \\ +28$$

$$3\overline{)243}$$

$$17 \\ +15$$

$$172 \\ \times 4$$

$$5\overline{)645}$$

$$51 \\ -19$$

$$16 \\ \times 2$$

$$2\overline{)1376}$$

$$94 \\ +35$$

$$1260 \\ -572$$

Four broken congruent squares. Cut them out and mend them. Use the numbers to help you.

Grids and Drigs
(Mixed Operations)

Name..

Fill in the tables.

1.

	6	15	48	102
+ 7	13			
− 5				
× 2				
÷ 3				

2.

	8	24	88	212
+	17			
−		18		
×			264	
÷ 4				53

3.

	35	80	215	1760
+ 28				
− 23			192	
× 4				
÷ 5				

4.

		63		
+ 35				2149
− 14			91	
× 5		315		
÷ 7	4			

5.

	60	96	204	4272
+ 44				
− 54				
× 23				
÷ 12	5			

6.

	50		325	4000
+ 16			341	
−		33		
×	800			
÷		3		160

WHOLE NUMBER ARITHMETIC

Grids and Drigs
(Blank)

Name ....

Fill in the tables.

1.

+				
−				
×				
÷				

2.

+				
−				
×				
÷				

3.

+				
−				
×				
÷				

4.

+				
−				
×				
÷				

5.

+				
−				
×				
÷				

6.

+				
−				
×				
÷				

Hi! My name is Ima Blank-
page. Turn the page and
BEHOLD!

Algo Onslaught Gameboard
Left side
Color, back, and laminate.

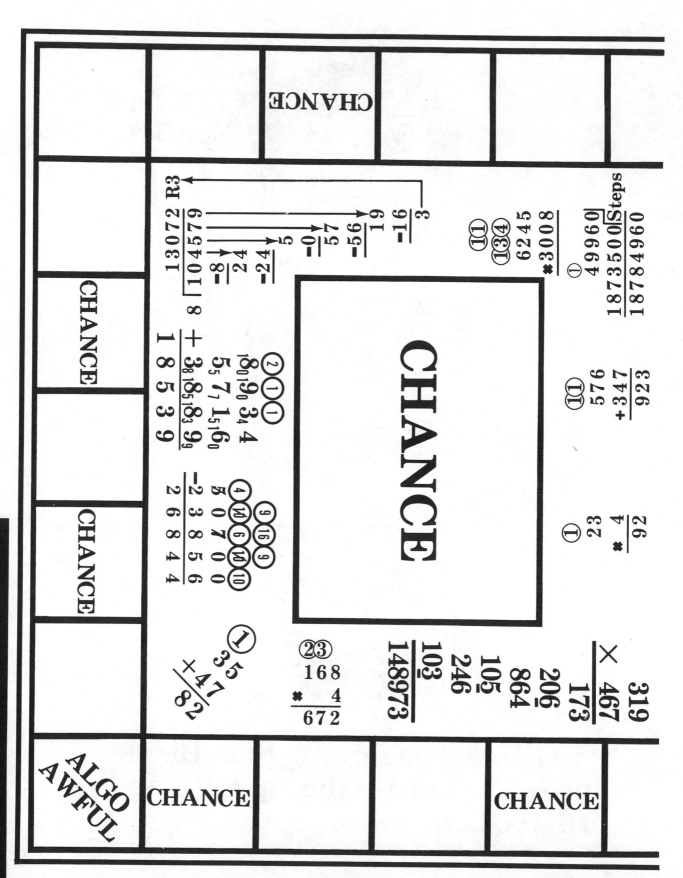

Algo Onslaught Gameboard
Right side
Color, back, and laminate.

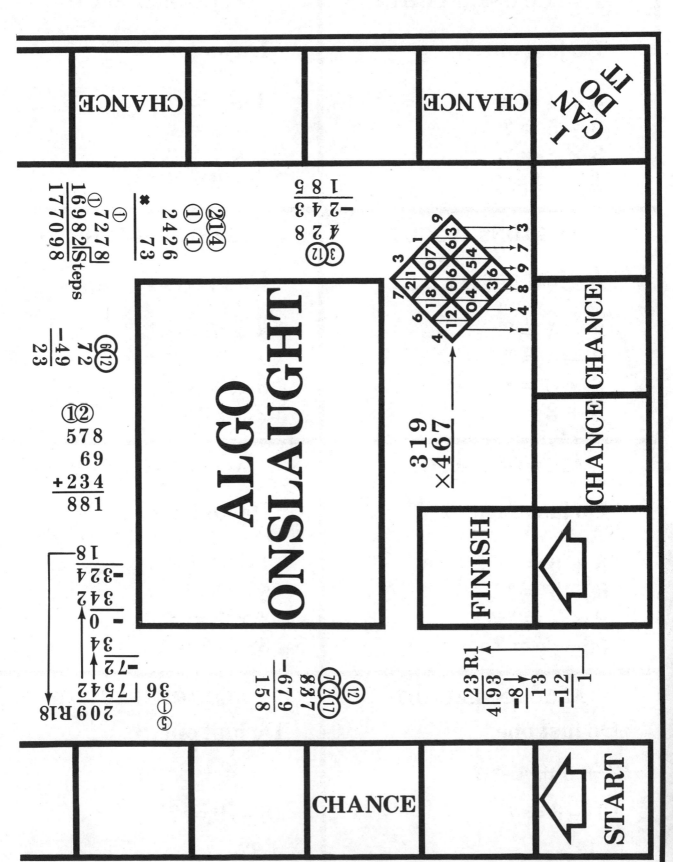

Algo Onslaught Operations Cards
(Page 1 of six pages)
Back, laminate, and cut along solid lines.

WHOLE NUMBER ARITHMETIC

1

ALGO ONSLAUGHT

Do just one.

$4 + 4 = ?$
$9 - 5 = ?$
$3 \times 2 = ?$
$12 \div 4 = ?$

2

ALGO ONSLAUGHT

Do just one.

$3 + 1 = ?$
$7 - 2 = ?$
$4 \times 1 = ?$
$8 \div 2 = ?$

3

ALGO ONSLAUGHT

Do just one.

$2 + 5 = ?$
$8 - 4 = ?$
$8 \times 0 = ?$
$6 \div 3 = ?$

4

ALGO ONSLAUGHT

Do just one.

$8 + 7 = ?$
$4 - 1 = ?$
$6 \times 8 = ?$
$27 \div 9 = ?$

5

ALGO ONSLAUGHT

Do just one.

$6 + 6 = ?$
$6 - 5 = ?$
$9 \times 7 = ?$
$56 \div 7 = ?$

6

ALGO ONSLAUGHT

Do just one.

$1 + 9 = ?$
$5 - 5 = ?$
$3 \times 5 = ?$
$42 \div 6 = ?$

7

ALGO ONSLAUGHT

Do just one.

$2 + 3 + 4 = ?$

$13 - 6 = ?$

$$\begin{array}{r} 13 \\ \times\ 3 \\ \hline \end{array}$$

$3\overline{)75}$

8

ALGO ONSLAUGHT

Do just one.

$1 + 4 + 8 = ?$

$18 - 9 = ?$

$$\begin{array}{r} 32 \\ \times\ 1 \\ \hline \end{array}$$

$4\overline{)48}$

Algo Onslaught Operations Cards
(Page 2 of six pages)
Back, laminate, and cut along solid lines.

9

ALGO ONSLAUGHT

Do just one.

$3 + 7 + 2 = ?$

$12 - 7 = ?$

$\begin{array}{r} 40 \\ \times\ 2 \\ \hline \end{array}$

$7\overline{)91}$

10

ALGO ONSLAUGHT

Do just one.

$5 + 2 + 8 = ?$

$15 - 8 = ?$

$\begin{array}{r} 213 \\ \times\ \ 2 \\ \hline \end{array}$

$5\overline{)55}$

11

ALGO ONSLAUGHT

Do just one.

$9 + 9 + 1 = ?$

$10 - 5 = ?$

$\begin{array}{r} 121 \\ \times\ \ 4 \\ \hline \end{array}$

$8\overline{)25}$

12

ALGO ONSLAUGHT

Do just one.

$3 + 4 + 7 = ?$

$10 - 3 = ?$

$\begin{array}{r} 222 \\ \times\ \ 3 \\ \hline \end{array}$

$9\overline{)70}$

13

ALGO ONSLAUGHT

Do just one.

$\begin{array}{r} 172 \\ +425 \\ \hline \end{array}$ $\qquad$ $\begin{array}{r} 485 \\ -132 \\ \hline \end{array}$

$\begin{array}{r} 35 \\ \times\ 2 \\ \hline \end{array}$

$3\overline{)735}$

14

ALGO ONSLAUGHT

Do just one.

$\begin{array}{r} 271 \\ +\ 14 \\ \hline \end{array}$ $\qquad$ $\begin{array}{r} 789 \\ -\ 56 \\ \hline \end{array}$

$\begin{array}{r} 46 \\ \times\ 2 \\ \hline \end{array}$

$4\overline{)571}$

15

ALGO ONSLAUGHT

Do just one.

$\begin{array}{r} 43 \\ +32 \\ \hline \end{array}$ $\qquad$ $\begin{array}{r} 85 \\ -23 \\ \hline \end{array}$

$\begin{array}{r} 28 \\ \times\ 3 \\ \hline \end{array}$

$7\overline{)854}$

16

ALGO ONSLAUGHT

Do just one.

$\begin{array}{r} 32 \\ +\ 3 \\ \hline \end{array}$ $\qquad$ $\begin{array}{r} 48 \\ -\ 3 \\ \hline \end{array}$

$\begin{array}{r} 136 \\ \times\ \ 2 \\ \hline \end{array}$

$9\overline{)108}$

WHOLE NUMBER ARITHMETIC

Algo Onslaught Operations Cards
(Page 3 of six pages)
Back, laminate, and cut along solid lines.

17

ALGO ONSLAUGHT

Do just one.

$$3078 \\ +1521$$ $$4302 \\ -2101$$

$$1224 \\ \times \quad 3$$ $$8\overline{)691}$$

18

ALGO ONSLAUGHT

Do just one.

$$608 \\ +271$$ $$378 \\ -254$$

$$26 \\ \times 3$$ $$2\overline{)553}$$

19

ALGO ONSLAUGHT

Do just one.

$$27 \\ +34$$ $$54 \\ -25$$

$$153 \\ \times \quad 3$$ $$5\overline{)73}$$

20

ALGO ONSLAUGHT

Do just one.

$$43 \\ + 7$$ $$73 \\ -38$$

$$272 \\ \times \quad 2$$ $$4\overline{)535}$$

21

ALGO ONSLAUGHT

Do just one.

$$29 \\ +38$$ $$47 \\ -18$$

$$180 \\ \times \quad 5$$ $$8\overline{)8920}$$

22

ALGO ONSLAUGHT

Do just one.

$$7 \\ +25$$ $$23 \\ - 8$$

$$92 \\ \times 4$$ $$7\overline{)63852}$$

23

ALGO ONSLAUGHT

Do just one.

$$234 \\ +157$$ $$475 \\ -349$$

$$1142 \\ \times \quad 3$$ $$2\overline{)45}$$

24

ALGO ONSLAUGHT

Do just one.

$$15 \\ +35$$ $$36 \\ -17$$

$$394 \\ \times \quad 2$$ $$3\overline{)458}$$

WHOLE NUMBER ARITHMETIC

46

Algo Onslaught Operations Cards
(Page 4 of six pages)
Back, laminate, and cut along solid lines.

25 ALGO ONSLAUGHT

Do just one.

$$
\begin{array}{r} 461 \\ +283 \\ \hline \end{array}
\qquad
\begin{array}{r} 456 \\ -283 \\ \hline \end{array}
$$

$$
\begin{array}{r} 259 \\ \times\ \ 3 \\ \hline \end{array}
\qquad
2\overline{)613}
$$

26 ALGO ONSLAUGHT

Do just one.

$$
\begin{array}{r} 283 \\ +461 \\ \hline \end{array}
\qquad
\begin{array}{r} 359 \\ -\ 84 \\ \hline \end{array}
$$

$$
\begin{array}{r} 114 \\ \times\ \ 8 \\ \hline \end{array}
\qquad
5\overline{)2545}
$$

27 ALGO ONSLAUGHT

Do just one.

$$
\begin{array}{r} 395 \\ +264 \\ \hline \end{array}
\qquad
\begin{array}{r} 518 \\ -235 \\ \hline \end{array}
$$

$$
\begin{array}{r} 243 \\ \times\ \ 4 \\ \hline \end{array}
\qquad
8\overline{)12038}
$$

28 ALGO ONSLAUGHT

Do just one.

$$
\begin{array}{r} 478 \\ +\ 51 \\ \hline \end{array}
\qquad
\begin{array}{r} 208 \\ -\ 47 \\ \hline \end{array}
$$

$$
\begin{array}{r} 97 \\ \times\ \ 8 \\ \hline \end{array}
\qquad
3\overline{)922}
$$

29 ALGO ONSLAUGHT

Do just one.

$$
\begin{array}{r} 2475 \\ +\ 372 \\ \hline \end{array}
\qquad
\begin{array}{r} 4736 \\ -\ 395 \\ \hline \end{array}
$$

$$
\begin{array}{r} 1146 \\ \times\ \ \ 6 \\ \hline \end{array}
\qquad
6\overline{)1824}
$$

30 ALGO ONSLAUGHT

Do just one.

$$
\begin{array}{r} 264 \\ +354 \\ \hline \end{array}
\qquad
\begin{array}{r} 555 \\ -264 \\ \hline \end{array}
$$

$$
\begin{array}{r} 128 \\ \times\ \ 7 \\ \hline \end{array}
\qquad
9\overline{)58540}
$$

31 ALGO ONSLAUGHT

Do just one.

$$
\begin{array}{r} 478 \\ +356 \\ \hline \end{array}
\qquad
\begin{array}{r} 523 \\ -276 \\ \hline \end{array}
$$

$$
\begin{array}{r} 23456 \\ \times\ \ \ \ 4 \\ \hline \end{array}
\qquad
26\overline{)552}
$$

32 ALGO ONSLAUGHT

Do just one.

$$
\begin{array}{r} 123 \\ +479 \\ \hline \end{array}
\qquad
\begin{array}{r} 473 \\ -189 \\ \hline \end{array}
$$

$$
\begin{array}{r} 12547 \\ \times\ \ \ \ 5 \\ \hline \end{array}
\qquad
19\overline{)824}
$$

WHOLE NUMBER ARITHMETIC

Algo Onslaught Operations Cards
(Page 5 of six pages)
Back, laminate, and cut along solid lines.

	33
ALGO ONSLAUGHT	
Do just one.	

$$355 + 255 \qquad 325 - 136$$

$$16253 \times 3 \qquad 45\overline{)513}$$

	34
ALGO ONSLAUGHT	
Do just one.	

$$476 + 58 \qquad 764 - 86$$

$$217292 \times 2 \qquad 72\overline{)145}$$

	35
ALGO ONSLAUGHT	
Do just one.	

$$1296 + 534 \qquad 4788 - 2699$$

$$15978 \times 7 \qquad 30\overline{)750}$$

	36
ALGO ONSLAUGHT	
Do just one.	

$$136 + 274 \qquad 831 - 652$$

$$23389 \times 4 \qquad 55\overline{)660}$$

	37
ALGO ONSLAUGHT	
Do just one.	

$$\begin{array}{r} 456 \\ 31 \\ +275 \end{array} \qquad \begin{array}{r} 43210 \\ -14563 \end{array}$$

$$4506 \times 27 \qquad 25\overline{)5234}$$

	38
ALGO ONSLAUGHT	
Do just one.	

$$\begin{array}{r} 18 \\ 543 \\ +257 \end{array} \qquad \begin{array}{r} 37421 \\ -18745 \end{array}$$

$$3725 \times 81 \qquad 50\overline{)70000}$$

	39
ALGO ONSLAUGHT	
Do just one.	

$$\begin{array}{r} 389 \\ 298 \\ +74 \end{array} \qquad \begin{array}{r} 84762 \\ -35989 \end{array}$$

$$406 \times 92 \qquad 17\overline{)353651}$$

	40
ALGO ONSLAUGHT	
Do just one.	

$$\begin{array}{r} 121 \\ 321 \\ +458 \end{array} \qquad \begin{array}{r} 739483 \\ -256567 \end{array}$$

$$2803 \times 242 \qquad 254\overline{)5103}$$

WHOLE NUMBER ARITHMETIC

Algo Onslaught Operations Cards
(Page 6 of six pages)
Back, laminate, and cut along solid lines.

ALGO ONSLAUGHT — 41

Do just one.

```
 2378
 1359
+ 198
```

```
 84837
-45949
```

```
 3214
× 523
```

```
377 86720
```

ALGO ONSLAUGHT — 42

Do just one.

```
  36
 457
+182
```

```
 96340
-58581
```

```
 487
×345
```

```
2050 9375601
```

ALGO ONSLAUGHT — 43

Do just one.

```
 34657
 21967
+11728
```

```
 60800
-23941
```

```
 43521
×50000
```

Divide 18 by 4 and write the remainder as a fraction. Simplify if you know how.

ALGO ONSLAUGHT — 44

Do just one.

```
 58739
  4192
+13129
```

```
 7400
-2536
```

```
 71439
×   700
```

Divide 60 by 25 and write the remainder as a fraction. Simplify if you know how.

ALGO ONSLAUGHT — 45

Do just one.

```
 23013
  2584
+45103
```

```
 502
-236
```

```
 62231
×  3500
```

Divide 815 by 37 and write the remainder as a fraction. Simplify if you know how.

ALGO ONSLAUGHT — 46

Do just one.

```
 930254
  85843
   7630
+ 10391
```

```
 600000
-125483
```

```
 3117
×2005
```

Determine 642 ÷ 7 to three decimal places.

ALGO ONSLAUGHT — 47

Do just one.

```
 23232
 15463
+46590
```

```
 40200
-12538
```

```
 4059
×5002
```

Determine 527 ÷ 8 to two decimal places.

ALGO ONSLAUGHT — 48

Do just one.

```
  3007
 49876
+32579
```

```
 3100
- 243
```

```
 4231
× 203
```

Determine 826 ÷ 9 to one decimal place.

WHOLE NUMBER ARITHMETIC

Algo Onslaught Chance Cards
(Page 1 of two pages)
Back, laminate, and cut along solid lines.

WHOLE NUMBER ARITHMETIC

ALGO ONSLAUGHT

CHANCE

You finally learned the basic facts. Advance five spaces.

ALGO ONSLAUGHT

CHANCE

You just remembered to check your work. Advance three spaces.

ALGO ONSLAUGHT

CHANCE

You just solved a word problem. Advance seven spaces.

ALGO ONSLAUGHT

CHANCE

You just understood what your teacher was saying. Advance three spaces.

ALGO ONSLAUGHT

CHANCE

You just had a fight with your parents over your homework. Go back five spaces.

ALGO ONSLAUGHT

CHANCE

You just helped a neighbor with his / her homework. Advance three spaces.

ALGO ONSLAUGHT

CHANCE

You just copied a friends homework. Go back five spaces.

ALGO ONSLAUGHT

CHANCE

You just asked your teacher a question. Advance five spaces.

Algo Onslaught Chance Cards
(Page 2 of two pages)
Back, laminate, and cut along solid lines.

ALGO ONSLAUGHT

CHANCE

Just in case you ever thought that in adding all you ever carried was a one, go back three spaces.

ALGO ONSLAUGHT

CHANCE

Just in case you ever used to just subtract the smaller number from the larger number, go back three spaces.

ALGO ONSLAUGHT

CHANCE

Add 38, 27, and 16. If you get 81, advance to I CAN DO IT. If you get 72, go to ALGO AWFUL.

ALGO ONSLAUGHT

CHANCE

Subtract 162 from 325. If you get 163, advance to I CAN DO IT. If you get 243, go to ALGO AWFUL.

ALGO ONSLAUGHT

CHANCE

Your pencil just broke. Go back one space.

ALGO ONSLAUGHT

CHANCE

The batteries in your calculator just ran down. Go back one space.

ALGO ONSLAUGHT

CHANCE

You just made a careless mistake. Go back one space.

ALGO ONSLAUGHT

CHANCE

You just finished your homework. Advance five spaces.

WHOLE NUMBER ARITHMETIC

ALGO ONSLAUGHT

KEY

Card	+	−	×	÷	Card	+	−	×	÷
1	8	4	6	3	25	744	173	777	306 R1
2	4	5	4	4	26	744	275	912	509
3	7	4	0	2	27	659	283	972	1504 R6
4	15	3	48	3	28	529	161	776	307 R1
5	12	1	63	8	29	2847	4341	6876	304
6	10	0	15	7	30	618	291	896	6504 R4
7	9	7	39	25	31	834	247	93,824	21 R6
8	13	9	32	12	32	602	284	62,735	43 R7
9	12	5	80	13	33	610	189	48,759	11 R18
10	15	7	426	11	34	534	678	434,584	2 R1
11	19	5	484	3 R1	35	1830	2089	111,846	25
12	14	7	666	7 R7	36	410	179	93,556	12
13	597	353	70	245	37	762	28,647	121,662	209 R9
14	285	733	92	142 R3	38	818	18,676	301,725	1400
15	75	62	84	122	39	761	48,773	37,352	20,803
16	35	45	272	12	40	900	482,916	678,326	20 R23
17	4599	2201	3672	86 R3	41	3935	38,888	1,680,922	230 R10
18	879	124	78	276 R1	42	675	37,759	168,015	4573 R951
19	61	29	459	14 R3	43	68,352	36,859	2,176,050,000	$4\frac{1}{2}$
20	50	35	544	133 R3	44	76,060	4864	50,007,300	$2\frac{2}{5}$
21	67	29	900	1115	45	70,700	266	217,808,500	$22\frac{1}{37}$
22	32	15	368	9121 R5	46	1,034,118	474,517	6,249,585	91.714
23	391	126	3426	22 R1	47	85,285	27,662	20,303,118	65.87
24	50	19	788	152 R2	48	85,462	2857	858,893	91.7

WHOLE NUMBER ARITHMETIC

Algo Onslaught Scorecard

Name . . . .   Date . . . .

Card	Operation				Card	Operation			
	+	−	×	÷		+	−	×	÷
	Hit Miss	Hit Miss	Hit Miss	Hit Miss		Hit Miss	Hit Miss	Hit Miss	Hit Miss
1	— —	— —	— —	— —	25	— —	— —	— —	— —
2	— —	— —	— —	— —	26	— —	— —	— —	— —
3	— —	— —	— —	— —	27	— —	— —	— —	— —
4	— —	— —	— —	— —	28	— —	— —	— —	— —
5	— —	— —	— —	— —	29	— —	— —	— —	— —
6	— —	— —	— —	— —	30	— —	— —	— —	— —
7	— —	— —	— —	— —	31	— —	— —	— —	— —
8	— —	— —	— —	— —	32	— —	— —	— —	— —
9	— —	— —	— —	— —	33	— —	— —	— —	— —
10	— —	— —	— —	— —	34	— —	— —	— —	— —
11	— —	— —	— —	— —	35	— —	— —	— —	— —
12	— —	— —	— —	— —	36	— —	— —	— —	— —
13	— —	— —	— —	— —	37	— —	— —	— —	— —
14	— —	— —	— —	— —	38	— —	— —	— —	— —
15	— —	— —	— —	— —	39	— —	— —	— —	— —
16	— —	— —	— —	— —	40	— —	— —	— —	— —
17	— —	— —	— —	— —	41	— —	— —	— —	— —
18	— —	— —	— —	— —	42	— —	— —	— —	— —
19	— —	— —	— —	— —	43	— —	— —	— —	— —
20	— —	— —	— —	— —	44	— —	— —	— —	— —
21	— —	— —	— —	— —	45	— —	— —	— —	— —
22	— —	— —	— —	— —	46	— —	— —	— —	— —
23	— —	— —	— —	— —	47	— —	— —	— —	— —
24	— —	— —	— —	— —	48	— —	— —	— —	— —

WHOLE NUMBER ARITHMETIC

Motley Crab Adder

54

The Scruffy Twin Subtractors

UNDERSTANDING ARITHMETIC WORD PROBLEMS

Sir Crab Multiplier

The Impeccable Twin Dividers

The Great Legalizer

The Magnificent Equalizer

Motley and Mates
(Miniatures)

Addition (Combining) Dominoes
(Page 1 of three pages)
Back, laminate, and cut along dotted lines.

3 + 2

1 + 3

Two
plus
5

One
plus
3

Two
combined
with
4

One
combined
with
3

Five
combined
with
4

Three
combined
with
1

3 + 5

3 + 1

Four
plus
6

Three
plus
1

Two
combined
with
5

Two
combined
with
3

2 + 4

2 + 3

Addition (Combining) Dominoes
(Page 2 of three pages)
Back, laminate, and cut along dotted lines.

UNDERSTANDING ARITHMETIC WORD PROBLEMS

Two plus 3	Five plus 3	Three combined with 2	Four combined with 5
Three plus 2	Six plus 4		
Two plus 4	Five plus 2	4 + 2	5 + 3
Four combined with 2	4 + 5	Four plus 2	6 + 4
		2 + 5	Three combined with 5

Addition (Combining) Dominoes
(Page 3 of three pages)
Back, laminate, and cut along dotted lines.

Six combined with 4

Five combined with 2

4 + 5

5 + 2

Four plus 5

Three plus 5

Four combined with 6

Five combined with 3

Five plus 4

4 + 6

Multiplication (Combining Neatly) Dominoes
(Page 1 of three pages)
Back, laminate, and cut along dotted lines.

2 × 4

2 × 3

Three combined neatly four times

Two combined neatly three times

Two times 5

Two times 3

Five times 3

Three times 2

7 × 2

3 × 2

Two combined neatly four times

Two combined neatly four times

Two combined neatly eight times

Three combined neatly two times

2 × 5

Three times 4

Two times 4

Multiplication (Combining Neatly) Dominoes
(Page 2 of three pages)
Back, laminate, and cut along dotted lines.

3×5

Four
times
2

4×2

Two
times
7

Four
combined
neatly
two
times

Eight
combined
neatly
two
times

2×7

5×2

Four
times
3

Two
combined
neatly
five
times

8×8

8×2

Five
combined
neatly
two
times

Five
times
2

Three
times
5

3×4

Seven
times
2

Multiplication (Combining Neatly) Dominoes
(Page 3 of three pages)
Back, laminate, and cut along dotted lines.

UNDERSTANDING ARITHMETIC WORD PROBLEMS

Eight times 2

Four combined neatly three times

5 × 3

4 × 3

Three combined neatly five times

Two combined neatly seven times

Seven combined neatly two times

2 × 8

Two times 8

Five combined neatly three times

Subtraction (Separating) Rummy Cards
(Page 1 of seven pages)
Back, laminate, and cut along solid lines.

One
sptd
from
4

One separated from 4

Four
minus
1

Four minus 1

$4-1$

$4-1$

Two
sptd
from
3

Two separated from 3

Three
minus
2

Three minus 2

$3-2$

$3-2$

Subtraction (Separating) Rummy Cards
(Page 2 of seven pages)
Back, laminate, and cut along solid lines.

Four
sptd
from
6

**Four
separated
from
6**

Six
minus
4

**Six
minus
4**

6 — 4

6 — 4

Two
sptd
from
7

**Two
separated
from
7**

Seven
minus
2

**Seven
minus
2**

7 — 2

7 — 2

Subtraction (Separating) Rummy Cards
(Page 3 of seven pages)
Back, laminate, and cut along solid lines.

Four separated from 8

Four
sptd
from
8

Eight minus 4

Eight
minus
4

8 — 4

8 — 4

Five separated from 11

Five
sptd
from
11

Eleven minus 5

Eleven
minus
5

11 — 5

11 — 5

Subtraction (Separating) Rummy Cards
(Page 4 of seven pages)
Back, laminate, and cut along solid lines.

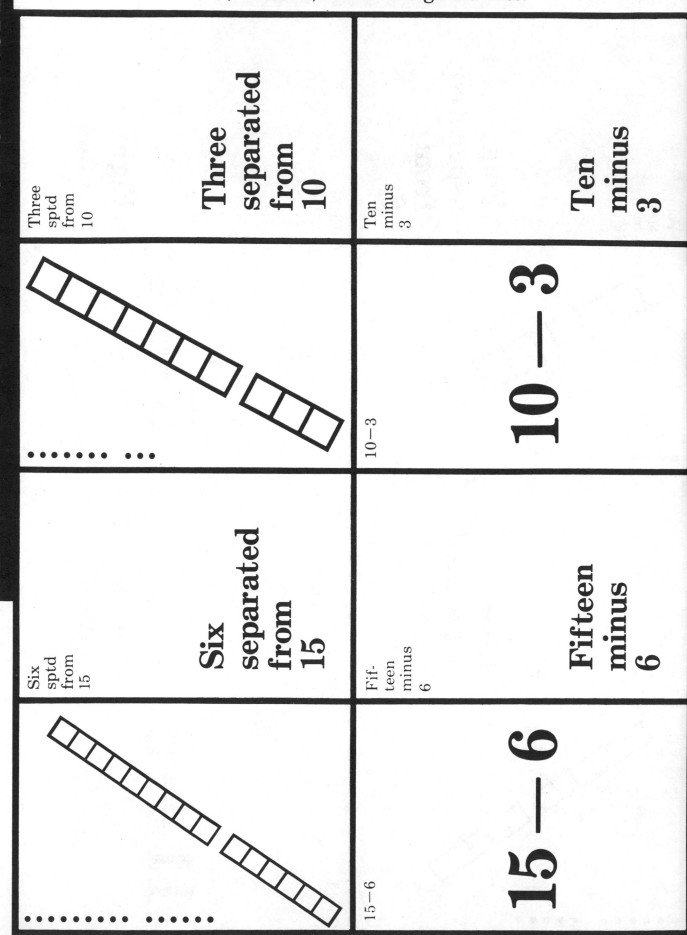

Three sptd from 10

Three separated from 10

Ten minus 3

Ten minus 3

10 — 3

10 — 3

Six sptd from 15

Six separated from 15

Fif- teen minus 6

Fifteen minus 6

15 — 6

15 — 6

Subtraction (Separating) Rummy Cards
(Page 5 of seven pages)
Back, laminate, and cut along solid lines.

Two
sptd
from
12

Two separated from 12

Twelve
minus
2

Twelve minus 2

....

12 — 2

12 — 2

Three
sptd
from
11

Three separated from 11

Eleven
minus
3

Eleven minus 3

....

11 — 3

11 — 3

Subtraction (Separating) Rummy Cards
(Page 6 of seven pages)
Back, laminate, and cut along solid lines.

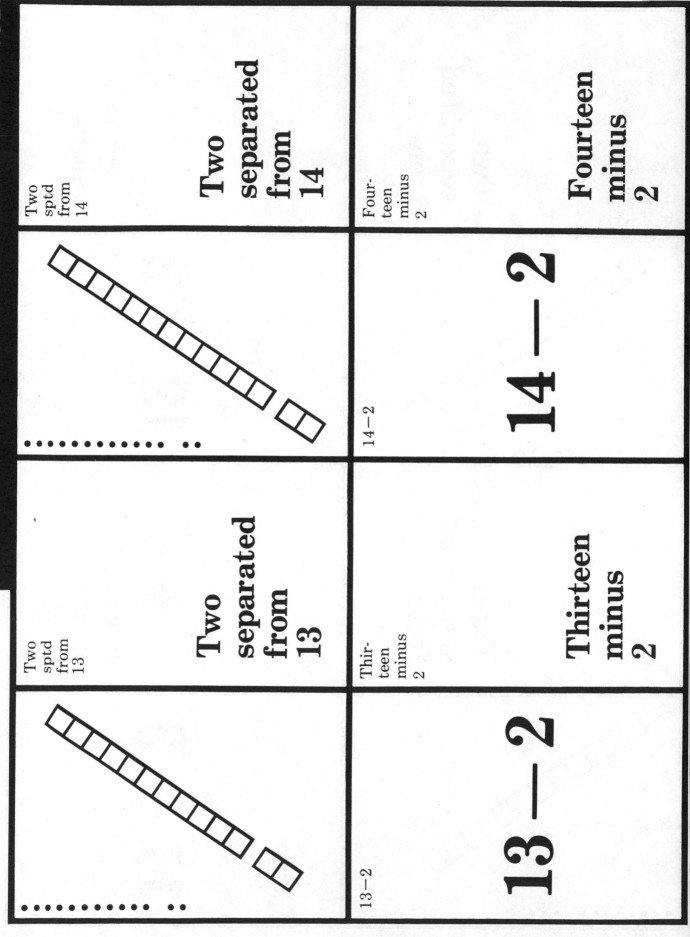

Two
sptd
from
14

Two separated from 14

Four-
teen
minus
2

Fourteen minus 2

14 − 2

14 — 2

Two
sptd
from
13

Two separated from 13

Thir-
teen
minus
2

Thirteen minus 2

13 − 2

13 — 2

Subtraction (Separating) Rummy Cards
(Page 7 of seven pages)
Back, laminate, and cut along solid lines.

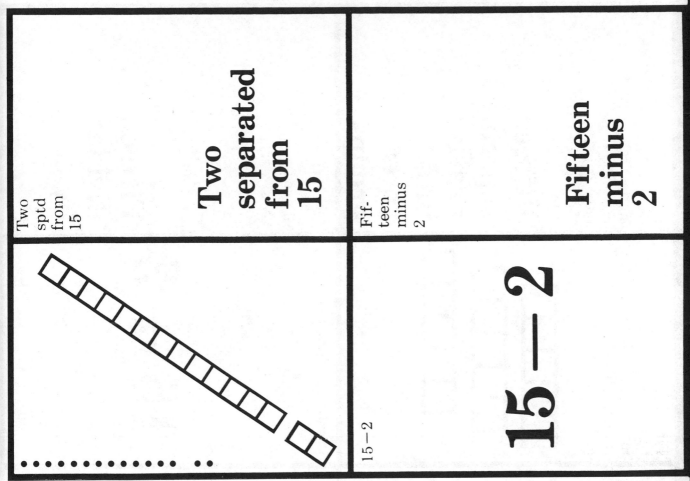

Two sptd from 15

Two separated from 15

Fif- teen minus 2

Fifteen minus 2

15 − 2

15 — 2

Division (Separating Neatly) Rummy Cards
(Page 1 of seven pages)
Back, laminate, and cut along solid lines.

UNDERSTANDING ARITHMETIC WORD PROBLEMS

Fif-
teen
sptd
ntly
into
three
grps

Fifteen separated neatly into three groups

Fif-
teen
divided
by
3

Fifteen divided by 3

Fif-
teen
into
three
grps

15 ÷ 3

15 ÷ 3

Four
sptd
ntly
into
twos

Four separated neatly into twos

Four
divided
by
2

Four divided by 2

Four
into
twos

4 ÷ 2

4 ÷ 2

Division (Separating Neatly) Rummy Cards
(Page 2 of seven pages)
Back, laminate, and cut along solid lines.

Nine
sptd
ntly
into
three
grps

Nine separated neatly into three groups

Nine
divided
by
3

Nine divided by 3

Nine
into
three
grps

9 ÷ 3

9 ÷ 3

Eight
sptd
ntly
into
ones

Eight separated neatly into ones

Eight
divided
by
1

Eight divided by 1

Eight
into
ones

8 ÷ 1

8 ÷ 1

Division (Separating Neatly) Rummy Cards
(Page 3 of seven pages)
Back, laminate, and cut along solid lines.

Twelve
sptd
ntly
into
two
grps

Twelve separated neatly into two groups

Twelve
divided
by
2

Twelve divided by 2

Twelve
into
two
grps

12÷2

12 ÷ 2

Eigh-
teen
sptd
ntly
into
twos

Eighteen separated neatly into twos

Eigh-
teen
divided
by
2

Eighteen divided by 2

Eigh-
teen
into
twos

18÷2

18 ÷ 2

Division (Separating Neatly) Rummy Cards
(Page 4 of seven pages)
Back, laminate, and cut along solid lines.

Twenty-two sptd ntly into two grps

Twenty-two separated neatly into two groups

Twenty-two divided by 2

Twenty-two divided by 2

Twenty-two into two grps

22 ÷ 2

22 ÷ 2

Thirty sptd ntly into threes

Thirty separated neatly into threes

Thirty divided by 3

Thirty divided by 3

Thirty into threes

30 ÷ 3

30 ÷ 3

Division (Separating Neatly) Rummy Cards
(Page 5 of seven pages)
Back, laminate, and cut along solid lines.

UNDERSTANDING ARITHMETIC WORD PROBLEMS

Twelve
sptd
ntly
into
one
grp

Twelve separated neatly into one group

Twelve
divided
by
1

Twelve divided by 1

Twelve
into
one
grp

$12 \div 1$

$12 \div 1$

Sixteen
sptd
ntly
into
fours

Sixteen separated neatly into fours

Sixteen
divided
by
4

Sixteen divided by 4

Sixteen
into
fours

$16 \div 4$

$16 \div 4$

Division (Separating Neatly) Rummy Cards
(Page 6 of seven pages)
Back, laminate, and cut along solid lines.

UNDERSTANDING ARITHMETIC WORD PROBLEMS

Twenty-one sptd ntly into three grps

Twenty-one separated neatly into three groups

Twenty-one divided by 3

Twenty-one divided by 3

Twenty-one into three grps

21 ÷ 3

21 ÷ 3

Twenty-six sptd ntly into twos

Twenty-six separated neatly into twos

Twenty-six divided by 2

Twenty-six divided by 2

Twenty-six into twos

26 ÷ 2

26 ÷ 2

Division (Separating Neatly) Rummy Cards
(Page 7 of seven pages)
Back, laminate, and cut along solid lines.

UNDERSTANDING ARITHMETIC WORD PROBLEMS

Twenty-eight sptd ntly into twos

Twenty-eight separated neatly into twos

Twenty-eight into twos

Twenty-eight divided by 2

Twenty-eight divided by 2

28÷2

28 ÷ 2

McDonald's Hamburgers Worksheet

Name..

Look at a McDonald's Hamburgers sign and determine the number of hamburgers McDonald's has sold to date. Then, for each problem below, write the number numerically in the space provided and solve the problem for that amount of hamburgers. If allowed, use a calculator for the computations.

1. Given that a McDonald's hamburger is about 2 inches high, that there are 12 inches in a foot, and that there are 5280 feet in a mile,

   a. Calculate the approximate height in miles of a stack of _____ McDonald's hamburgers.

   b. Make a comparison between a stack of hamburgers this high and the approximate distance from the earth to the moon (238,857 miles).

2. Given that a McDonald's hamburger is about 4 inches wide,

   a. Calculate the approximate length of a 6-lane highway with 12-foot wide traffic lanes and 10-foot wide shoulders "paved" with _____ McDonald's hamburgers laid side by side.

   b. List some major cities that could be connected with this highway.

3. Given that a McDonald's hamburger weighs about 3.7 ounces, that there are 16 ounces in a pound, and that there are 2000 pounds in a ton,

   a. Calculate the approximate weight in tons of _____ McDonald's hamburgers.

   b. Make a comparison between the weight of this many hamburgers and the approximate weight of a male African bush elephant (6 tons), the largest land mammal in the world.

4. Given that McDonald's uses about 1 gallon of mustard for every 2400 hamburgers it makes,

   a. Calculate the approximate number of gallons of mustard McDonald's has used to make _____ hamburgers.

   b. Make a comparison between this much mustard and the capacity of a railroad tank car (about 26,000 gallons).

5. Given that McDonald's uses about 1 gallon of ketchup for every 300 hamburgers it makes,

   a. Calculate the approximate number of gallons of ketchup McDonald's has used to make _____ hamburgers.

   b. Given that 1 gallon of ketchup will paint about 650 square feet, make a comparison between this much ketchup and the area of the District of Columbia (69.245 square miles).

6. Given that McDonald's uses about 1 gallon of pickles for every 350 hamburgers it makes,

   a. Calculate the approximate number of gallons of pickles McDonald's has used to make _____ hamburgers.

   b. Given that the dimensions of a gallon pickle jar are about 6½ inches wide by 9½ inches tall, make a comparison between this many gallons of pickles and the distance around Long Island, New York (about 300 miles).

Make-a-Whole Spinners
Color in keeping with fraction cakes.
Back and laminate.
Pin to boards or pencils with thumbtacks.

MATH GAMES & ACTIVITIES. COPYRIGHT © 1984

Fraction Cake
(unit)
Back, laminate, and cut out.

Fraction Cake
(Halves)
Color red.
Back, laminate, and cut along solid lines.

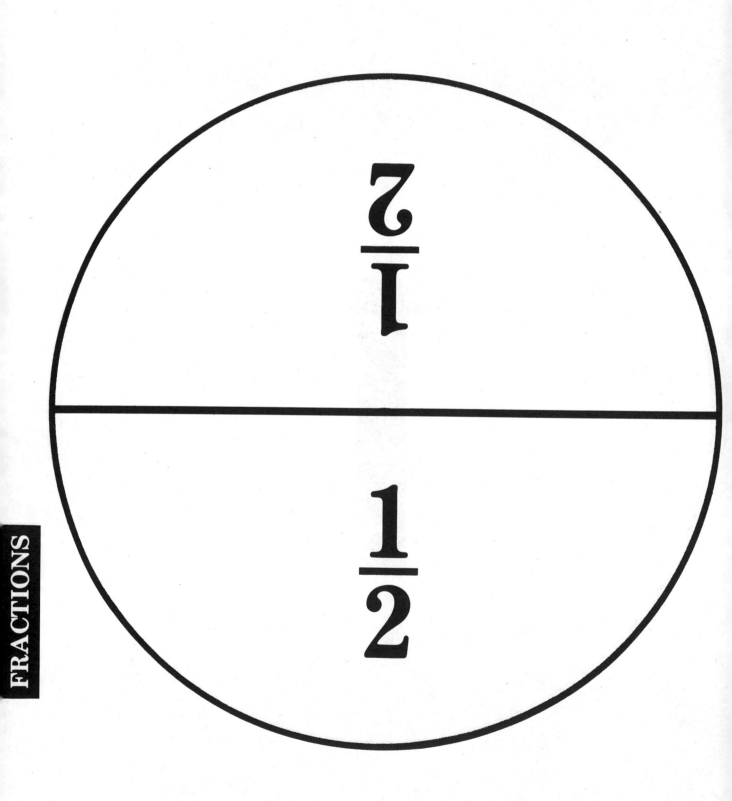

Fraction Cake
(Thirds)
Color green.
Back, laminate, and cut along solid lines.

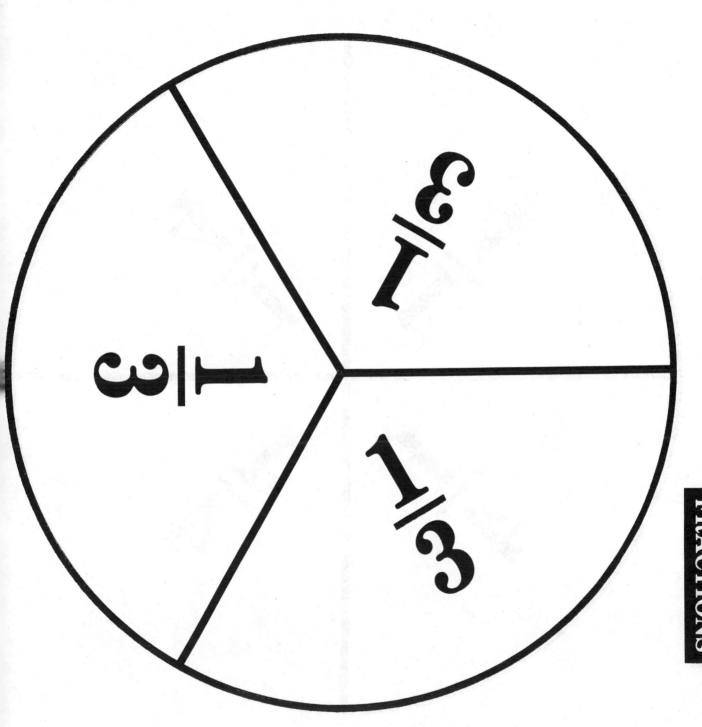

Fraction Cake
(Fourths)
Color yellow.
Back, laminate, and cut along solid lines.

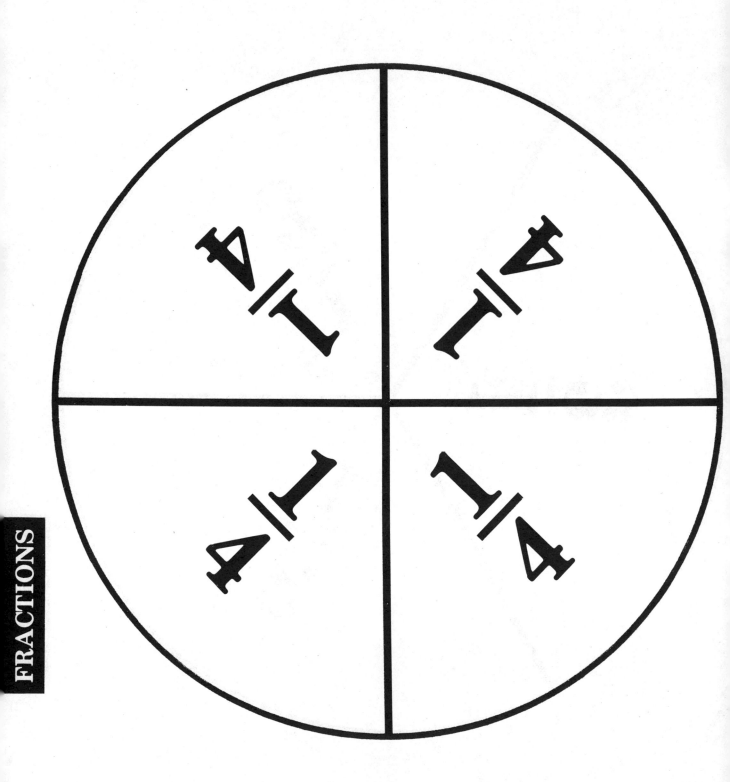

Fraction Cake
(Fifths)
Color blue.
Back, laminate, and cut along solid lines.

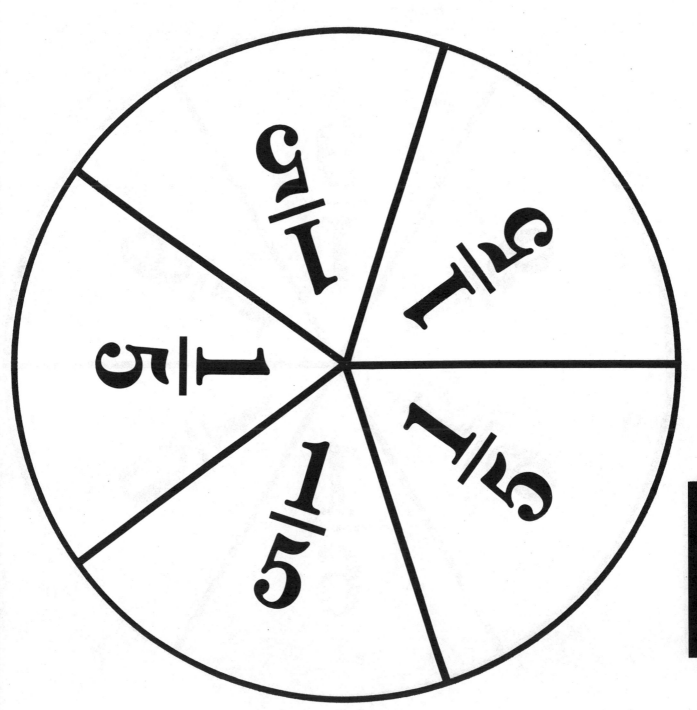

Fraction Cake
(Sixths)
Color brown.
Back, laminate, and cut along solid lines.

FRACTIONS

Fraction Cake
(Eighths)
Color pink.
Back, laminate, and cut along solid lines.

Fraction Cake
(Ninths)
Color purple.
Back, laminate, and cut along solid lines.

FRACTIONS

Fraction Cake
(Tenths)
Color orange.
Back, laminate, and cut along solid lines.

Fraction Cake
(Twelfths)
Color grey.
Back, laminate, and cut along solid lines.

Fraction Cakes
(Units, halves, thirds, and fourths)

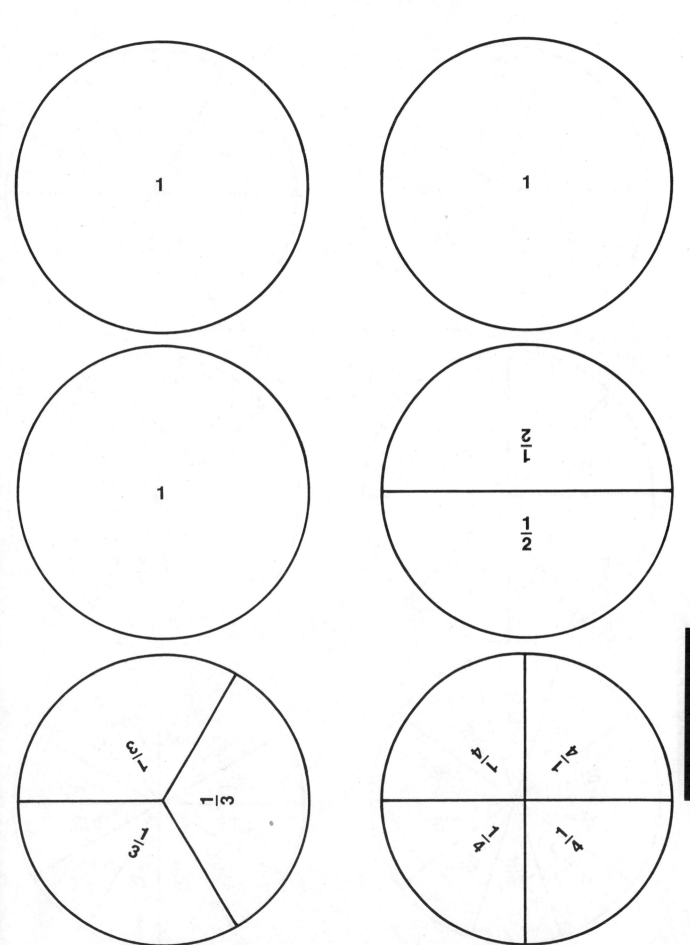

Fraction Cakes
(Fifths, sixths, eighths, ninths, tenths, and twelfths)

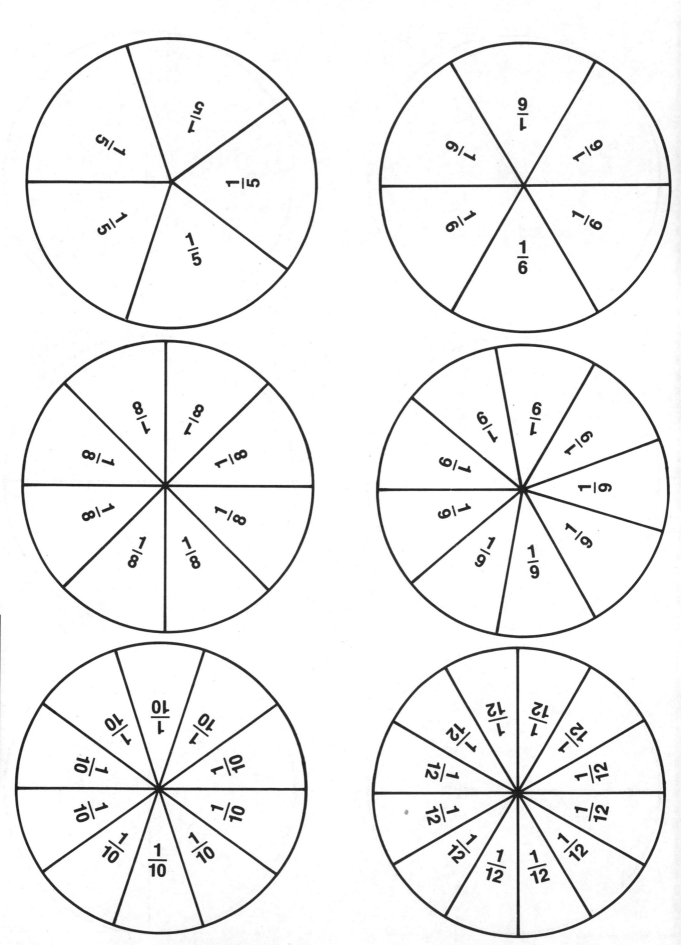

FRACTIONS

Equivalent Fraction Dominoes
(Page 1 of three pages)
Back, laminate, and cut along dotted lines.

One	$\dfrac{2}{2}$	$\dfrac{9}{5}$
1	$\dfrac{1}{2}$	One-half
	$\dfrac{1}{3}$	One-third
	$\dfrac{2}{3}$	Two-thirds
	$\dfrac{3}{4}$	$\dfrac{3}{6}$ Three-fourths

FRACTIONS

Equivalent Fraction Dominoes
(Page 2 of three pages)
Back, laminate, and cut along dotted lines.

Five-sixths

$\frac{4}{6}$

$\frac{3}{9}$

$\frac{12}{6}$

$\frac{9}{9}$

$\frac{8}{9}$

$\frac{2}{6}$

FRACTIONS

Equivalent Fraction Dominoes
(Page 3 of three pages)
Back, laminate, and cut along dotted lines.

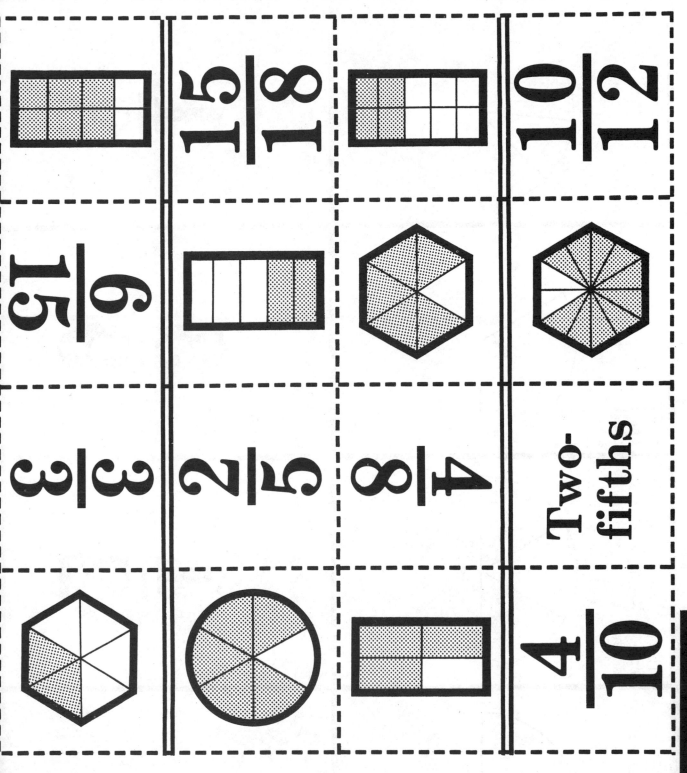

Equivalent Fraction Rummy Cards
(Page 1 of seven pages)
Back, laminate, and cut along solid lines.

FRACTIONS

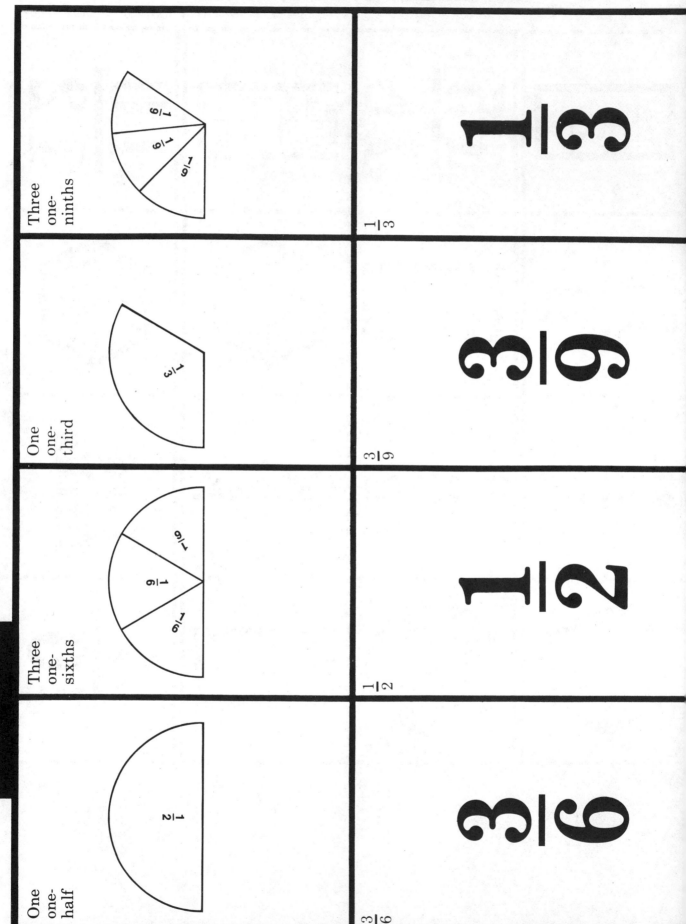

Three one-ninths

$\frac{1}{9}$ $\frac{1}{9}$ $\frac{1}{9}$

$\frac{1}{3}$

One one-third

$\frac{1}{3}$

$\frac{3}{6}$

Three one-sixths

$\frac{1}{6}$ $\frac{1}{6}$ $\frac{1}{6}$

$\frac{1}{2}$

One one-half

$\frac{1}{2}$

$\frac{3}{6}$

98

Equivalent Fraction Rummy Cards
(Page 2 of seven pages)
Back, laminate, and cut along solid lines.

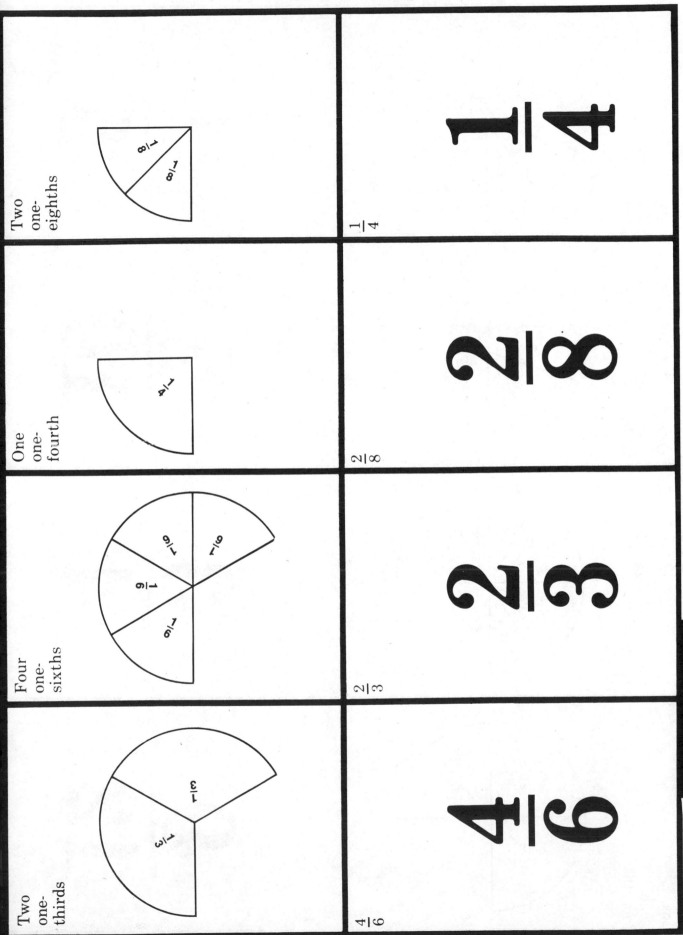

Two one-eighths

$\dfrac{1}{4}$

One one-fourth

$\dfrac{2}{8}$

Four one-sixths

$\dfrac{2}{3}$

Two one-thirds

$\dfrac{4}{6}$

FRACTIONS

Equivalent Fraction Rummy Cards
(Page 3 of seven pages)
Back, laminate, and cut along solid lines.

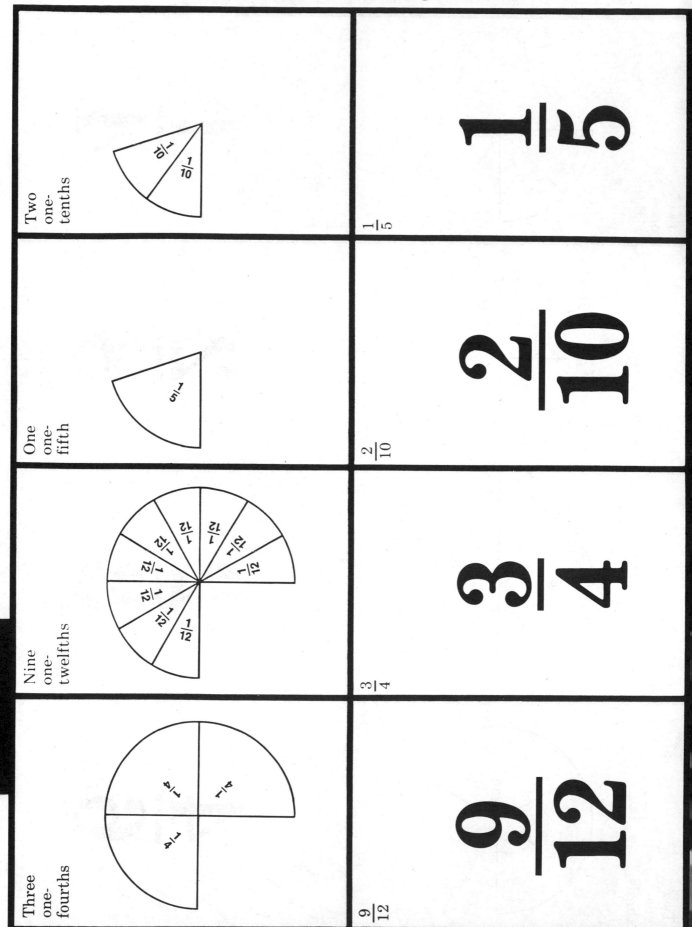

Two one-tenths

$\frac{1}{5}$

$\frac{1}{5}$

One one-fifth

$\frac{2}{10}$

$\frac{2}{10}$

Nine one-twelfths

$\frac{3}{4}$

$\frac{3}{4}$

Three one-fourths

$\frac{9}{12}$

$\frac{9}{12}$

FRACTIONS

Equivalent Fraction Rummy Cards
(Page 4 of seven pages)
Back, laminate, and cut along solid lines.

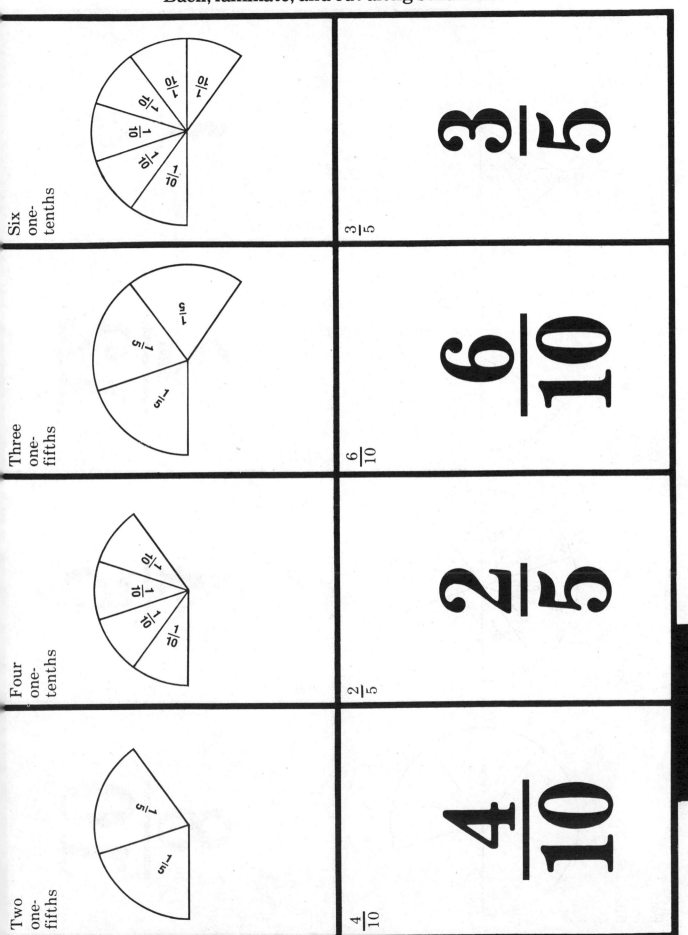

Six one-tenths

$\frac{3}{5}$

$\frac{3}{5}$

Three one-fifths

$\frac{6}{10}$

$\frac{6}{10}$

Four one-tenths

$\frac{2}{5}$

$\frac{2}{5}$

Two one-fifths

$\frac{4}{10}$

$\frac{4}{10}$

FRACTIONS

Equivalent Fraction Rummy Cards
(Page 5 of seven pages)
Back, laminate, and cut along solid lines.

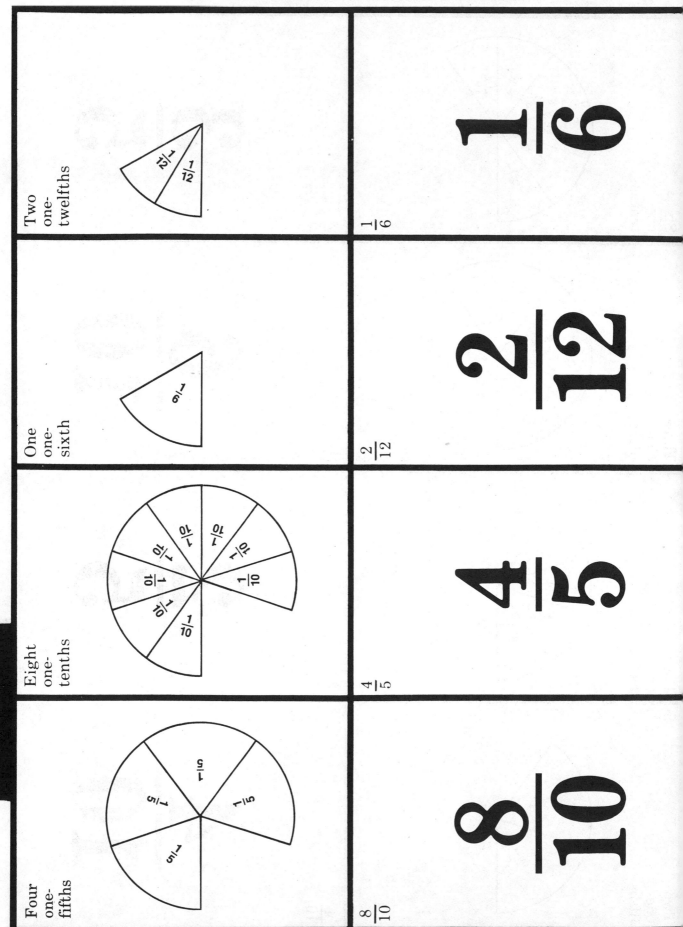

Two one-twelfths

$\frac{1}{12}$ $\frac{1}{12}$

$\frac{1}{6}$

$\frac{1}{6}$

One one-sixth

$\frac{1}{6}$

$\frac{2}{12}$

$\frac{2}{12}$

Eight one-tenths

$\frac{1}{10}$ $\frac{1}{10}$ $\frac{1}{10}$ $\frac{1}{10}$ $\frac{1}{10}$ $\frac{1}{10}$

$\frac{4}{5}$

$\frac{4}{5}$

Four one-fifths

$\frac{1}{5}$ $\frac{1}{5}$ $\frac{1}{5}$

$\frac{8}{10}$

$\frac{8}{10}$

FRACTIONS

Equivalent Fraction Rummy Cards
(Page 6 of seven pages)
Back, laminate, and cut along solid lines.

$$\frac{9}{20}$$

$\frac{6}{20}$

$$\frac{12}{40}$$

$\frac{12}{40}$

Three one-tenths

$$\frac{9}{30}$$

$\frac{9}{30}$

Ten one-twelfths

$$\frac{5}{6}$$

$\frac{5}{6}$

Five one-sixths

$$\frac{10}{12}$$

$\frac{10}{12}$

FRACTIONS

Equivalent Fraction Rummy Cards
(Page 7 of seven pages)
Back, laminate, and cut along solid lines.

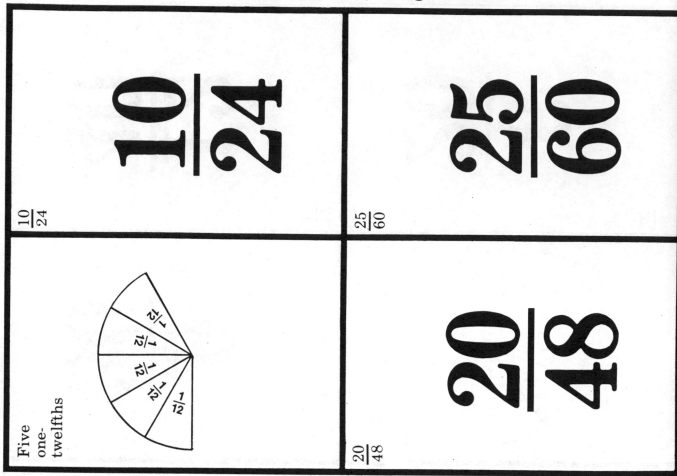

$$\frac{10}{24}$$

$$\frac{25}{60}$$

$$\frac{20}{48}$$

Five one-twelfths

FRACTIONS

Colored Squares Gameboard
Back and laminate.

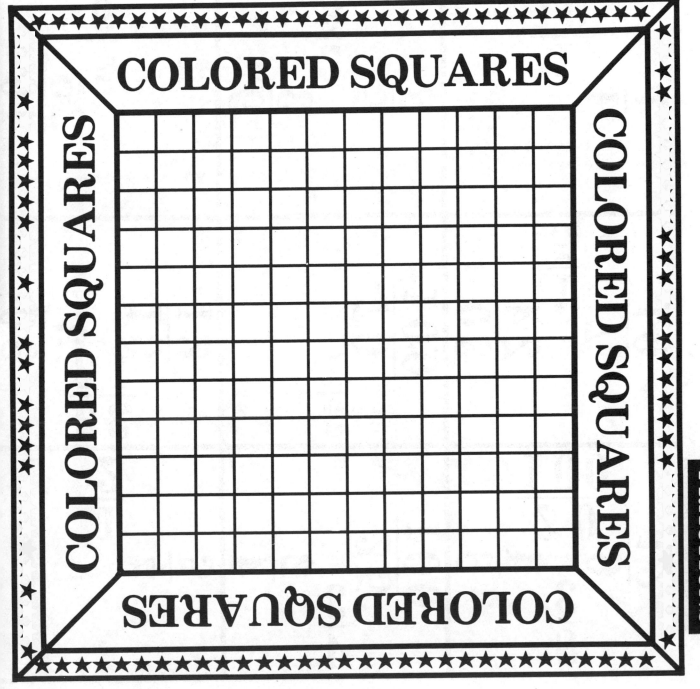

FRACTIONS

$\dfrac{5}{9}$ $\dfrac{25}{45}$ $\dfrac{40}{?}$	$\dfrac{2}{3}$ $\dfrac{6}{3}$ $\dfrac{5}{8}$	$\dfrac{1}{10}$ $\dfrac{1}{4}$
$\dfrac{30}{?}$ $\dfrac{10}{12}$ $\dfrac{3}{?}$ $\dfrac{12}{32}$	$\dfrac{70}{100}$ $\dfrac{1}{3}$	$\dfrac{1}{5}$ $\dfrac{7}{10}$ $\dfrac{24}{30}$
$\dfrac{1}{2}$ $\dfrac{4}{5}$ $\dfrac{4}{2}$	$\dfrac{25}{100}$ $\dfrac{3}{4}$	$\dfrac{12}{?}$ $\dfrac{6}{9}$ $\dfrac{20}{100}$ $\dfrac{3}{8}$

Bank It or Clear It Gameboard
Color in keeping with counters.
Back and laminate.

DECIMALS

BANK IT

CLEAR IT

DECIMALS

DECIMALS

Bank It or Clear It Spinners
Color in keeping with counters.
Back and laminate.
Pin to boards or pencils with thumbtacks.

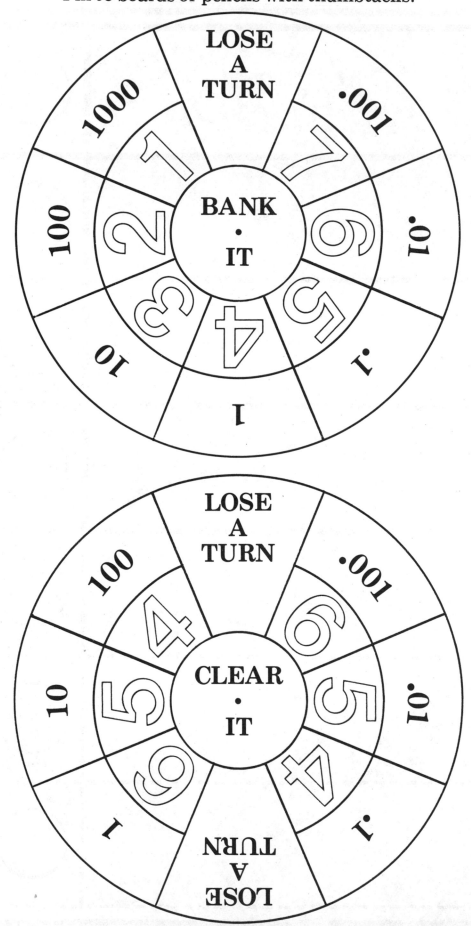

Deci-Builder or Deci-Buster Gameboard
Right side **and** left side
Color in keeping with counters.
Back and laminate.

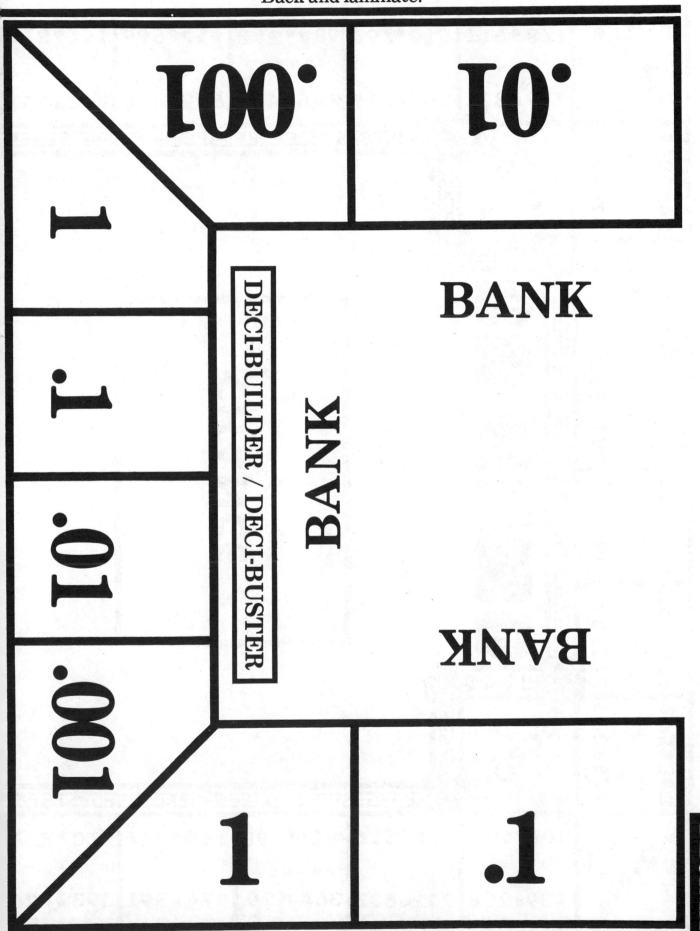

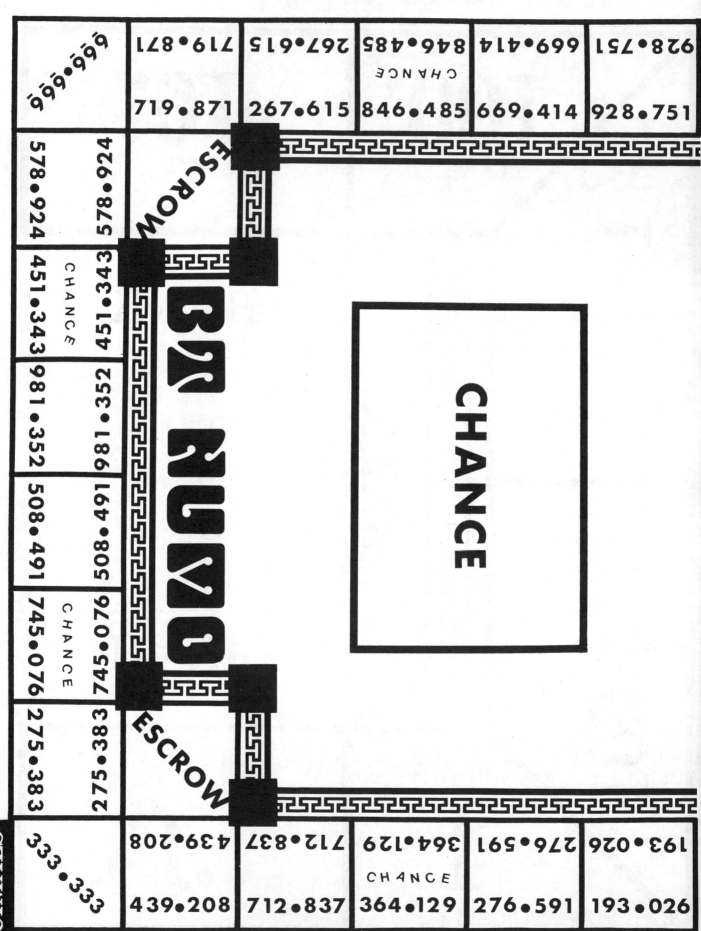

666.666

719.871

267.615

846.485
CHANCE

669.414

928.751

578.924

451.343
CHANCE

981.352

508.491

745.076
CHANCE

275.383

ESCROW

BT NUMO

ESCROW

CHANCE

439.208

712.837

364.129
CHANCE

276.591

193.026

333.333

DECIMALS

BT NUMO

ESCROW

640.958 | 687.507 CHANCE | 390.464 | 136.172 | 130.239 CHANCE | 999.999

524.514 | 524.514

923.105 | CHANCE | 923.105

561.807 | 561.807

452.763 | 452.763

882.748 | CHANCE | 882.748

494.096 | CHANCE | 494.096

GO

ESCROW

805.843 | 207.689 | 317.262 CHANCE | 183.912 | 359.635 | **START** 000.000

BT Numo Go Cards
(Page 1 of seven pages)
Back, laminate, and cut along solid lines.

BT NUMO GO

0.

Zero in the one's place

BT NUMO GO

1.

One in the one's place

BT NUMO GO

2.

Two in the one's place

BT NUMO GO

3.

Three in the one's place

BT NUMO GO

4.

Four in the one's place

BT NUMO GO

5.

Five in the one's place

BT NUMO GO

6.

Six in the one's place

BT NUMO GO

7.

Seven in the one's place

BT NUMO GO

8.

Eight in the one's place

BT NUMO GO

9.

Nine in the one's place

DECIMALS

BT Numo Go Cards
(Page 2 of seven pages)
Back, laminate, and cut along solid lines.

BT NUMO GO

Zero in the tenth's place

BT NUMO GO

One in the tenth's place

BT NUMO GO

Two in the tenth's place

BT NUMO GO

Three in the tenth's place

BT NUMO GO

Four in the tenth's place

BT NUMO GO

Five in the tenths place

BT NUMO GO

Six in the tenth's place

BT NUMO GO

Seven in the tenth's place

BT NUMO GO

Eight in the tenth's place

BT NUMO GO

Nine in the tenth's place

BT Numo Go Cards
(Page 3 of seven pages)
Back, laminate, and cut along solid lines.

BT NUMO GO

Zero in the ten's place

BT NUMO GO

One in the ten's place

BT NUMO GO

Two in the ten's place

BT NUMO GO

Three in the ten's place

BT NUMO GO

Four in the ten's place

BT NUMO GO

Five in the ten's place

BT NUMO GO

Six in the ten's place

BT NUMO GO

Seven in the ten's place

BT NUMO GO

Eight in the ten's place

BT NUMO GO

Nine in the ten's place

BT Numo Go Cards
(Page 4 of seven pages)
Back, laminate, and cut along solid lines.

BT NUMO GO

Zero in the hundredth's place

BT NUMO GO

One in the hundredth's place

BT NUMO GO

Two in the hundredth's place

BT NUMO GO

Three in the hundredth's place

BT NUMO GO

Four in the hundredth's place

BT NUMO GO

Five in the hundredth's place

BT NUMO GO

Six in the hundredth's place

BT NUMO GO

Seven in the hundredth's place

BT NUMO GO

Eight in the hundredth's place

BT NUMO GO

Nine in the hundredth's place

DECIMALS

BT Numo Go Cards
(Page 5 of seven pages)
Back, laminate, and cut along solid lines.

BT NUMO GO

1▮▮.▮▮▮

One in the hundred's place

BT NUMO GO

2▮▮.▮▮▮

Two in the hundred's place

BT NUMO GO

3▮▮.▮▮▮

Three in the hundred's place

BT NUMO GO

4▮▮.▮▮▮

Four in the hundred's place

BT NUMO GO

5▮▮.▮▮▮

Five in the hundred's place

BT NUMO GO

6▮▮.▮▮▮

Six in the hundred's place

BT NUMO GO

7▮▮.▮▮▮

Seven in the hundred's place

BT NUMO GO

8▮▮.▮▮▮

Eight in the hundred's place

BT NUMO GO

9▮▮.▮▮▮

Nine in the hundred's place

BT NUMO GO

▮▮.▮▮**1**

One in the thousandth's place

DECIMALS

MATH GAMES & ACTIVITIES. COPYRIGHT © 1984

BT Numo Go Cards
(Page 6 of seven pages)
Back, laminate, and cut along solid lines.

BT NUMO GO

■■■.■■2

Two in the thousandth's place

BT NUMO GO

■■■.■■3

Three in the thousandth's place

BT NUMO GO

■■■.■■4

Four in the thousandth's place

BT NUMO GO

■■■.■■5

Five in the thousandth's place

BT NUMO GO

■■■.■■6

Six in the thousandth's place

BT NUMO GO

■■■.■■7

Seven in the thousandth's place

BT NUMO GO

■■■.■■8

Eight in the thousandth's place

BT NUMO GO

■■■.■■9

Nine in the thousandth's place

BT NUMO GO

Go to your deed card.

BT NUMO GO

Go to your deed card.

DECIMALS

BT Numo Go Cards
(Page 7 of seven pages)
Back, laminate, and cut along solid lines.

BT NUMO GO

Go to the 000.000 corner.

BT NUMO GO

Go to the 333.333 corner.

BT NUMO GO

Go to the 666.666 corner.

BT NUMO GO

Go to the 999.999 corner.

BT NUMO GO

Go to the smallest number.

BT NUMO GO

Go to the largest number.

BT NUMO GO

Go back one space.

BT NUMO GO

Go back two spaces.

BT NUMO GO

Go back three spaces.

BT NUMO GO

Go back four spaces.

BT Numo Chance Cards
(Page 1 of three pages)
Back, laminate, and cut along solid lines.

BT NUMO **CHANCE** Pay **$0.10** to each Escrow square.	**BT NUMO** **CHANCE** Pay **$0.10** to each Escrow square.
BT NUMO **CHANCE** Pay **$0.10** to each Escrow square.	**BT NUMO** **CHANCE** Pay **$0.10** to each Escrow square.
BT NUMO **CHANCE** Pay **$1** to each Escrow square.	**BT NUMO** **CHANCE** Pay **$1** to each Escrow square.
BT NUMO **CHANCE** Pay **$1** to each Escrow square.	**BT NUMO** **CHANCE** Pay **$1** to each Escrow square.
BT NUMO **CHANCE** Pay **$0.10** to the 333.333 Escrow square.	**BT NUMO** **CHANCE** Pay **$1 to the 333.333** Escrow square.

DECIMALS

BT Numo Chance Cards
(Page 2 of three pages)
Back, laminate, and cut along solid lines.

BT NUMO **CHANCE** **Pay $10 to the 333.333 Escrow square.**	**BT NUMO** **CHANCE** **Pay $0.10 to the 666.666 Escrow square.**
BT NUMO **CHANCE** **Pay $1 to the 666.666 Escrow square.**	**BT NUMO** **CHANCE** **Pay $10 to the 666.666 Escrow square.**
BT NUMO **CHANCE** **Pay $0.10 to the 999.999 Escrow square.**	**BT NUMO** **CHANCE** **Pay $1 to the 999.999 Escrow square.**
BT NUMO **CHANCE** **Pay $10 to the 999.999 Escrow square.**	**BT NUMO** **CHANCE** **Pay $0.10 to the 000.000 Escrow square.**
BT NUMO **CHANCE** **Pay $1 to the 000.000 Escrow square.**	**BT NUMO** **CHANCE** **Pay $10 to the 000.000 Escrow square.**

DECIMALS

BT Numo Chance Cards
(Page 3 of three pages)
Back, laminate, and cut along solid lines.

BT NUMO **CHANCE** Collect $0.10 from each player.	**BT NUMO** **CHANCE** Collect $1 from each player.
BT NUMO **CHANCE** Collect $10 from each player.	**BT NUMO** **CHANCE** Collect the money from any two of the Escrow squares.
BT NUMO **CHANCE** Count your money. If it matches your scorecard, collect $10 from the bank. If otherwise, pay the bank $10.	**BT NUMO** **CHANCE** Count your money. If it matches your scorecard, collect $10 from the bank. If otherwise, pay the bank $10.
BT NUMO **CHANCE** Count your money. If it matches your scorecard, collect $10 from the bank. If otherwise, pay the bank $10.	**BT NUMO** **CHANCE** Count your money. If it matches your scorecard, collect $10 from the bank. If otherwise, pay the bank $10.
BT NUMO **CHANCE** Count your money. If it matches your scorecard, collect $10 from the bank. If otherwise, pay the bank $10.	**BT NUMO** **CHANCE** Count your money. If it matches your scorecard, collect $10 from the bank. If otherwise, pay the bank $10.

DECIMALS

BT Numo Deed Cards
(Page 1 of three pages)
Back, laminate, and cut along solid lines.

BT NUMO DEED	BT NUMO DEED
451.343	**578.924**
BT NUMO DEED	BT NUMO DEED
439.208	**719.871**
BT NUMO DEED	BT NUMO DEED
712.837	**267.615**
BT NUMO DEED	BT NUMO DEED
364.129	**846.485**
BT NUMO DEED	BT NUMO DEED
276.591	**669.414**

DECIMALS

BT Numo Deed Cards
(Page 2 of three pages)
Back, laminate, and cut along solid lines.

BT NUMO DEED	BT NUMO DEED
136.172	**130.239**
BT NUMO DEED	BT NUMO DEED
640.958	**805.843**
BT NUMO DEED	BT NUMO DEED
524.514	**923.105**
BT NUMO DEED	BT NUMO DEED
561.807	**452.763**
BT NUMO DEED	BT NUMO DEED
882.748	**494.096**

DECIMALS

BT Numo Deed Cards
(Page 3 of three pages)
Back, laminate, and cut along solid lines.

BT NUMO DEED	BT NUMO DEED
359.635	**183.912**
BT NUMO DEED	BT NUMO DEED
317.262	**207.689**
BT NUMO DEED	BT NUMO DEED
275.383	**928.751**
BT NUMO DEED	BT NUMO DEED
193.026	**745.076**
BT NUMO DOUBLE DEED	BT NUMO DOUBLE DEED
390.464 and 508.491	687.507 and 981.352

DECIMALS

$10 $10

$1 $1

$1 $1

$0.10 $0.10 $0.10 $0.10

DECIMALS

BT Numo Scorecard

Name _____

$50.00

BT Numo Scorecard

Name _____

$50.00

BT Numo Scorecard

Name _____

$50.00

BT Numo Scorecard

Name _____

$50.00

Decimal Rummy Cards
(Page 1 of seven pages)
Back, laminate, and cut along solid lines.

Three hun-dredths

.03

.03

$\frac{3}{100}$

$\frac{3}{100}$

Point zero three

Point zero three

Nine-hun-dredths

.09

.09

$\frac{9}{100}$

$\frac{9}{100}$

Point zero nine

Point zero nine

DECIMALS

Decimal Rummy Cards
(Page 2 of seven pages)
Back, laminate, and cut along solid lines.

Thirteen-hun-dredths

.13

.13

Point one three

$\frac{13}{100}$

Point one three

$\frac{13}{100}$

Two-tenths

.2

.2

Point two

$\frac{2}{10}$

Point two

$\frac{2}{10}$

Decimal Rummy Cards
(Page 3 of seven pages)
Back, laminate, and cut along solid lines.

Twenty-five-hun-dredths

.25

.25

Point two five

Point two five

Point three

$\frac{25}{100}$

$\frac{25}{100}$

Three-tenths

.3

.3

Point three

Point three

$\frac{3}{10}$

$\frac{3}{10}$

DECIMALS

129

Decimal Rummy Cards
(Page 4 of seven pages)
Back, laminate, and cut along solid lines.

Five-tenths

.5

.5

Point five

Point five

$\frac{5}{10}$

$\frac{5}{10}$

Sixty-two-hundredths

.62

.62

Point six two

Point six two

$\frac{62}{100}$

$\frac{62}{100}$

Decimal Rummy Cards
(Page 5 of seven pages)
Back, laminate, and cut along solid lines.

Seventy-five hun-dredths

.75

.75

Point seven five

$\frac{75}{100}$

$\frac{75}{100}$

Nine-tenths

.9

.9

Point nine

$\frac{9}{10}$

$\frac{9}{10}$

Decimal Rummy Cards
(Page 6 of seven pages)
Back, laminate, and cut along solid lines.

One
and
eight-
hun-
dredths

1.08

1.08

One
point
zero
eight

One point zero eight

$1\frac{8}{100}$

$1\frac{8}{100}$

One
and
twenty-
five-
hun-
dredths

1.25

1.25

One
point
two
five

One point two five

$1\frac{25}{100}$

$1\frac{25}{100}$

MATH GAMES & ACTIVITIES. COPYRIGHT © 1984

Decimal Rummy Cards
(Page 7 of seven pages)
Back, laminate, and cut along solid lines.

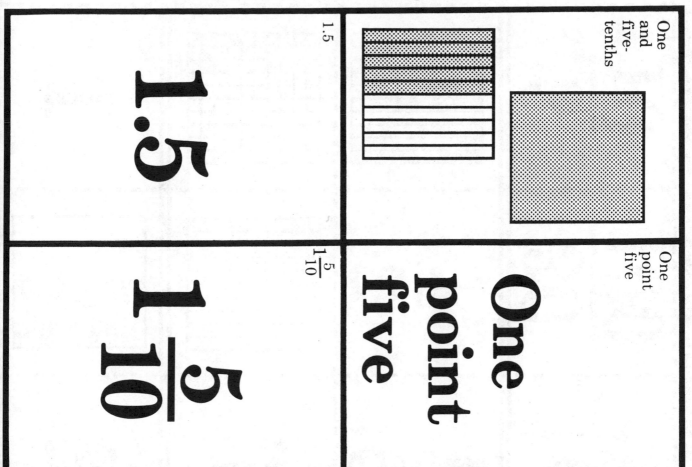

Fraction-Decimal-Percent Dominoes
(Page 1 of three pages)
Back, laminate, and cut along dotted lines.

FRACTIONS, DECIMALS, AND PERCENTS

$\frac{3}{10}$

$\frac{30}{100}$

.3

30%

Point three

$\frac{1}{2}$

$\frac{1}{5}$

$\frac{4}{5}$

$\frac{2}{25}$

1

.2

.5

50%

Point five

$\frac{4}{50}$

Fraction-Decimal-Percent Dominoes
(Page 2 of three pages)
Back, laminate, and cut along dotted lines.

$\dfrac{10}{10}$

.8

80%

Point eight

Eighty percent

$\dfrac{8}{100}$

20%

Point two

Twenty percent

.08

75%

100%

.75

8%

Fraction-Decimal-Percent Dominoes
(Page 3 of three pages)
Back, laminate, and cut along dotted lines.

FRACTIONS, DECIMALS, AND PERCENTS

Eight percent

One hundred percent

Seventy five percent

Thirty percent

$\dfrac{3}{4}$

Fifty percent

$\dfrac{75}{100}$

$\dfrac{100}{100}$

Point zero eight

Point seven five

Fraction-Decimal-Percent Array Cards
Back, laminate, and cut along solid lines.

$\frac{3}{4}$ $.3$ 25%

$\frac{1}{2}$ $.4$

$\frac{1}{8}$ $\frac{1}{10}$ $.6$

$.05$ 15% 50%

$\frac{3}{10}$ $\frac{1}{4}$ 90%

$.2$ 5% .125

$.75$ 20%

$\frac{4}{5}$ $.15$ 10%

$\frac{2}{5}$ 80%

Fraction-Decimal-Percent Rummy Cards
(Page 1 of seven pages)
Back, laminate, and cut along solid lines.

FRACTIONS, DECIMALS, AND PERCENTS

$\frac{1}{5}$

$\frac{1}{5}$

20%

20%

$\frac{2}{10}$

$\frac{2}{10}$

0.2

0.2

$\frac{1}{10}$

$\frac{1}{10}$

10%

10%

$\frac{2}{20}$

$\frac{2}{20}$

0.1

0.1

MATH GAMES & ACTIVITIES. COPYRIGHT © 1984

Fraction-Decimal-Percent Rummy Cards
(Page 2 of seven pages)
Back, laminate, and cut along solid lines.

$\dfrac{3}{10}$

$\dfrac{3}{10}$

30%

30%

$\dfrac{6}{20}$

$\dfrac{6}{20}$

0.3

0.3

$\dfrac{1}{4}$

$\dfrac{1}{4}$

25%

25%

$\dfrac{2}{8}$

$\dfrac{2}{8}$

0.25

0.25

Fraction-Decimal-Percent Rummy Cards
(Page 3 of seven pages)
Back, laminate, and cut along solid lines.

FRACTIONS, DECIMALS, AND PERCENTS

$\frac{2}{5}$

$\frac{2}{5}$

40%

40%

$\frac{4}{10}$

$\frac{4}{10}$

0.4

0.4

$\frac{1}{3}$

$\frac{1}{3}$

33%

33%

$\frac{2}{6}$

$\frac{2}{6}$

0.33

0.33

Fraction-Decimal-Percent Rummy Cards
(Page 4 of seven pages)
Back, laminate, and cut along solid lines.

FRACTIONS, DECIMALS, AND PERCENTS

$\dfrac{3}{5}$

$\dfrac{3}{5}$

60%

60%

$\dfrac{6}{10}$

$\dfrac{6}{10}$

0.6

0.6

$\dfrac{1}{2}$

$\dfrac{1}{2}$

50%

50%

$\dfrac{2}{4}$

$\dfrac{2}{4}$

0.5

0.5

Fraction-Decimal-Percent Rummy Cards
(Page 5 of seven pages)
Back, laminate, and cut along solid lines.

FRACTIONS, DECIMALS, AND PERCENTS

$\frac{3}{4}$

$\frac{3}{4}$

75%

75%

$\frac{6}{8}$

$\frac{6}{8}$

0.75

0.75

$\frac{2}{3}$

$\frac{2}{3}$

67%

67%

$\frac{4}{6}$

$\frac{4}{6}$

0.67

0.67

Fraction-Decimal-Percent Rummy Cards
(Page 6 of seven pages)
Back, laminate, and cut along solid lines.

$\frac{9}{10}$

$\frac{9}{10}$

90%

90%

$\frac{18}{20}$

$\frac{18}{20}$

0.9

0.9

$\frac{4}{5}$

$\frac{4}{5}$

80%

80%

$\frac{8}{10}$

$\frac{8}{10}$

0.8

0.8

Fraction-Decimal-Percent Rummy Cards
(Page 7 of seven pages)
Back, laminate, and cut along solid lines.

FRACTIONS, DECIMALS, AND PERCENTS

1

1

100%

100%

$$\frac{10}{10}$$

$\frac{10}{10}$

1.0

1.0

Tunnel Gameboard
(Fractions, decimals, and percents)
Color, back, and laminate.

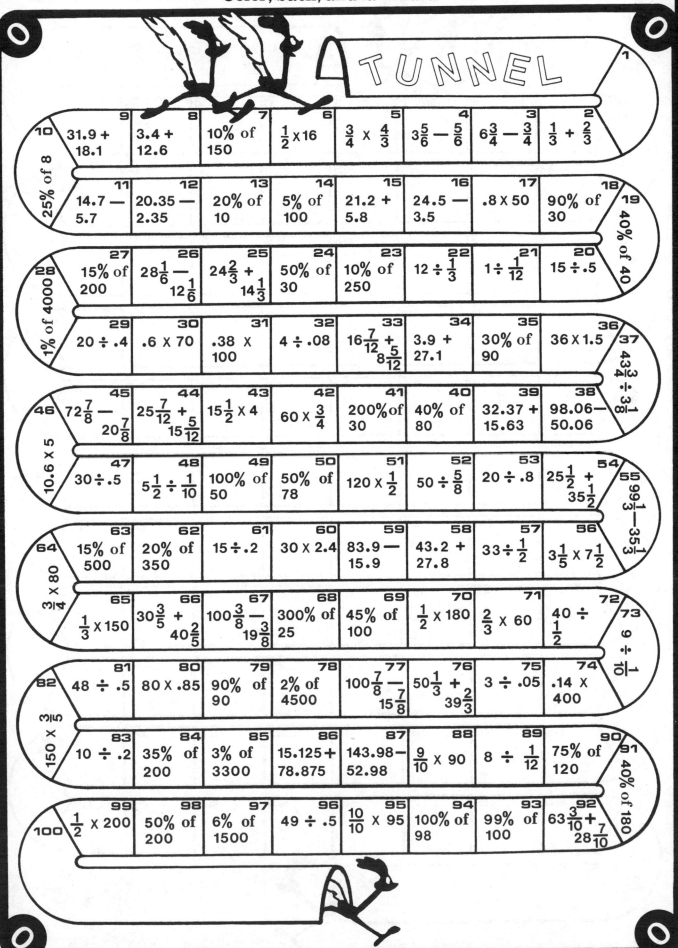

1 TUNNEL

2 $\frac{1}{3} + \frac{2}{3}$

3 $6\frac{3}{4} - \frac{3}{4}$

4 $3\frac{5}{6} - \frac{5}{6}$

5 $\frac{3}{4} \times \frac{4}{3}$

6 $\frac{1}{2} \times 16$

7 10% of 150

8 $3.4 + 12.6$

9 $31.9 + 18.1$

10 25% of 8

11 $14.7 - 5.7$

12 $20.35 - 2.35$

13 20% of 10

14 5% of 100

15 $21.2 + 5.8$

16 $24.5 - 3.5$

17 $.8 \times 50$

18 90% of 30

19 40% of 40

20 $15 \div .5$

21 $1 \div \frac{1}{12}$

22 $12 \div \frac{1}{3}$

23 10% of 250

24 50% of 30

25 $24\frac{2}{3} + 14\frac{1}{3}$

26 $28\frac{1}{6} - 12\frac{1}{6}$

27 15% of 200

28 1% of 4000

29 $20 \div .4$

30 $.6 \times 70$

31 $.38 \times 100$

32 $4 \div .08$

33 $16\frac{7}{12} + 8\frac{5}{12}$

34 $3.9 + 27.1$

35 30% of 90

36 36×1.5

37 $43\frac{3}{4} \div 3\frac{1}{8}$

38 $98.06 - 50.06$

39 $32.37 + 15.63$

40 40% of 80

41 200% of 30

42 $60 \times \frac{3}{4}$

43 $15\frac{1}{2} \times 4$

44 $25\frac{7}{12} + 15\frac{5}{12}$

45 $72\frac{7}{8} - 20\frac{7}{8}$

46 10.6×5

47 $30 \div .5$

48 $5\frac{1}{2} \div \frac{1}{10}$

49 100% of 50

50 50% of 78

51 $120 \times \frac{1}{2}$

52 $50 \div \frac{5}{8}$

53 $20 \div .8$

54 $25\frac{1}{2} + 35\frac{1}{2}$

55 $99\frac{1}{3} - 35\frac{1}{3}$

56 $3\frac{1}{5} \times 7\frac{1}{2}$

57 $33 \div \frac{1}{2}$

58 $43.2 + 27.8$

59 $83.9 - 15.9$

60 30×2.4

61 $15 \div .2$

62 20% of 350

63 15% of 500

64 $\frac{3}{4} \times 80$

65 $\frac{1}{3} \times 150$

66 $30\frac{3}{5} + 40\frac{2}{5}$

67 $100\frac{3}{8} - 19\frac{3}{8}$

68 300% of 25

69 45% of 100

70 $\frac{1}{2} \times 180$

71 $\frac{2}{3} \times 60$

72 $40 \div 1\frac{1}{2}$

73 $9 \div 1\frac{1}{10}$

74 $.14 \times 400$

75 $3 \div .05$

76 $50\frac{1}{3} + 39\frac{2}{3}$

77 $100\frac{7}{8} - 15\frac{7}{8}$

78 2% of 4500

79 90% of 90

80 $80 \times .85$

81 $48 \div .5$

82 $150 \times \frac{3}{5}$

83 $10 \div .2$

84 35% of 200

85 3% of 3300

86 $15.125 + 78.875$

87 $143.98 - 52.98$

88 $\frac{9}{10} \times 90$

89 $8 \div \frac{1}{12}$

90 75% of 120

91 40% of 180

92 $63\frac{3}{10} + 28\frac{7}{10}$

93 99% of 100

94 100% of 98

95 $\frac{10}{10} \times 95$

96 $49 \div .5$

97 6% of 1500

98 50% of 200

99 $\frac{1}{2} \times 200$

100

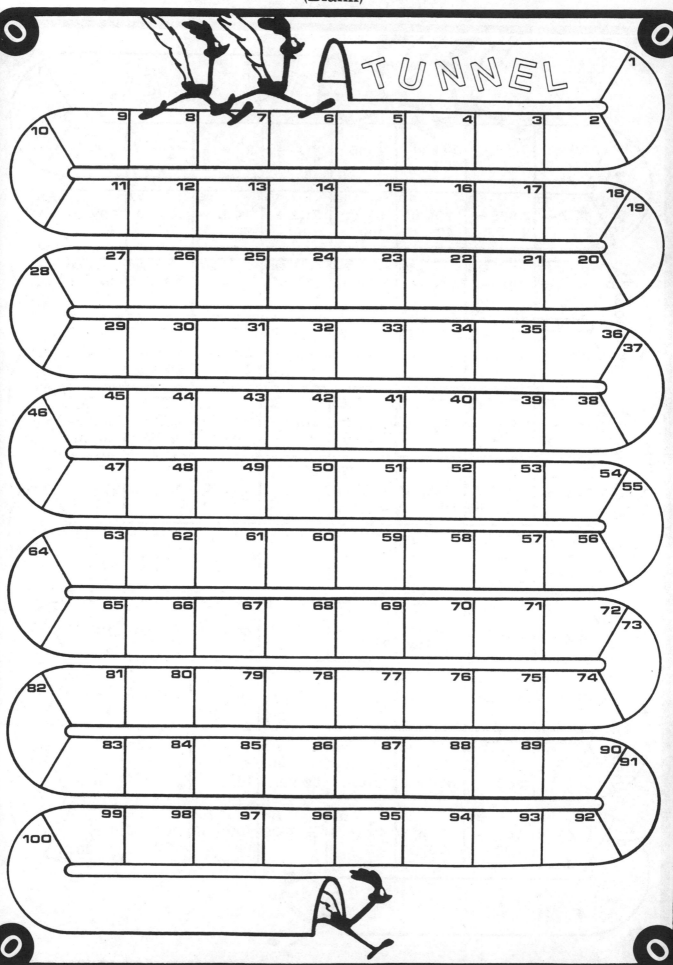

Hi! My name is Ima Blank-page. Turn the page and BEHOLD!

FDP Showdown Gameboard
Left side
Color, back, and laminate.

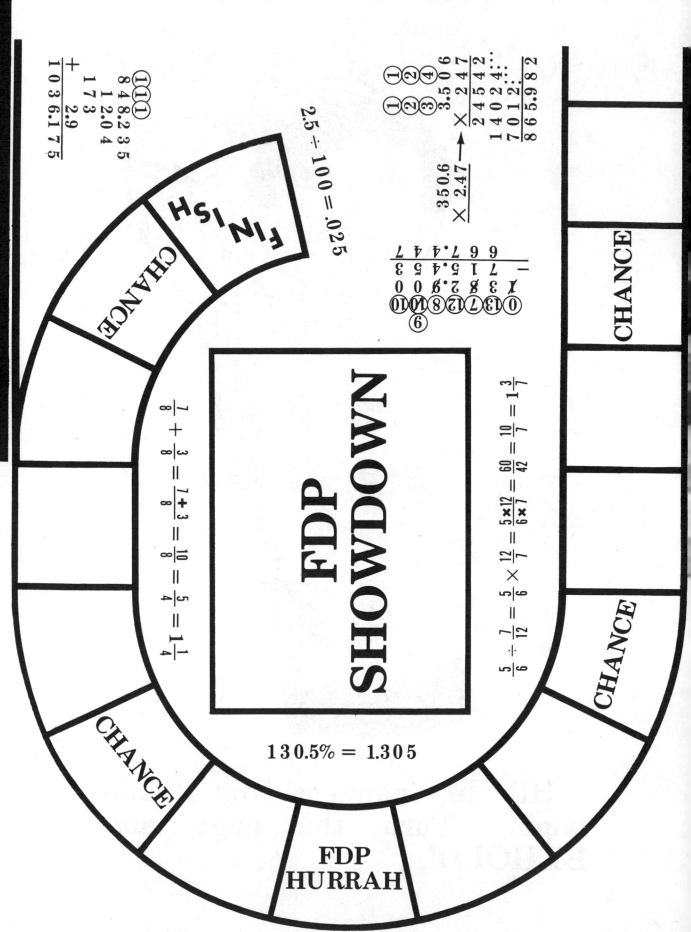

FDP Showdown Gameboard
Right side
Color, back, and laminate.

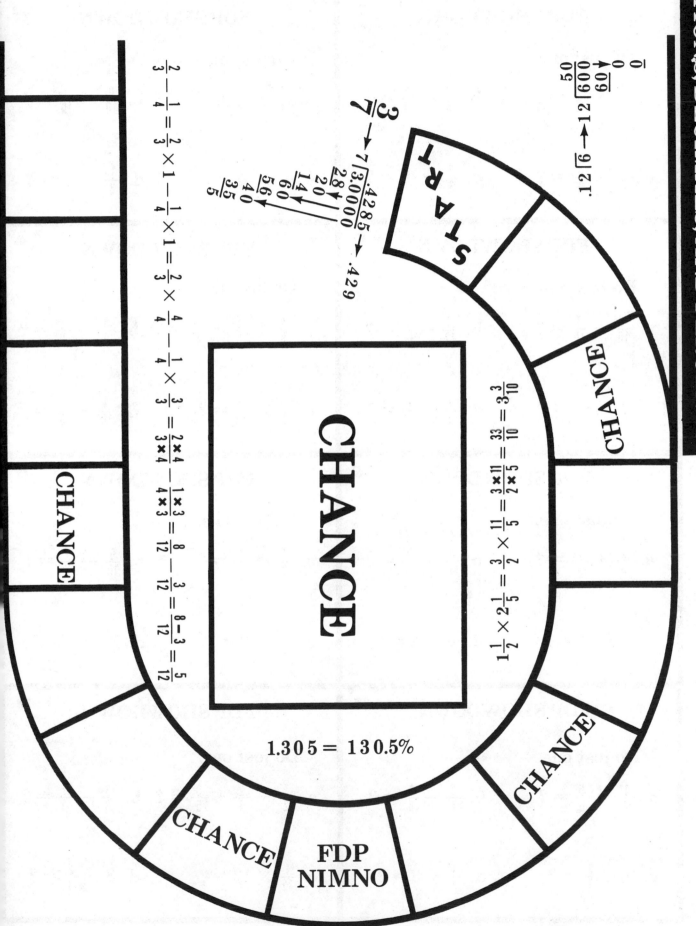

FDP Showdown Operations Cards
(Page 1 of five pages)
Back, laminate, and cut along solid lines.

FDP SHOWDOWN 1

Do just one.

a. $\frac{1}{7} + \frac{2}{7} = ?$ b. $\frac{7}{8} - \frac{5}{8} = ?$

c. $\frac{1}{3} \times \frac{3}{6} = ?$ d. $\frac{2}{3} \div \frac{1}{3} = ?$

FDP SHOWDOWN 2

Do just one.

a. $\frac{3}{4} + \frac{3}{4} = ?$ b. $\frac{9}{10} - \frac{3}{10} = ?$

c. $\frac{1}{2} \times \frac{4}{5} = ?$ d. $\frac{1}{2} \div \frac{1}{4} = ?$

FDP SHOWDOWN 3

Do just one.

a. $\frac{7}{10} + \frac{1}{10} = ?$ b. $\frac{7}{12} - \frac{1}{12} = ?$

c. $\frac{3}{4} \times \frac{4}{3} = ?$ d. $\frac{7}{8} \div \frac{1}{12} = ?$

FDP SHOWDOWN 4

Do just one.

a. $\frac{4}{9} + \frac{5}{9} + \frac{7}{9} = ?$ b. $\frac{8}{9} - \frac{5}{9} = ?$

c. $\frac{4}{9} \times \frac{5}{12} = ?$ d. $\frac{3}{10} \div \frac{1}{3} = ?$

FDP SHOWDOWN 5

Do just one.

a. $\frac{2}{3} + \frac{3}{4} = ?$ b. $\frac{1}{2} - \frac{1}{3} = ?$

c. $3 \times \frac{1}{6} = ?$ d. $\frac{4}{5} \div 2 = ?$

FDP SHOWDOWN 6

Do just one.

a. $\frac{1}{2} + \frac{1}{6} = ?$ b. $\frac{9}{10} - \frac{1}{2} = ?$

c. $\frac{3}{4} \times 2 = ?$ d. $1 \div \frac{1}{4} = ?$

FDP SHOWDOWN 7

Do just one.

a. $\frac{1}{4} + \frac{5}{6} = ?$ b. $\frac{3}{4} - \frac{1}{8} = ?$

c. $9 \times \frac{2}{3} = ?$ d. $\frac{1}{3} \div 3 = ?$

FDP SHOWDOWN 8

Do just one.

a. $\frac{1}{2} + \frac{2}{3} + \frac{3}{5} = ?$ b. $\frac{3}{8} - \frac{1}{3} = ?$

c. $\frac{1}{12} \times 12 = ?$ d. $8 \div \frac{2}{3} = ?$

FDP Showdown Operations Cards
(Page 2 of five pages)
Back, laminate, and cut along solid lines.

FDP SHOWDOWN 9

Do just one.

a. $3\frac{1}{3}$ $+2\frac{1}{6}$

b. $5\frac{1}{2}$ $-3\frac{1}{9}$

c. $\frac{2}{5} \times 1\frac{1}{9} = ?$

d. $1\frac{3}{4} \div \frac{1}{2} = ?$

FDP SHOWDOWN 10

Do just one.

a. 4 $+2\frac{1}{5}$

b. $2\frac{3}{4}$ $-\frac{1}{6}$

c. $2\frac{2}{5} \times \frac{2}{3} = ?$

d. $2\frac{2}{3} \div \frac{1}{3} = ?$

FDP SHOWDOWN 11

Do just one.

a. $3\frac{1}{2}$ $+\frac{1}{3}$

b. $9\frac{4}{5}$ -9

c. $\frac{3}{5} \times 4\frac{1}{2} = ?$

d. $1\frac{3}{5} \div \frac{2}{5} = ?$

FDP SHOWDOWN 12

Do just one.

a. $1\frac{2}{3}$ $+2\frac{1}{5}$

b. $4\frac{3}{8}$ $-1\frac{1}{10}$

c. $2\frac{1}{12} \times \frac{4}{5} = ?$

d. $\frac{2}{3} \div 3\frac{5}{6} = ?$

FDP SHOWDOWN 13

Do just one.

a. $2\frac{3}{4}$ $+4\frac{5}{6}$

b. $4\frac{1}{3}$ $-2\frac{3}{4}$

c. $2 \times 1\frac{3}{4} = ?$

d. $2\frac{2}{3} \div 2 = ?$

FDP SHOWDOWN 14

Do just one.

a. $3\frac{1}{4}$ $+\frac{7}{8}$

b. $9\frac{3}{10}$ $-5\frac{4}{5}$

c. $8 \times 2\frac{1}{6} = ?$

d. $5 \div 2\frac{1}{2} = ?$

FDP SHOWDOWN 15

Do just one.

a. $\frac{3}{4}$ $+5\frac{4}{5}$

b. $7 - \frac{7}{10} = ?$

c. $6\frac{1}{3} \times 9 = ?$

d. $3\frac{1}{6} \div 2 = ?$

FDP SHOWDOWN 16

Do just one.

a. $3\frac{3}{10}$ $+6\frac{8}{9}$

b. $1 - \frac{9}{16} = ?$

c. $3\frac{1}{2} \times 10 = ?$

d. $5 \div 6\frac{7}{8} = ?$

FDP Showdown Operations Cards
(Page 3 of five pages)
Back, laminate, and cut along solid lines.

FRACTIONS, DECIMALS, AND PERCENTS

FDP SHOWDOWN 17

Do just one.

a. What decimal fraction is shaded?

b. What percent is shaded?

c. $1\frac{1}{3} \times 3\frac{1}{3} = ?$

d. $3\frac{1}{6} \div 2\frac{5}{6} = ?$

FDP SHOWDOWN 18

Do just one.

a. What decimal fraction is shaded?

b. What percent is shaded?

c. $3\frac{3}{4} \times 4\frac{4}{5} = ?$

d. $5\frac{3}{8} \div 4\frac{1}{2} = ?$

FDP SHOWDOWN 19

Do just one.

a. What decimal fraction is shaded?

b. What percent is shaded?

c. $2\frac{5}{8} \times 4\frac{2}{3} = ?$

d. $2\frac{1}{12} \div 3\frac{1}{6} = ?$

FDP SHOWDOWN 20

Do just one.

a. What decimal fraction is shaded?

b. What percent is shaded?

c. $5\frac{5}{6} \times 4\frac{4}{5} = ?$

d. $3\frac{1}{8} \div 7\frac{2}{9} = ?$

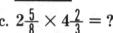
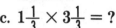
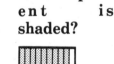
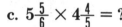

FDP SHOWDOWN 21

Do just one.

a. Convert .6 to a fraction.
b. Round .875 to the nearest tenth.
c. Convert .45 to a percent.
d. Convert $\frac{4}{25}$ to a percent.

FDP SHOWDOWN 22

Do just one.

a. Convert .75 to a fraction.
b. Round .932 to the nearest hundredth.
c. Convert .06 to a percent.
d. Convert $\frac{17}{50}$ to a percent.

FDP SHOWDOWN 23

Do just one.

a. Convert .125 to a fraction.
b. Round 1.0436 to the nearest thousandth.
c. Convert .025 to a percent.
d. Convert $\frac{3}{8}$ to a percent.

FDP SHOWDOWN 24

Do just one.

a. Convert 3.5 to a mixed number.
b. Round 13.045 to the nearest whole number.
c. Convert 2.2 to a percent.
d. Convert $1\frac{3}{5}$ to a percent.

FDP Showdown Operations Cards
(Page 4 of five pages)
Back, laminate, and cut along solid lines.

FRACTIONS, DECIMALS, AND PERCENTS

FDP SHOWDOWN 25

Do just one.

a. Convert $\frac{7}{25}$ to a decimal to the nearest tenth.

b. $38.6 + 42.71 = ?$

c. Convert 50% to a decimal.

d. Convert 45% to a fraction.

FDP SHOWDOWN 26

Do just one.

a. Convert $3\frac{5}{6}$ to a decimal to the nearest tenth.

b. $987.83 + 7.056 = ?$

c. Convert $1\frac{1}{2}$% to a decimal.

d. Convert $2\frac{1}{2}$% to a fraction.

FDP SHOWDOWN 27

Do just one.

a. Convert $\frac{4}{7}$ to a decimal to the nearest hundredth.

b. $\begin{array}{r} 21.3 \\ 8.7 \\ + 109.86 \\ \hline \end{array}$

c. Convert 150% to a decimal.

d. Convert 5% to a fraction.

FDP SHOWDOWN 28

Do just one.

a. Convert $1\frac{2}{3}$ to a decimal to the nearest thousandth.

b. $\begin{array}{r} 212.3 \\ 94.64 \\ + 6.382 \\ \hline \end{array}$

c. Convert $\frac{1}{2}$% to a decimal.

d. Convert 325% to a mixed number.

FDP SHOWDOWN 29

Do just one.

a. $12.3 - 3.57 = ?$
b. $23 \times .6 = ?$
c. 20% of 30 = ?
d. ?% of 80 = 20

FDP SHOWDOWN 30

Do just one.

a. $28.1 - 3.07 = ?$
b. $.12 \times 3.5 = ?$
c. 50% of 18 = ?
d. ?% of 60 = 84

FDP SHOWDOWN 31

Do just one.

a. $\begin{array}{r} 8003.9 \\ - 24.326 \\ \hline \end{array}$

b. $\begin{array}{r} 103 \\ \times 2.4 \\ \hline \end{array}$

c. 10% of 75 = ?

d. ?% of 16 = 2

FDP SHOWDOWN 32

Do just one.

a. $\begin{array}{r} 436.952 \\ - 82.37 \\ \hline \end{array}$

b. $\begin{array}{r} .401 \\ \times .1016 \\ \hline \end{array}$

c. 99% of 150 = ?

d. ?% of 18 = 5.4

FDP Showdown Operations Cards
(Page 5 of five pages)
Back, laminate, and cut along solid lines.

FRACTIONS, DECIMALS, AND PERCENTS

FDP SHOWDOWN 33

Do just one.

a. $3.82 \div .5 = ?$
b. $4.3 \times 100 = ?$
c. Convert $\frac{2}{3}$ to a repeating decimal.
d. 15% of ? = 60

FDP SHOWDOWN 34

Do just one.

a. $.08 \div 2 = ?$
b. $3.5 \div 1000 = ?$
c. Convert $\frac{35}{99}$ to a repeating decimal.
d. 4% of ? = 12

FDP SHOWDOWN 35

Do just one.

a. $24 \div .06 = ?$
b. $.85 \times 1000 = ?$
c. Convert $\frac{2}{9}$ to a repeating decimal.
d. 80% of ? = 100

FDP SHOWDOWN 36

Do just one.

a. $121.73 \div 3.29 = ?$
b. $17.3 \div 10 = ?$
c. Convert $\frac{3}{7}$ to a repeating decimal.
d. 6% of ? = 27

154

FDP Showdown Chance Cards
(Page 1 of two pages)
Back, laminate, and cut along solid lines.

FDP SHOWDOWN

CHANCE

Divide $\frac{2}{3}$ by $\frac{1}{6}$. If you get 4, go to FDP HURRAH. If you get $\frac{1}{4}$, go to FDP NIMNO.

FDP SHOWDOWN

CHANCE

Convert 5% to a decimal. If you get .05, go to FDP HURRAH. If you get 500, go to FDP NIMNO.

FDP SHOWDOWN

CHANCE

Just in case you ever thought that all you had to do to add fractions was add "tops and bottoms," go back three spaces.

FDP SHOWDOWN

CHANCE

Just in case you ever forgot to simplify your answer when working with fractions, go back three spaces.

FDP SHOWDOWN

CHANCE

Just in case you ever forgot to turn a mixed number into an improper fraction before multiplying, go back three spaces.

FDP SHOWDOWN

CHANCE

Just in case you ever turned the wrong fraction upside down when dividing fractions, go back three spaces.

FDP SHOWDOWN

CHANCE

You finally moved the decimal point two places to the left in converting a percent into a decimal. Advance five spaces.

FDP SHOWDOWN

CHANCE

You finally remembered that "percent" means per 100. Advance five spaces.

FDP Showdown Chance Cards
(Page 2 of two pages)
Back, laminate, and cut along solid lines.

FRACTIONS, DECIMALS, AND PERCENTS

FDP SHOWDOWN

CHANCE

You finally lined up the decimal points in adding decimals. Advance five spaces.

FDP SHOWDOWN

CHANCE

You finally moved both decimal points equally much in dividing decimals. Advance five spaces.

FDP SHOWDOWN

CHANCE

You just saved 20% at a sale. Advance five spaces.

FDP SHOWDOWN

CHANCE

You just borrowed some money at 18% interest. Go back five spaces.

FDP SHOWDOWN

CHANCE

You just figured out how to share two-thirds of a pie with four people. Advance five spaces.

FDP SHOWDOWN

CHANCE

You just made $1\frac{1}{2}$ sandwiches for each of six people. Advance five spaces.

FDP SHOWDOWN

CHANCE

You just forgot to enter the decimal point in a calculator. Go back five spaces.

FDP SHOWDOWN

CHANCE

Just in case you ever forget how to enter a fraction in a calculator, go back five spaces.

FDP SHOWDOWN

KEY

Card	Problem				Card	Problem			
	a	b	c	d		a	b	c	d
1	$\frac{3}{7}$	$\frac{1}{4}$	$\frac{1}{6}$	2	19	.21	30%	$12\frac{1}{4}$	$\frac{25}{38}$
2	$1\frac{1}{2}$	$\frac{3}{5}$	$\frac{2}{5}$	2	20	.74	90%	28	$\frac{45}{104}$
3	$\frac{4}{5}$	$\frac{1}{2}$	1	$10\frac{1}{2}$	21	$\frac{3}{5}$	.9	45%	16%
4	$1\frac{7}{9}$	$\frac{1}{3}$	$\frac{5}{27}$	$\frac{9}{10}$	22	$\frac{3}{4}$	.93	6%	34%
5	$1\frac{5}{12}$	$\frac{1}{6}$	$\frac{1}{2}$	$\frac{2}{5}$	23	$\frac{1}{8}$	1.044	2.5%	37.5%
6	$\frac{2}{3}$	$\frac{2}{5}$	$1\frac{1}{2}$	4	24	$3\frac{1}{2}$	13	220%	160%
7	$1\frac{1}{12}$	$\frac{5}{8}$	6	$\frac{1}{9}$	25	.3	81.31	.5	$\frac{9}{20}$
8	$1\frac{23}{30}$	$\frac{1}{24}$	1	12	26	3.8	994.886	.015	$\frac{1}{40}$
9	$5\frac{1}{2}$	$2\frac{7}{18}$	$\frac{4}{9}$	$3\frac{1}{2}$	27	.57	139.86	1.5	$\frac{1}{20}$
10	$6\frac{1}{5}$	$2\frac{7}{12}$	$1\frac{3}{5}$	8	28	1.667	313.322	.005	$3\frac{1}{4}$
11	$3\frac{5}{6}$	$\frac{4}{5}$	$2\frac{7}{10}$	4	29	8.73	13.8	6	25%
12	$3\frac{13}{15}$	$3\frac{11}{40}$	$1\frac{2}{3}$	$\frac{4}{23}$	30	25.03	.42	9	140%
13	$7\frac{7}{12}$	$1\frac{7}{12}$	$3\frac{1}{2}$	$1\frac{1}{3}$	31	7979.574	247.2	7.5	12.5%
14	$4\frac{1}{8}$	$3\frac{1}{2}$	$17\frac{1}{3}$	2	32	354.582	.0407416	148.5	30%
15	$6\frac{11}{20}$	$6\frac{3}{10}$	57	$1\frac{7}{12}$	33	7.64	430	$.\overline{6}$	400
16	$10\frac{17}{90}$	$\frac{7}{16}$	35	$\frac{8}{11}$	34	.04	.0035	$.\overline{35}$	300
17	.1	27%	$4\frac{4}{9}$	$1\frac{2}{17}$	35	400	850	$.\overline{2}$	125
18	.9	74%	18	$1\frac{7}{36}$	36	37	1.73	$.\overline{428571}$	450

FDP Showdown Scorecard

Name .... Date ....

Card	Problem a		b		c		d		Card	Problem a		b		c		d	
	Hit	Miss	Hit	Miss	Hit	Miss	Hit	Miss		Hit	Miss	Hit	Miss	Hit	Miss	Hit	Miss
1	—	—	—	—	—	—	—	—	21	—	—	—	—	—	—	—	—
2	—	—	—	—	—	—	—	—	22	—	—	—	—	—	—	—	—
3	—	—	—	—	—	—	—	—	23	—	—	—	—	—	—	—	—
4	—	—	—	—	—	—	—	—	24	—	—	—	—	—	—	—	—
5	—	—	—	—	—	—	—	—	25	—	—	—	—	—	—	—	—
6	—	—	—	—	—	—	—	—	26	—	—	—	—	—	—	—	—
7	—	—	—	—	—	—	—	—	27	—	—	—	—	—	—	—	—
8	—	—	—	—	—	—	—	—	28	—	—	—	—	—	—	—	—
9	—	—	—	—	—	—	—	—	29	—	—	—	—	—	—	—	—
10	—	—	—	—	—	—	—	—	30	—	—	—	—	—	—	—	—
11	—	—	—	—	—	—	—	—	31	—	—	—	—	—	—	—	—
12	—	—	—	—	—	—	—	—	32	—	—	—	—	—	—	—	—
13	—	—	—	—	—	—	—	—	33	—	—	—	—	—	—	—	—
14	—	—	—	—	—	—	—	—	34	—	—	—	—	—	—	—	—
15	—	—	—	—	—	—	—	—	35	—	—	—	—	—	—	—	—
16	—	—	—	—	—	—	—	—	36	—	—	—	—	—	—	—	—
17	—	—	—	—	—	—	—	—									
18	—	—	—	—	—	—	—	—									
19	—	—	—	—	—	—	—	—									
20	—	—	—	—	—	—	—	—									

Place Value Words

Name . . . .

1000	100	10	1
A	G	M	T
B	H	N	U
C	I	O	V
D	J	P	W
E	K	Q	X
F	L	R	Y
		S	Z

1. The word "flow" is worth 1111 points. Can you find six or more other words worth the same?

_____   _____   _____   _____

_____   _____   _____   _____

2. What are these words worth?

    a. Stop ____   d. Best ____   g. Seven ____

    b. Moon ____   e. Roll ____   h. What ____

    c. Play ____   f. Dime ____   i. Beat ____

3. Can you find a four-letter word worth between 200 and 250 points? _____

4. What is your name worth? ____

5. Which day of the week is worth the most? _____

6. What is the name of your school worth? ____

MATH / LANGUAGE ARTS

Homonym Hunt

Name..............................

A = 1	F = 5	K = 7	P = 2	U = 2
B = 2	G = 4	L = 5	Q = 4	V = 3
C = 3	H = 3	M = 3	R = 6	W = 10
D = 4	I = 2	N = 1	S = 8	X = 2
E = 5	J = 1	O = 2	T = 10	Y,Z = 10

1. For each clue, find the word and its homonym. Then figure your score by adding the values of the letters the words have in common. The first one has been done for you. A total score of more than 120 is OUTSTANDING!

Clue	Word	Homonym	Score
One twenty-fourth of a day	Hour	Our	2 + 2 + 6 = 10
One.............street sign			
The opposite of day			
Sixteen divided by 8			
The window .... was broken			
A father's boy			
A deaf person can't do this			
Ships sail in this body of water			
A cub's mother			
A fruit			
A vegetable			
		Total	

2. How many tri-homonyms can you find? Example: To - Two - Too. Score one point for each one you find. Eight is excellent, 7 good, 6 fair, 5 HHN (homonym help needed).

Name......................

A	E	I	O	U
5	4	3	2	1

1. The word "chair" is worth eight points. How much are these words worth?

   a. Boat ____   d. Teacher ____   g. Use ____

   b. Moon ____   e. Area ____   h. Inside ____

   c. Money ____   f. Ruin ____   i. Outer ____

2. What are the values of these sentences?

   a. The duck likes water. _____

   b. Where are you? _____

   c. Please come in here. _____

   d. John likes trains. _____

   e. Can Sue play today? _____

3. How much is your name worth? _____

4. Which day of the week is worth the most? _____

5. Which month has the smallest value? _____

6. What names have small values? _____

Name......................

ABCDE   FGHIJ   KLMNO   PQRST   UVWXY

1. Use the arrangement of letters above to decode these numbers. The first one has been done for you.

    a. 13 . 11 . 45 <u>Cat</u>

    b. 44 . 45 . 43 . 35 . 34 . 22 <u>   </u>

    c. 12 . 35 . 54 <u>   </u>

    d. 21 . 24 . 22 <u>   </u>

    e. 12 . 11 . 14 <u>   </u>

    f. 31 . 24 . 13 . 31 <u>   </u>

2. How much are these words (without claps) worth?

a. P =	b. S =	c. O =	d. C =
O =	I =	P =	A =
R =	N =	E =	L =
T =	G =	N =	L =

3. Make a five-letter word using only one letter from each group of letters. How much is it worth?

MATH GAMES & ACTIVITIES. COPYRIGHT © 1984

MATH / LANGUAGE ARTS

Name....................

1. For each category, find a word that has three and only three vowels in it. Then find the word's value by adding the values of the word's vowels. The first one has been done for you.

a. Holiday $\underline{\text{Easter, } \frac{1}{4} + \frac{1}{2} + \frac{1}{4} = 1}$ f. Animal _____

b. Color _____   g. Boy _____

c. Food _____   h. Planet _____

d. Car _____   i. City _____

e. Girl _____   j. State _____

2. Find at least three words that have a repeating vowel and no other vowel. Then find each word's value.

Examples: Bleed, $\frac{1}{2}$

Iris, $\frac{1}{4}$

Fool, 1

Name..................................

A = 19	I = 20	Q = 21
B = 22	J = 23	R = 24
C = 13	K = 14	S = 15
D = 16	L = 17	T = 18
E = 7	M = 8	U = 9
F = 10	N = 11	V = 12
G = 4	O = 5	W = 6
H = 1	P = 2	X, Y, Z = 3

1. For each hint, find the word that contains S.E.A.. Then find the word's value by adding the values of the letters in the word. The first one has been done for you.

HINT	WORD	VALUE
a. A vapor	S t e a m	15 + 18 + 7 + 19 + 8 = 67
b. A bottom rester	S e a _	_____
c. Butter is used this way	S _ _ e a _	_____
d. A sport	_ _ s e _ a _ _	_____
e. A fishing place	S _ _ e a _	_____
f. A ball balancer	S e a _	_____
g. A weapon	S _ e a _	_____
h. A direction	S _ _ _ _ e a _ _	_____
i. A major western city	S e a _ _ _ _	_____
j. A join between two pieces of material	S e a _	_____

2. Find some words that contain the month of M.A.Y., the names S.U.E. or T.O.M., or your name. Then determine each word's value. A total score of more than 500 makes you a word whiz.

MATH / LANGUAGE ARTS

Name . . . .

Name the tree for each clue. Then figure your score by multiplying the number of letters in the name of the tree by the number given. The first one has been done for you. A total score of more than 250 makes you "aboreal."

Clue	Tree	Score
The seashore	Beech	$2 \times \underline{5} = 10$
The hand		$5 \times \_\_ =$
An inlet of the sea		$4 \times \_\_ =$
Sadness		$6 \times \_\_ =$
A country bumpkin		$3 \times \_\_ =$
The dead part of a fire		$7 \times \_\_ =$
A winter coat		$1 \times \_\_ =$
Neat appearance		$6 \times \_\_ =$
Gracefully tall and slender		$9 \times \_\_ =$
A kind of grasshopper		$8 \times \_\_ =$
	Total	

MATH / LANGUAGE ARTS

Fast Fill-ins

Name. . . . .

A = 2	H = 16	N = 3	T = 15
B = 4	I = 18	O = 5	U = 17
C = 6	J = 20	P = 7	V = 19
D = 8	K = 22	Q = 9	W = 21
E = 10	L = 24	R = 11	X = 23
F = 12	M = 1	S = 13	Y = 25
G = 14			Z = 27

For each clue, find the word for the number of letters and the two letters given. Then figure your score by adding the values of the letters in the word. The first one has been done for you. A total score of less than 500 is HW (help wanted).

Clue	Number of letters	Two of the letters	Word	Score
A honey eater	4	A.B.	Bear	4 + 10 + 2 + 11 = 27
A president	7	L.L.		
A part of a boat	4	M.T.		
A number	5	E.T.		
A month	5	I.L.		
A part of your body	3	E.Y.		
A snake	5	A.R.		
A bird	5	N.R.		
A city	7	E.K.		
A state	5	A.O.		
A river	11	P.P.		
			Total	

Missing Letter Problem Solving

Name. . . . .

1. Hw mny dys n tw wks? _____

2. Tw dys r th sm s hw mny hrs? _____

3. Wht s 6 tms 9? _____

4. Cntng by tns, wht cms ftr 34? _____

5. Hw mny ggs n thr dzn ggs? _____

6. f Mry s svn, nd Bll s twc hr g, hw ld s Bll? _____

7. Whch s lrgr, 5 tms 4 r 8 tms 2? _____

8. Hw mny pnts n 3 qrts? _____

9. Hw mny sds d 10 sqrs hv? _____

10. Lp yr hs hw mny dys? _____

11. Wht s th dffrnc btwn 20 nd 7? _____

12. Sxty s hw mch mr thn 42? _____

Creating Creatures

Name...............................

For each clue, find the word and the animal that rhymes with the word. Then figure your score by multiplying the number of letters in the word by the number of letters in the name of the animal. The first one has been done for you. A total score of more than 275 makes you a zoo keeper.

Clue	Word	Animal	Score
I am a yard cleaning tool.	Rake	Drake	4 × 5 = 20
What Bugs Bunny likes			
"At present" is another meaning for me.			
I am the opposite of skinny.			
I am the opposite of hate.			
I am a water crosser.			
This is very close to jelly.			
I am on the top of a person's head.			
This word means not tight.			
I lie on the grass in the morning.			
I am the opposite of far.			
The first name of Tatum O'Neal's father			
The biggest part of a tree			
A wet baby often does this.			
The back part of a shoe			
This is the sound a dog makes.			
		Total	

Name . . . .

1. Many words contain "food" words -- words of things we eat. For each of the following words, circle the food word it contains and multiply the number of letters in the food word by the number of letters remaining. The first one has been done for you.

   a. D(nut) $2 \times 3 = 6$ f. Scrapple _____

   b. Corner _____   g. Startle _____

   c. Begging _____   h. Scrabble _____

   d. Appear _____   i. Copier _____

   e. Bundle _____   j. Curdle _____

2. For each of the following words, find a word that contains it. Then multiply the number of letters in the word you've found by six.

   a. Fig _____ ___   d. Ham _____ ___

   b. Meat _____ ___   e. Ice _____ ___

   c. Tea _____ ___   f. Sauce _____ ___

3. For each of the following words, find three words that contain it. Then multiply the number of letters in each word you've found by nine.

   a. Pea _____ ___   b. Bean _____ ___

   _____ ___   _____ ___

   _____ ___   _____ ___

MATH / LANGUAGE ARTS

PMDAS

Name..............................

For each problem, do four things: One, solve the problem with a calculator. Two, write the answer to the problem in the space provided. Three, turn the calculator upside down and write the "word answer" to the problem in the space provided. And four, compare the word answer to the clue for the problem. If the two agree, you solved the problem correctly.

In solving the problems, remember to use PMDAS: parentheses (P), then multiplication (M) or division (D), whichever comes first, and finally addition (A) or subtraction (S), whichever comes first. The key is to always work from left to right.

1. $160 \times 5 + 7$ ___ _____ A tennis shot
2. $46 + 4 \times 150 - 9$ ___ _____ What a flamingo stands on
3. $33\,624 \div 6$ ___ _____ Mature pigs
4. $394\,752 \div 512$ ___ _____ Sick
5. $2715 + 330$ ___ _____ What goes on a foot
6. $584\,831 - 123\,456$ ___ _____ Vehicle for riding on snow
7. $8^3 + 2$ ___ _____ Not hers, but ___
8. $12\,345 + 23\,456 - 465$ ___ _____ Their message is "honk, honk."
9. $7 + 50 \times 110$ ___ _____ Not a gain, but a ___
10. $(654\,321 \div 3 - 214\,238) \times 2$ ___ _____ It rings.
11. $5787 \div 3 \times 4$ ___ _____ A fish organ
12. 22% of 2900 ___ _____ To plead
13. $17^2 + 7^2$ ___ _____ It buzzes about.
14. $706 - 99$ ___ _____ A ___ cabin
15. $1884 + 1623$ ___ _____ To fail to win
16. $64\,118 - 80^2$ ___ _____ Another word for "beak"
17. $279^2 - 16 \times 31$ ___ _____ The outer covering of a peanut
18. 15×247 ___ _____ The bottom of a shoe
19. $987\,654 - 984\,150$ ___ _____ Fire truck equipment
20. $59^2 + 223$ ___ _____ A pit

MATH / LANGUAGE ARTS

Name......................

Some numbers on a calculator look like letters when the calculator is turned upside down. The 0 looks like an "O," the 1 an "I," the 3 an "E," the 4 an "h," the 5 an "S," the 6 a "g," the 7 an "L," and the 8 a "B." Thus a calculator can be used to "write" with.

Find a word that can be written on a calculator and write a question for it. For the word "globe," the question might be "What's another name for a small earth?" Then write a problem that has the word for its answer. A sample problem for the word globe would be the following:

1. Enter the number of days it takes the earth to circle the sun (365).

2. Multiply by 100.

3. Subtract the number of hours it takes the earth to revolve on its axis (24).

4. Add the diameter of the earth (8000) divided by five and turn the calculator upside down.

Note how the problem was written in keeping with the "theme" suggested by the question.

Write questions and problems for the following words or expressions that can be "written" on a calculator:

1. Goose

2. Leg

3. Shell

4. High hill

5. Boil eggs

6. Big Bill

Figure Four Rabbit Trap
(One-half actual size)

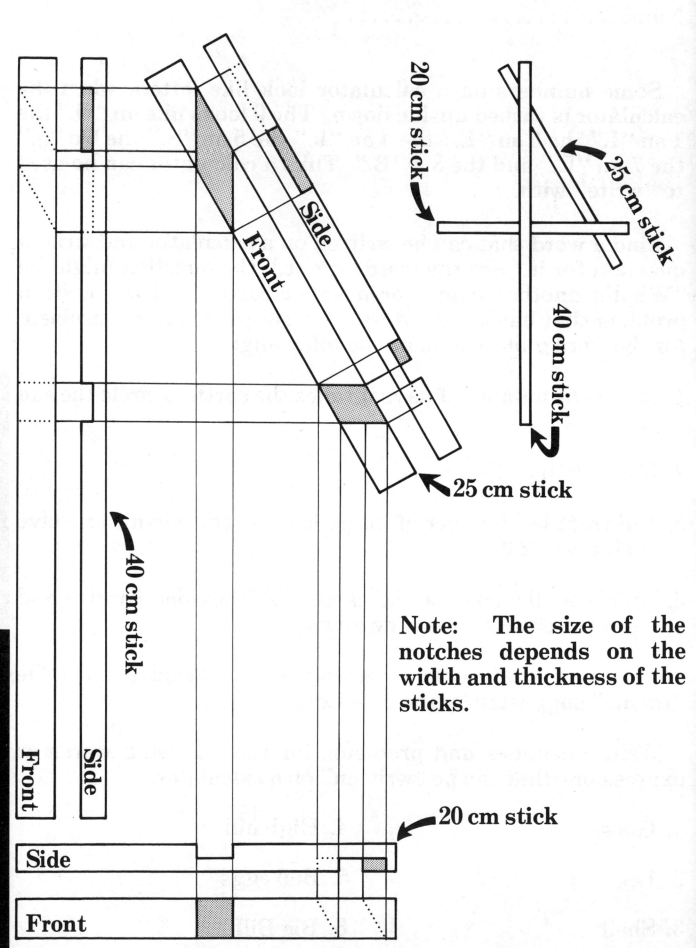

20 cm stick

25 cm stick

40 cm stick

25 cm stick

Side

Front

Side

Front

40 cm stick

Note: The size of the notches depends on the width and thickness of the sticks.

20 cm stick

Side

Front

Geo Piece Cutouts
(Page 1 of two pages)
Color, back, and laminate.

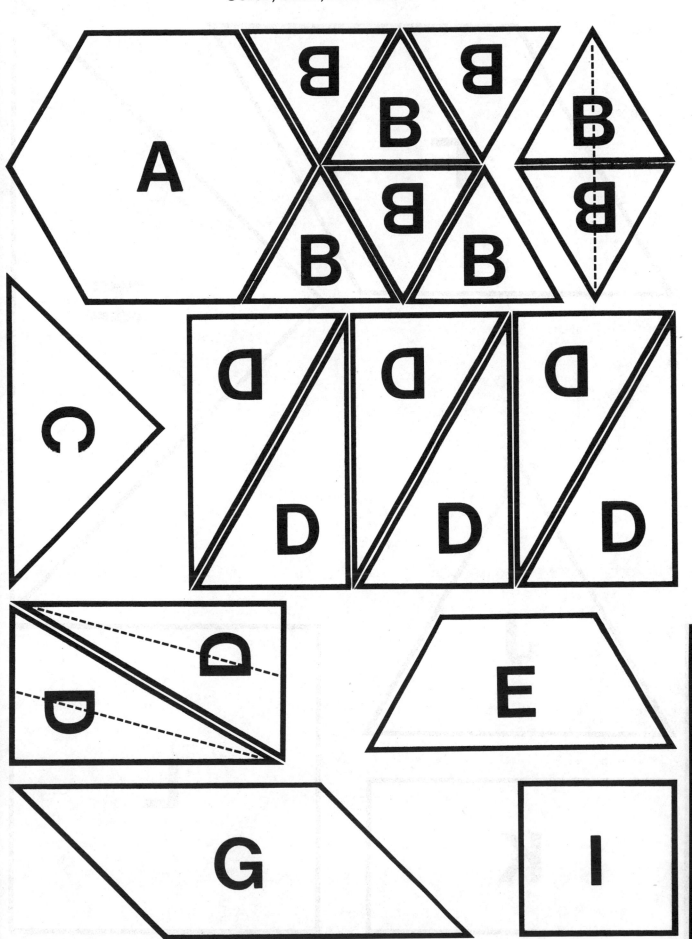

Geo Piece Cutouts
(Page 2 of two pages)
Color, back, and laminate.

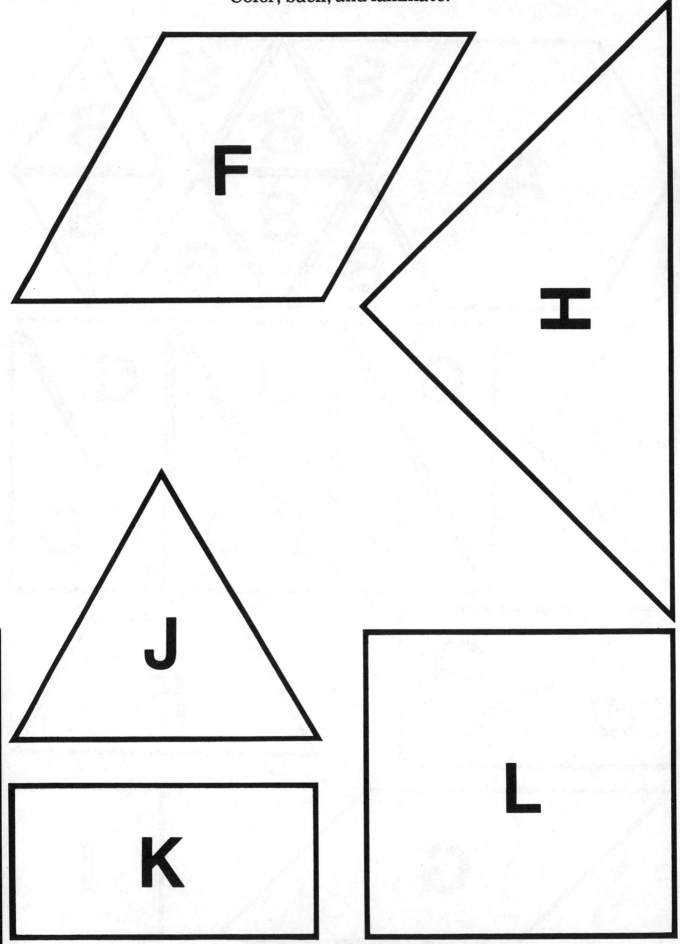

Circular Dot Paper
(Large)

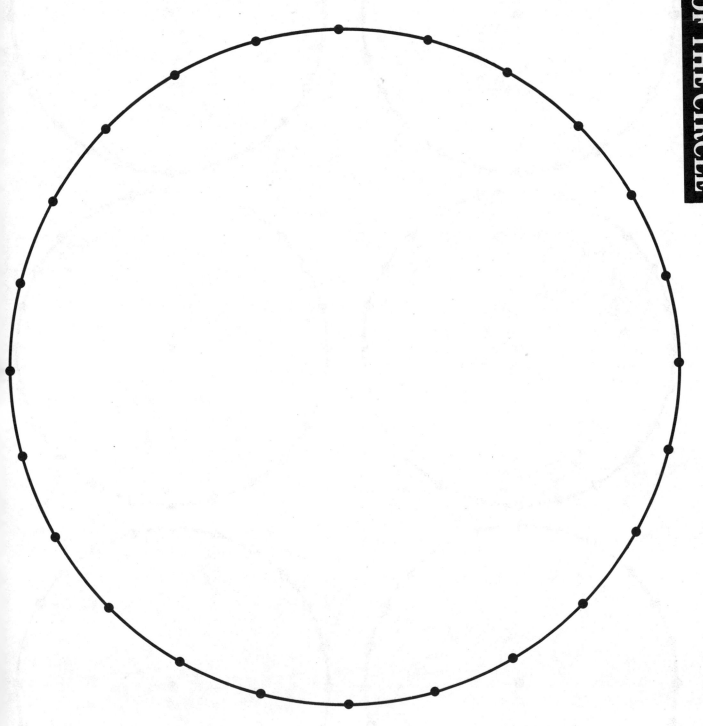

175

Circular Dot Paper
(Small)

Regular Tetrahedron Cutout

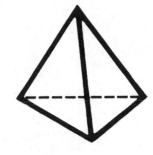

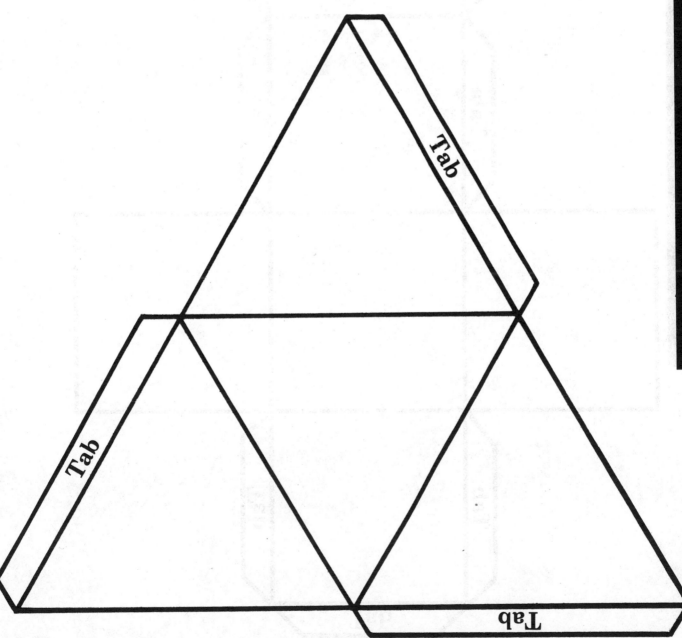

Tab

Tab

Tab

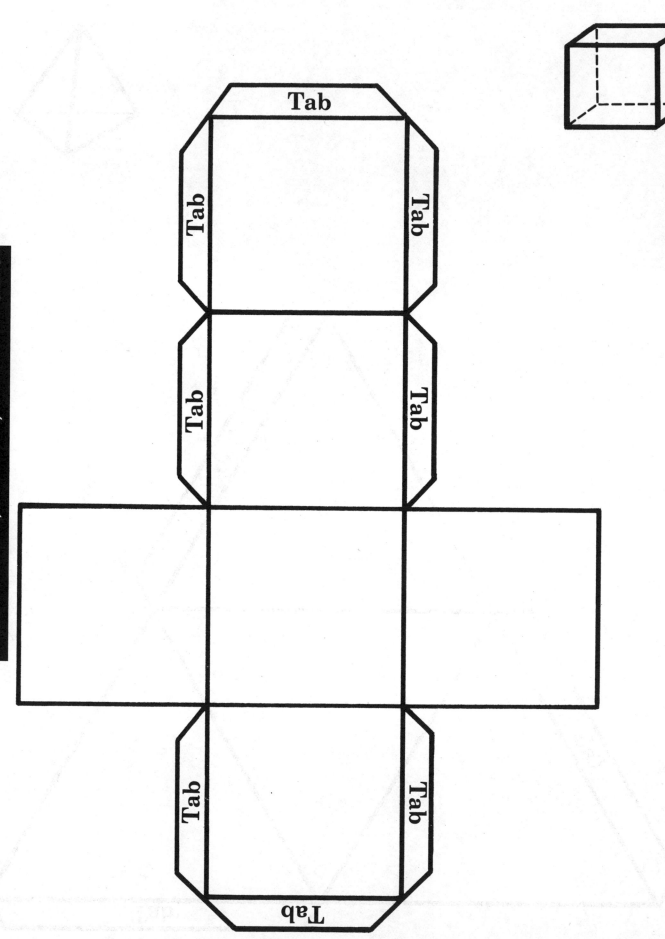

VERTICES, FACES, AND EDGES

Regular Octahedron Cutout

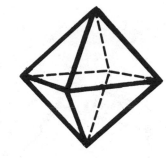

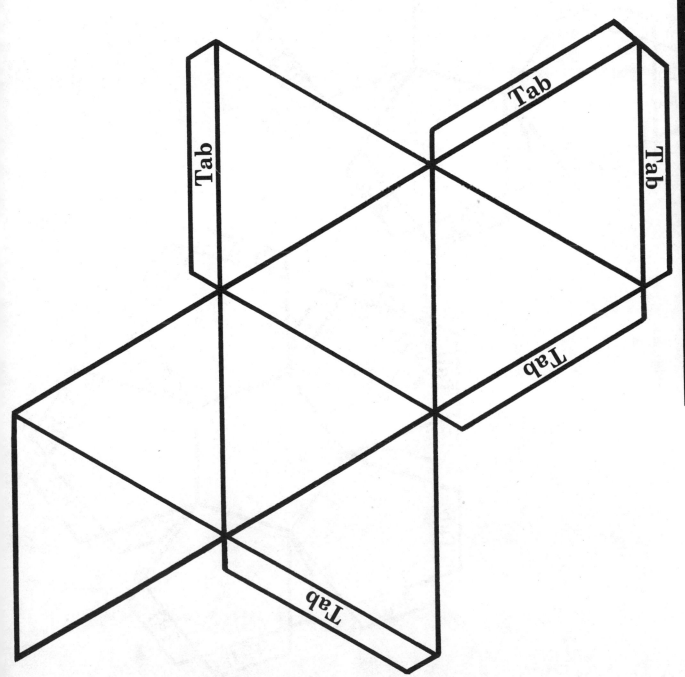

VERTICES, FACES, AND EDGES

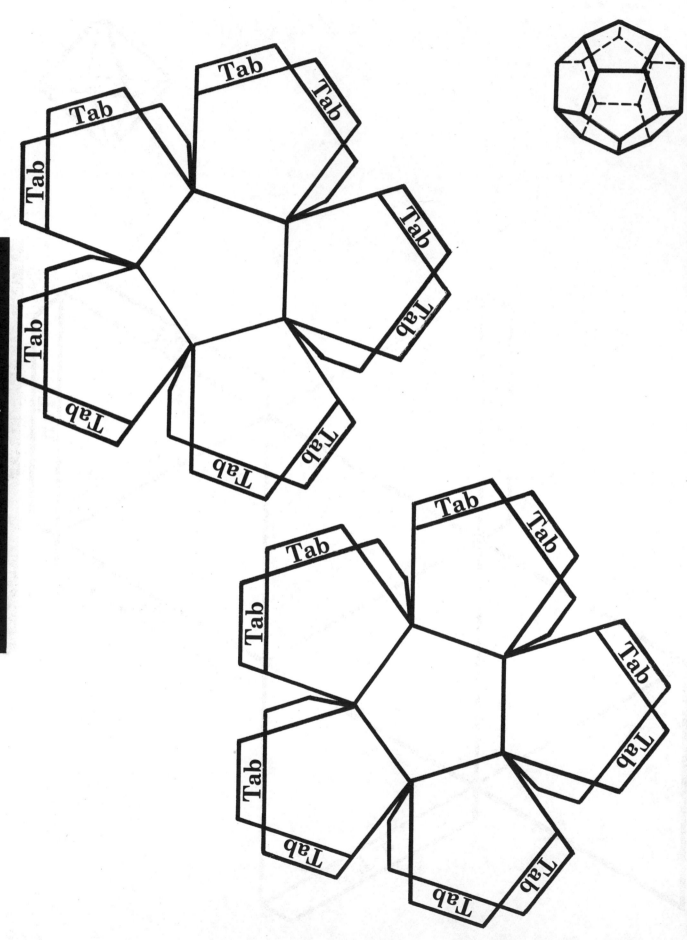

VERTICES, FACES, AND EDGES

Regular Icosahedron Cutout

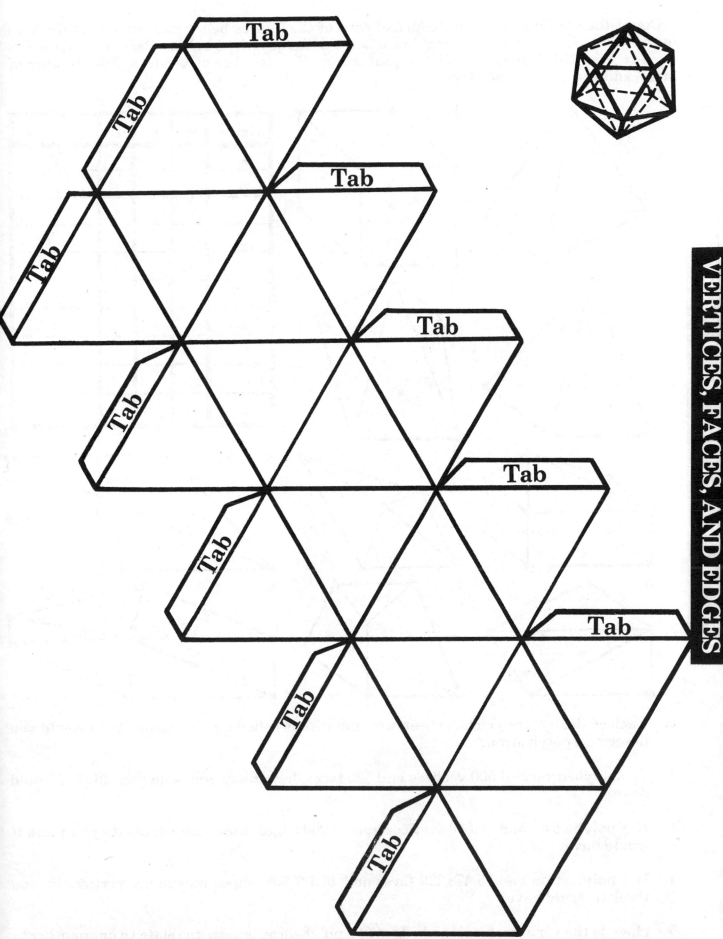

Vertices, Faces, and Edges
(First of two)

Name..

Count the vertices, faces, and edges of each of the figures below and enter your findings in the table. Then complete the table and answer the questions below. Part of the table has already been filled in as a check for your work. V = number of vertices, F = number of faces, and E = number of edges.

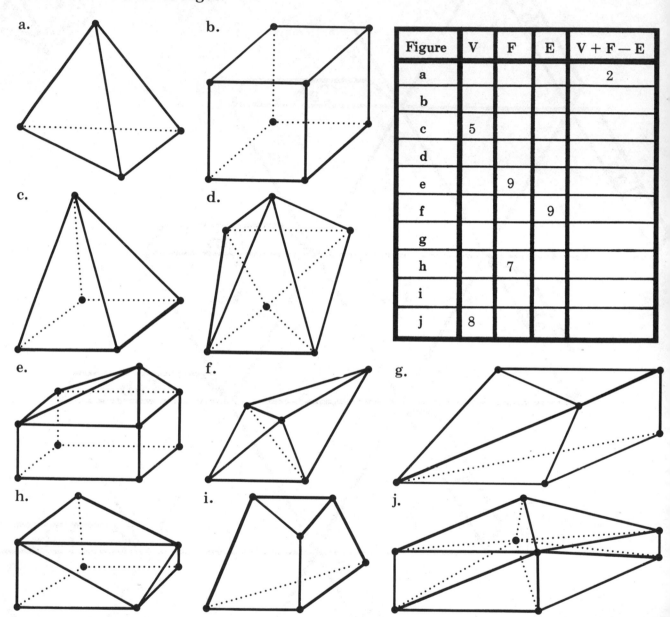

Figure	V	F	E	V + F — E
a				2
b				
c	5			
d				
e		9		
f			9	
g				
h		7		
i				
j	8			

1. Each of the figures you have been working with is called a polyhedron. How would you describe a polyhedron?

2. If a polyhedron had 500 vertices and 500 faces, how many edges do you think it would have?

3. If a polyhedron had 10,000 vertices and 15,000 edges, how many faces do you think it would have?

4. If a polyhedron had 25,478,329 faces and 45,327,908 edges, how many vertices do you think it would have?

5. How do the vertices, faces, and edges of a polyhedron appear to relate to one another?

Vertices, Faces, and Edges
(Second of two)

Name . . . .

Find the rule relating the number of vertices, faces, and edges of polyhedra with one hole. V = number of vertices, F = number of faces, and E = number of edges. Some of them have already been counted for you as a check for your work.

a.

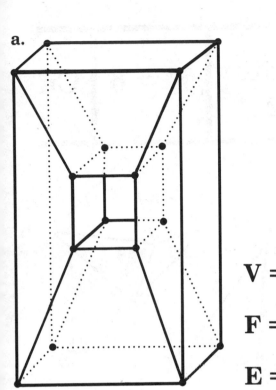

$V = \underline{\quad 16 \quad}$

$F = \underline{\qquad}$

$E = \underline{\qquad}$

$V + F - E = \underline{\qquad}$

b.

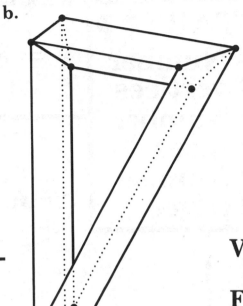

$V = \underline{\qquad}$

$F = \underline{\quad 9 \quad}$

$E = \underline{\qquad}$

$V + F - E = \underline{\qquad}$

c.

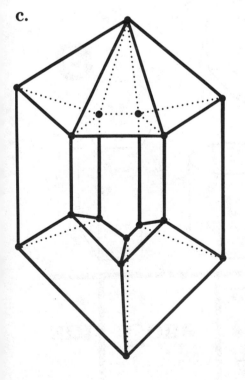

$V = \underline{\qquad}$

$F = \underline{\qquad}$

$E = \underline{\quad 35 \quad}$

$V + F - E = \underline{\qquad}$

d.

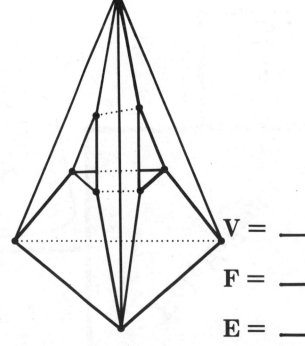

$V = \underline{\qquad}$

$F = \underline{\qquad}$

$E = \underline{\qquad}$

$V + F - E = \underline{\qquad}$

MATH GAMES & ACTIVITIES. COPYRIGHT © 1984

183

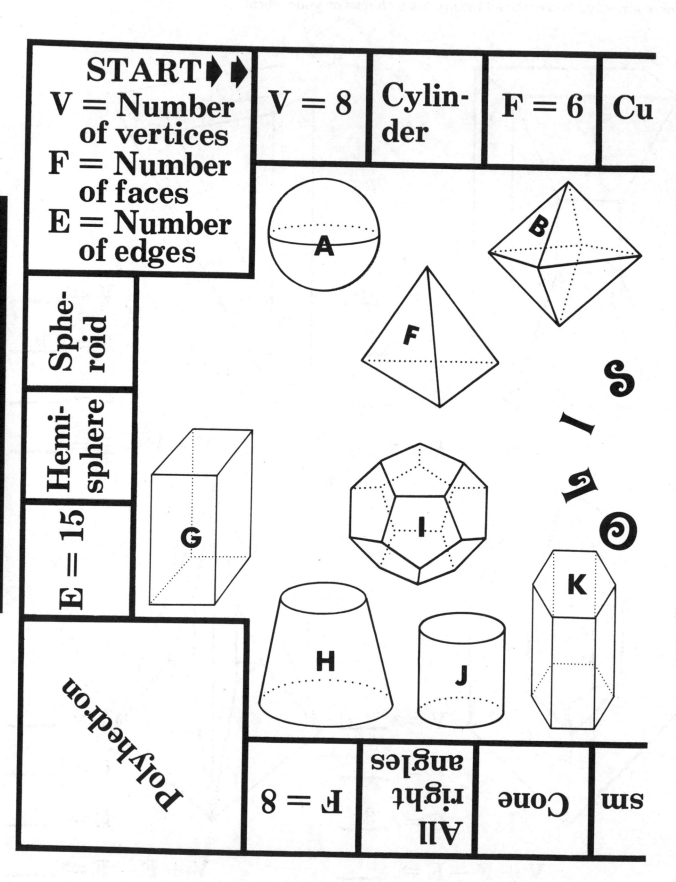

VERTICES, FACES, AND EDGES

START ▶ ▶

V = Number
of vertices
F = Number
of faces
E = Number
of edges

V = 8

Cylin-der

F = 6

Cu

Sphe-roid

Hemi-sphere

E = 15

Polyhedron

F = 8

All right angles

Cone

sm

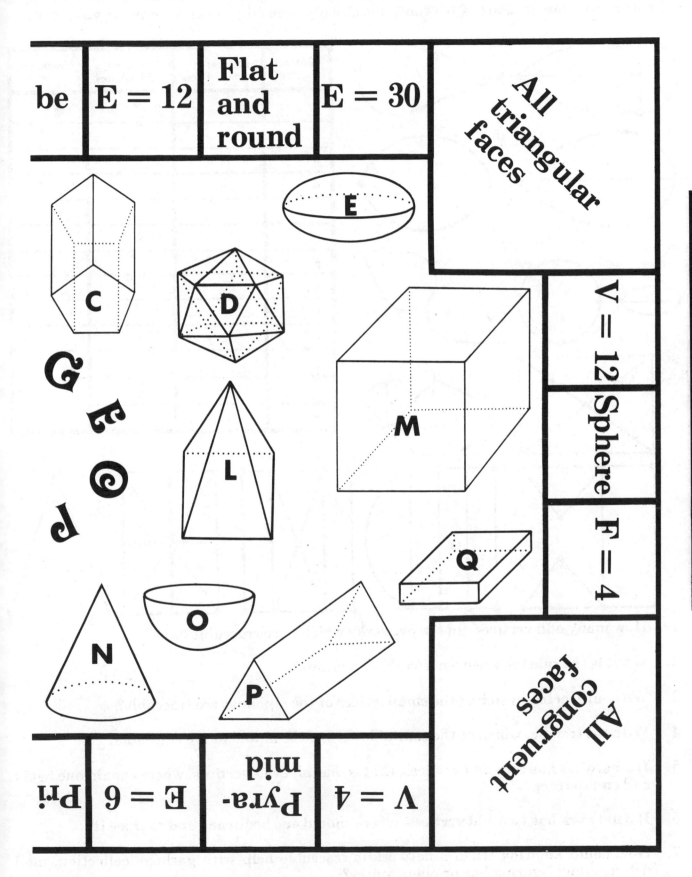

VERTICES, FACES, AND EDGES

be | E = 12 | Flat and round | E = 30

All triangular faces

V = 12 | Sphere | F = 4

All congruent faces

Pri | E = 6 | Pyra-mid | V = 4

Traceable Networks

Name . . . .

Trace as many of the following networks as you can without lifting your pen or pencil or drawing the same line twice and enter your findings in the table below. Then complete the table and answer the questions below. An "even" vertex is a vertex with an even number of edges "shooting out" from it, an "odd" vertex a vertex with an odd number of edges shooting out from it. Part of the table has already been filled in as a check for your work.

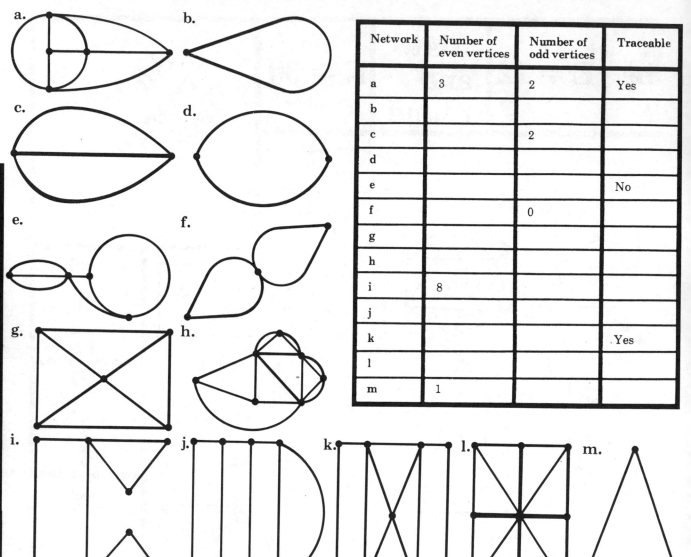

Network	Number of even vertices	Number of odd vertices	Traceable
a	3	2	Yes
b			
c		2	
d			
e			No
f		0	
g			
h			
i	8		
j			
k			Yes
l			
m	1		

1. How many odd vertices did the networks which were traceable have?

2. What is the rule for when a network is traceable?

3. Without tracing, which of the small letters of the alphabet are traceable?

4. Without tracing, which of the capital letters of the alphabet are traceable?

5. If a network has zero odd vertices, that is, has all even vertices, where should one begin and end to trace it?

6. If a network has two odd vertices, where should one begin and end to trace it?

7. How could knowing when a network is traceable help with garbage collection, mail delivery, and figuring bus or plane routes?

MATH GAMES & ACTIVITIES. COPYRIGHT © 1984

Traceable Houses

Name...........................

Which houses can you walk through by walking through each doorway exactly once? What's the rule for being able to do this?

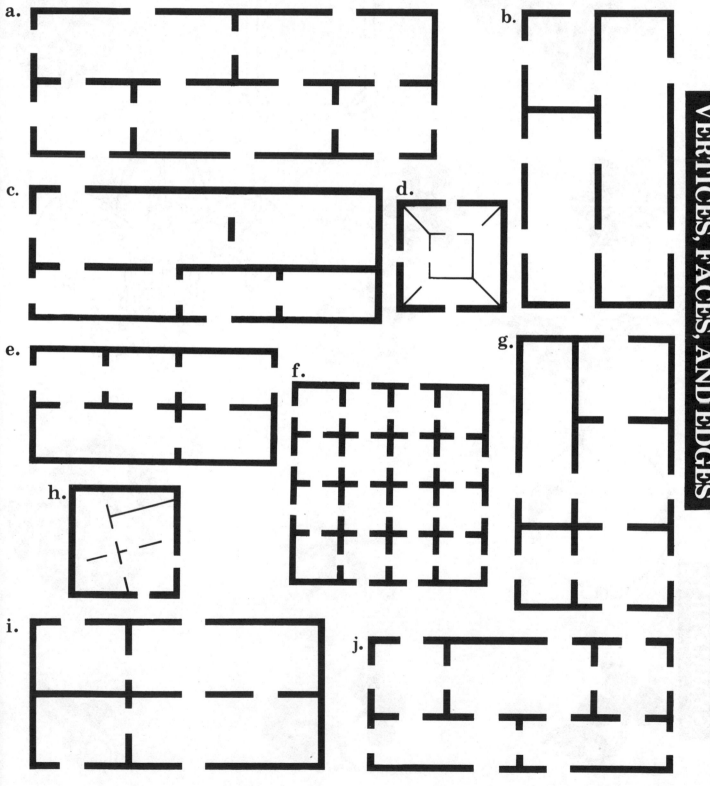

Mirror Symmetry
(Mirror symmetric figures)

Name............................

Seven of the figures below are mirror symmetric. Find all seven of them. Use a mirror to help you.

a.

b.

c.

d.

e.

f.

g.

h.

i.

j.

k.

l.

m.

n.

Mirror Symmetry
(Lines of symmetry)

Name...

1. Make a kaleidoscope. Tape two mirrors together as in Figure 1 and open the mirrors until you see three lines of symmetry. Then sprinkle some pieces of colored paper between the mirrors and blow on the pieces of paper to change the design.

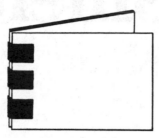

Figure 1

2. Draw a line about six inches long. Then place the hinged mirrors on the line and adjust them until you see an equilateral triangle as in Figure 2.

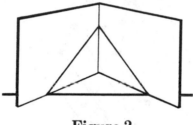

Figure 2

Now do the following:

a. Slowly move the mirrors together to form as many of the following figures as you can: right triangle, square, rhombus (other than a square), rectangle (other than a square), five-pointed star, six-pointed star, pentagon, hexagon, octagon, decagon, dodecagon, 60-sided figure, circle.

b. Adjust the mirrors to form an equilateral triangle again. Now try to form a figure with fewer than three sides. What happens?

3. Knowing that there are 360⁰ in a circle, find the degree measures of the following angles by placing the hinged mirrors along the sides of the angles.

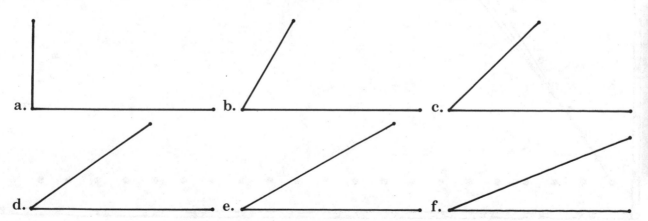

a.   b.   c.

d.   e.   f.

SYMMETRY

Shield

Name...........................

Complete the pattern.

Dart

Name............................

Complete the pattern.

SYMMETRY

Black Hole

Name..........................

Complete the pattern.

Frosty Window

Name............................

Complete the pattern.

SYMMETRY

Flying Saucer

Name..........................

Complete the pattern.

SYMMETRY

Web

Name.........................

Complete the pattern.

SYMMETRY

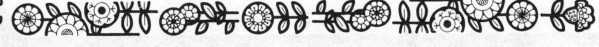

Whirlpool

Name...........................

Complete the pattern.

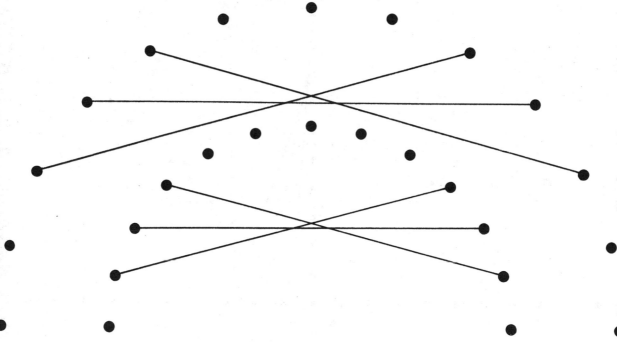

SYMMETRY

Kaleidoscope

Name.........................

Complete the pattern.

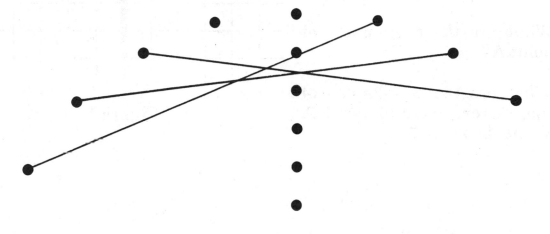

SYMMETRY

Mirror Symmetry
(In a coordinate system)

Name.............................

1. Hold a mirror along the x-axis of the coordinate system in Figure 1 and answer the following questions:

   a. How far below the x-axis does the mirror image of point A appear to be?

   b. How far to the right of the y-axis does the mirror image of point A appear to be?

   c. What are the coordinates of point A?

   d. What are the coordinates of the mirror image of point A about the x-axis?

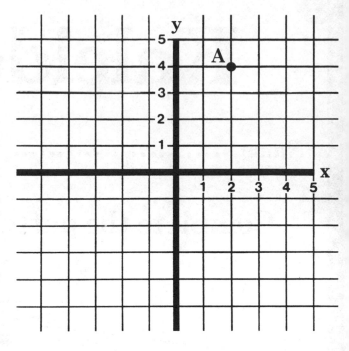

Figure 1

2. Hold a mirror along the y-axis of the coordinate system in Figure 2 and answer the following questions.

   a. How far to the left of the y-axis does the mirror image of point B appear to be?

   b. How far above the x-axis does the mirror image of point B appear to be?

   c. What are the coordinates of point B?

   d. What are the coordinates of the mirror image of point B about the y-axis?

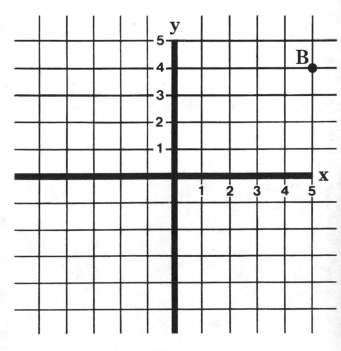

Figure 2

SYMMETRY

198

Name........................

Thinking of the x-axis as a mirror, draw the mirror images
of the following graphs.

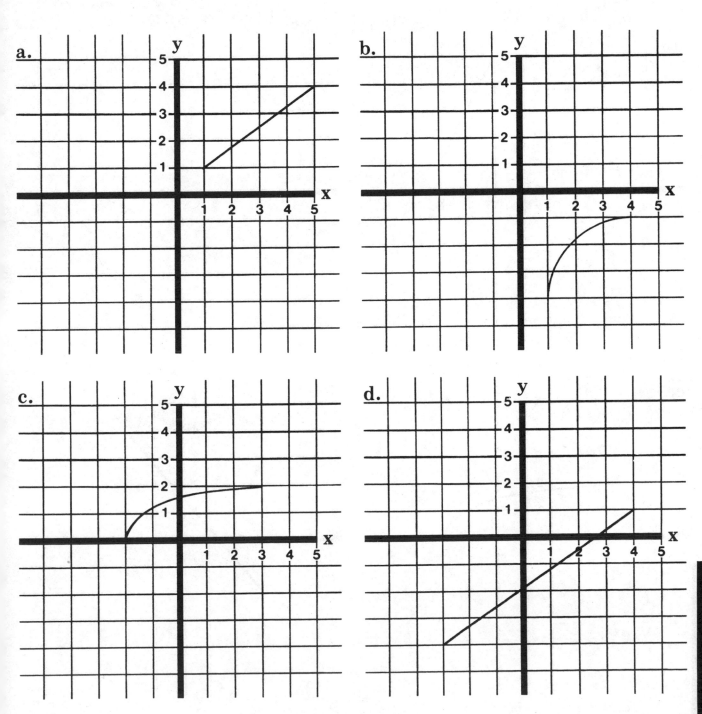

SYMMETRY

Name............................

Thinking of the y-axis as a mirror, draw the mirror images of the following graphs.

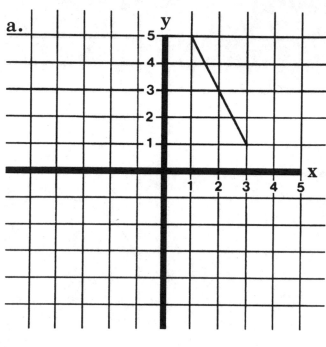

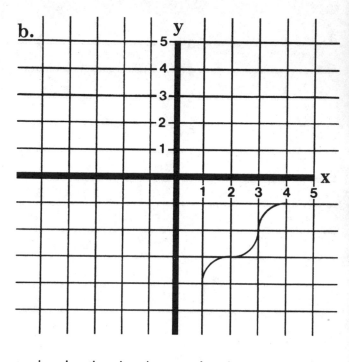

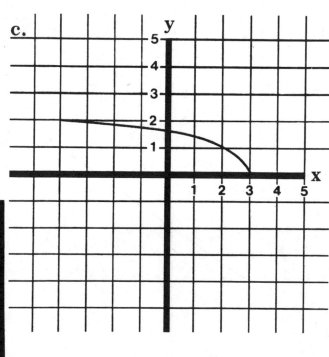

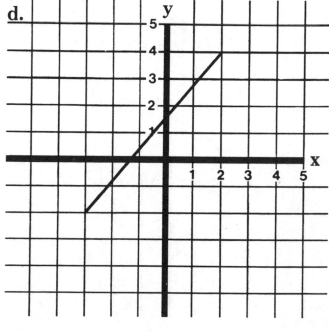

SYMMETRY

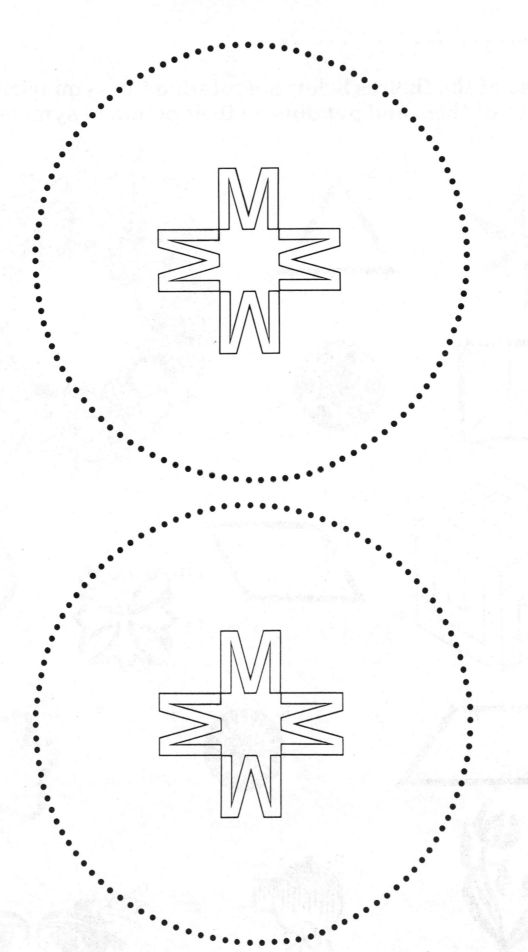

SYMMETRY

Name........................

Nine of the figures below are rotationally symmetric.   Find all nine of them and put dots on their points of symmetry.

a.

b.

c.

d.

e.

f.

g.

h.

i.

j.

k.

l.

m.

n.

o.

SYMMETRY

Name........................

1. **All of the figures below are rotationally symmetric. What is the degree of rotational symmetry for each one?**

2. **The capital letter H is 180° rotationally symmetric as are five other capital letters. Find all five of them.**

Slide Symmetry Cutouts

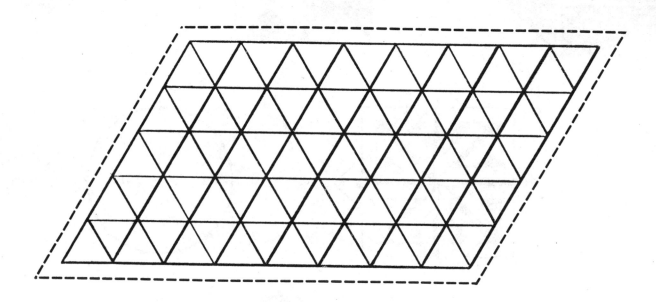

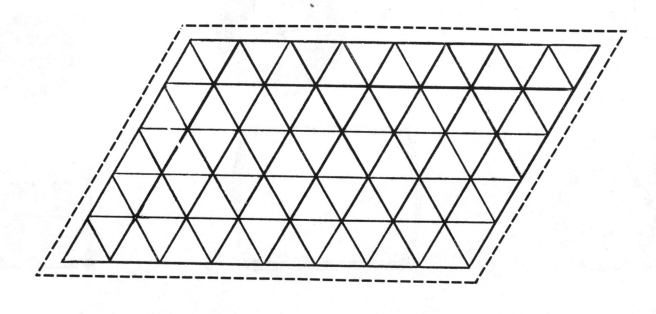

SYMMETRY

Name.....................

Six of the figures below are slide symmetric. Find all six of them and indicate a slide on each of them with an arrow.

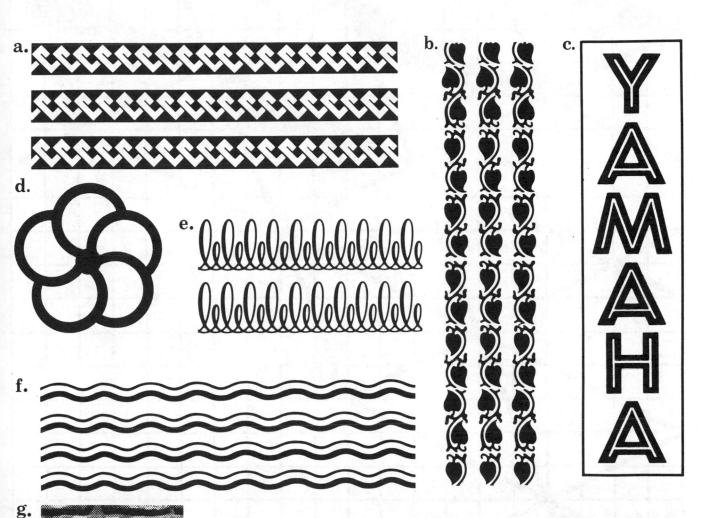

a.

b.

c.

d.

e.

f.

g.

h.

i.

j.

SYMMETRY

Name ....

Complete the pattern.

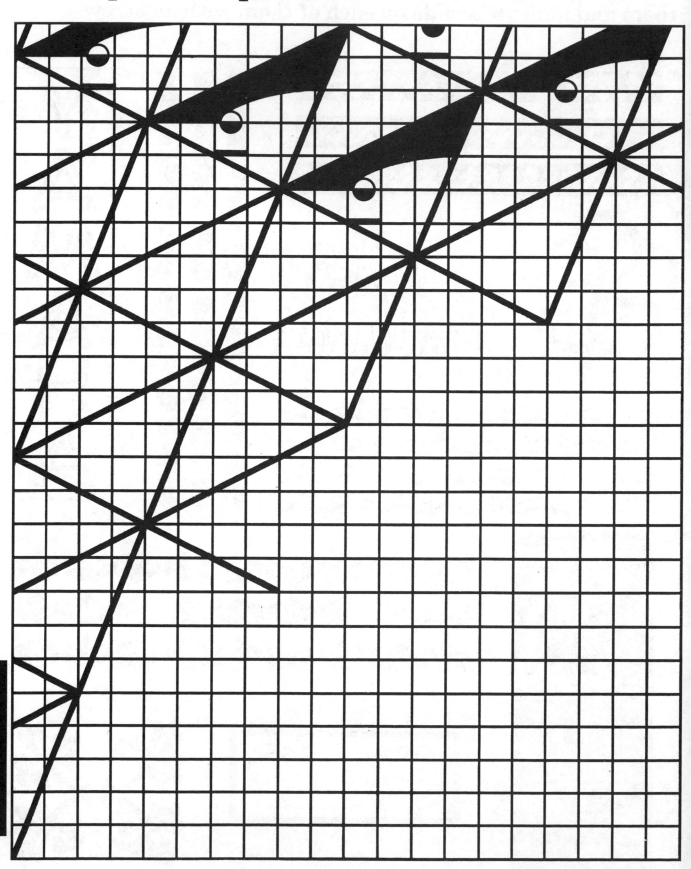

Name ....

Complete the pattern.

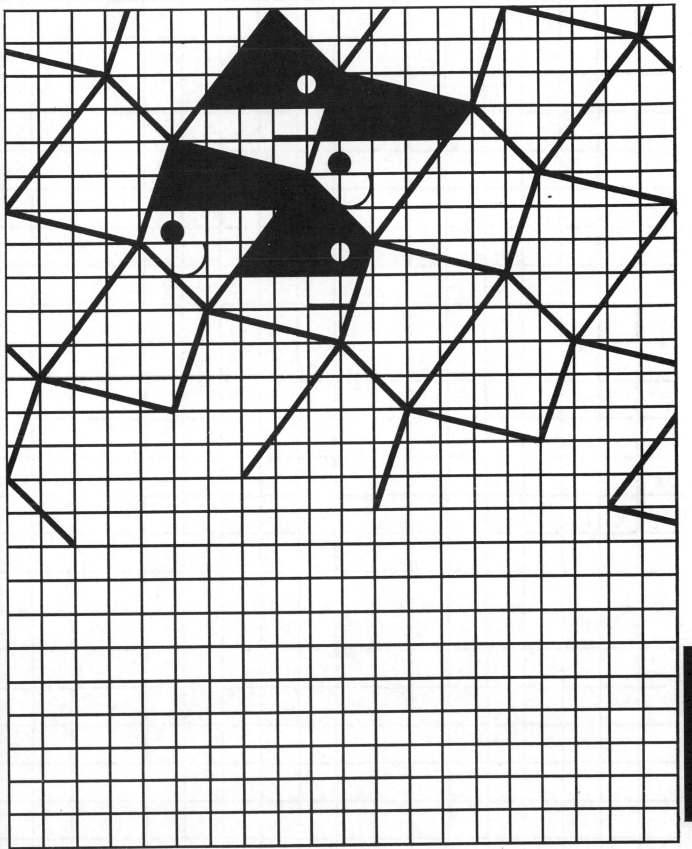

REPRINTED FROM THE MATHEMATICS TEACHER WITH THE PERMISSION OF THE NATIONAL
COUNCIL OF TEACHERS OF MATHEMATICS

207

SYMMETRY

Grid Paper

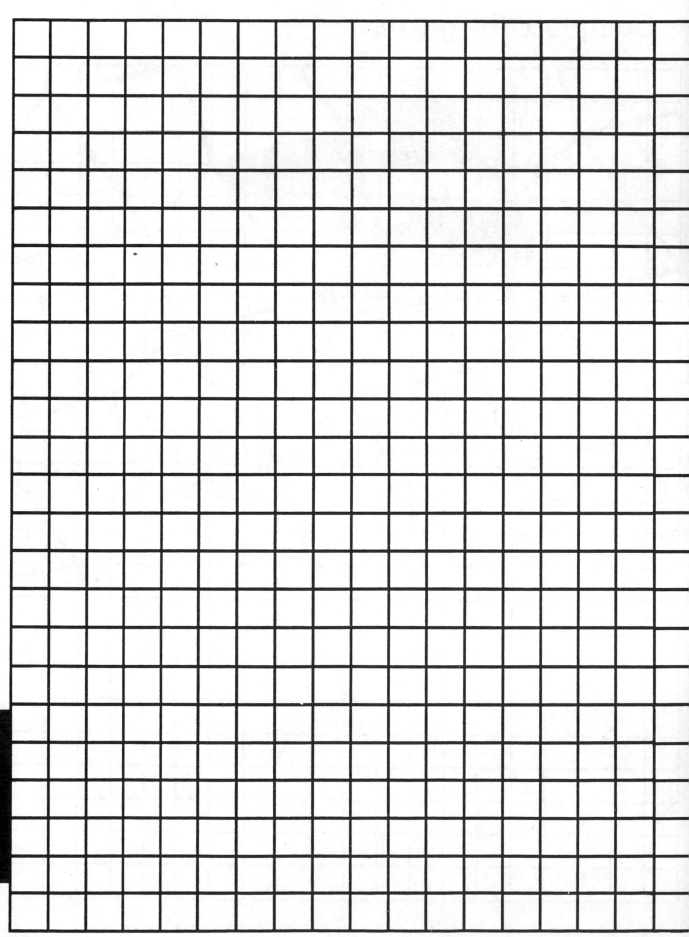

SYMMETRY

AREA

Areas (A) of Triangles

Name.......................................

The area of the triangle in Figure 1 is four because the triangle is half of a rectangle of area 8 as shown in Figure 2.

Find the areas of triangles a through v by enclosing them in rectangles. The rectangles should be as small as possible with horizontal bases and vertical sides. Some of the areas of the triangles have already been found for you as a check for your work.

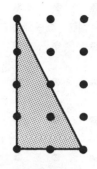

Figure 1

Figure 2

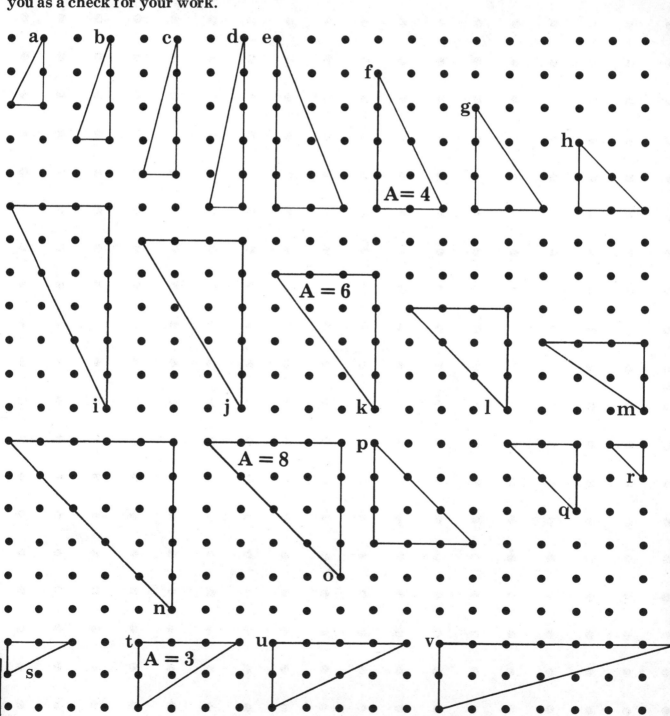

AREA

Areas (A) of Polygons
(First of two)

Name ....

The area of the pentagon in Figure 1 is 6½ because the pentagon can be divided into five units of area and three half-units of area as shown in Figure 2.

Find the areas of polygons a through o by dividing them into units and half units of area. Some of the areas of the polygons have already been found for you as a check for your work.

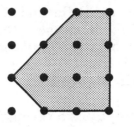

Figure 1   Figure 2

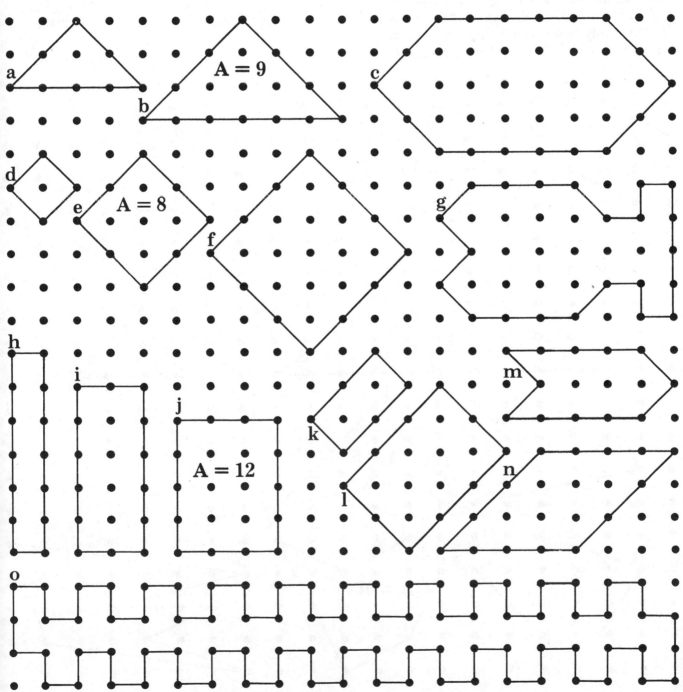

a

b   A = 9   c

d
e   A = 8   f   g

h   i   j   A = 12   k   m   l   n

o

AREA

Areas (A) of Polygons
(Second of two)

Name ....

The area of the quadrilateral in Figure 1 is 5½ because the quadrilateral is part of a rectangle of area 15 and 15 − (1 + 1 + 1½ + 2 + 2 + 2) = 5½ as shown in Figure 2.

Find the areas of polygons a through p by enclosing them in rectangles and subtracting all but the areas of the polygons themselves from the areas of the rectangles. The rectangles should be as small as possible with horizontal and vertical sides. Some of the areas of the polygons have already been found for you as a check for your work.

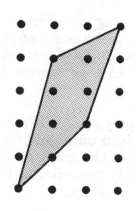

Figure 1

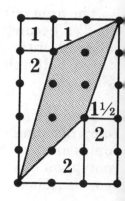

Figure 2

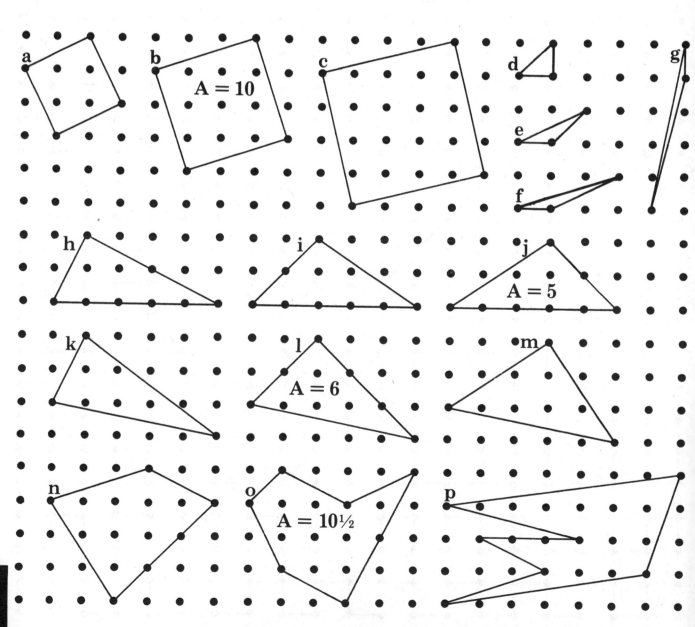

a

b A = 10

c

d

e

f

g

h

i

j A = 5

k

l A = 6

m

n

o A = 10½

p

AREA

Areas (A) of Similar Figures on the Sides of Right Triangles
(First of two)

Name ....

For each configuration, find the areas of the figures on the sides of the right triangle. Do NOT find the area of the right triangle. Some of the areas of the figures have already been found for you as a check for your work.

How do the areas for each configuration relate to one another?

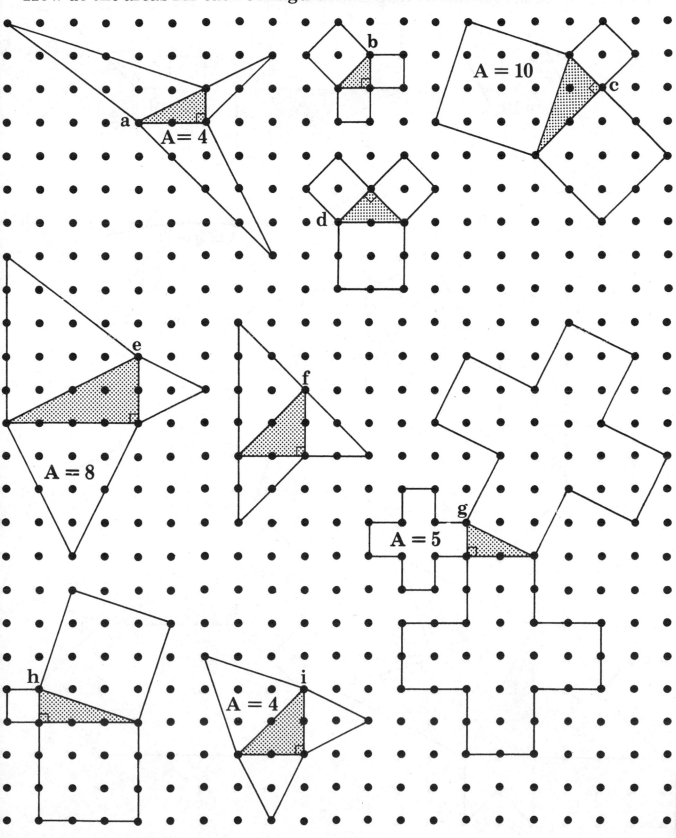

AREA

Areas (A) of Similar Figures on the Sides of Right Triangles
(Second of two)

Name.....................................

For each configuration, find the areas of the figures on the sides of the right triangle. Do NOT find the area of the right triangle. Some of the areas of the figures have already been found for you as a check for your work.

How do the areas for each configuration relate to one another?

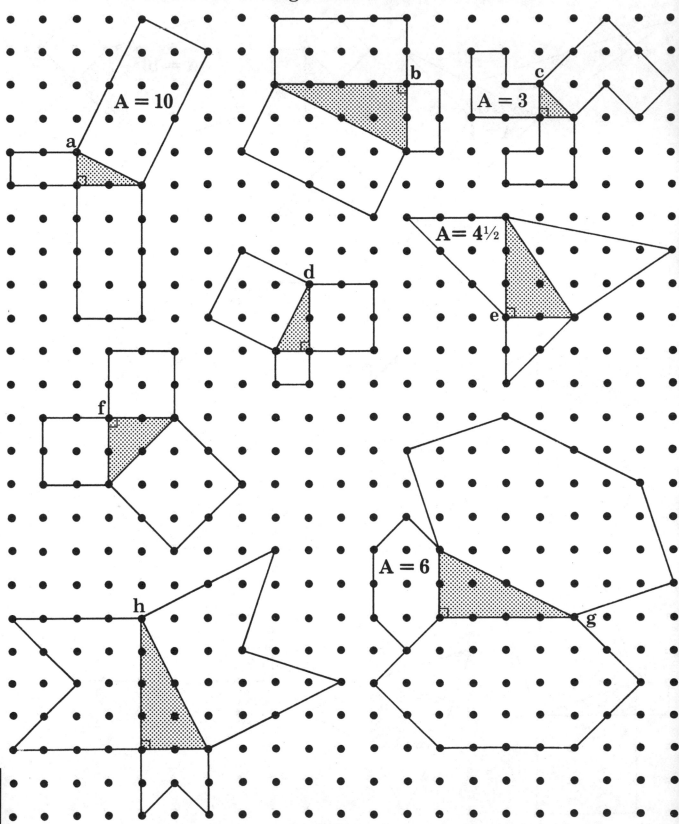

1. **What is the area of the square in Figure 1?** _____

2. **Cut the square in Figure 1 into four pieces by cutting along the dotted lines. Then make a rectangle with the four pieces.**

3. **What is the area of the rectangle?** _____

4. **Explain.**

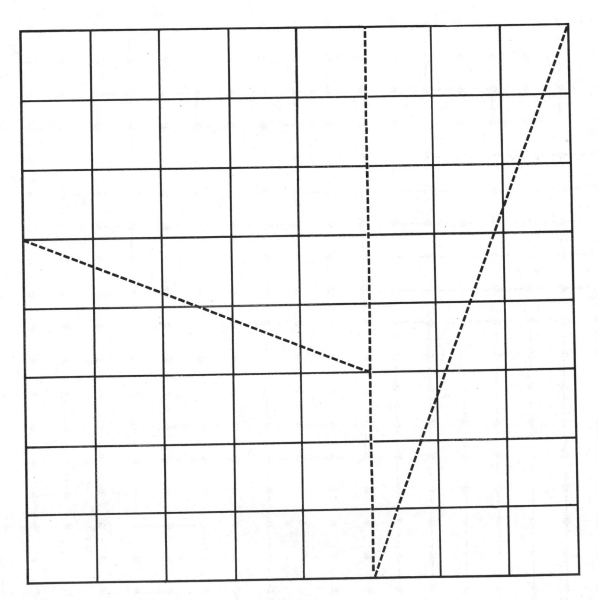

Figure 1

AREA

Name...

The length of the curve in Figure 1 is 11 because the curve can be traversed with 11 jumps of unit length as shown in Figure 2.

Find the lengths of curves a through i by traversing them with jumps of unit length. Some of the lengths of the curves have already been found for you as a check for your work.

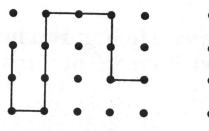

Figure 1

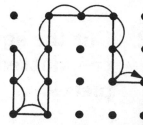

Figure 2

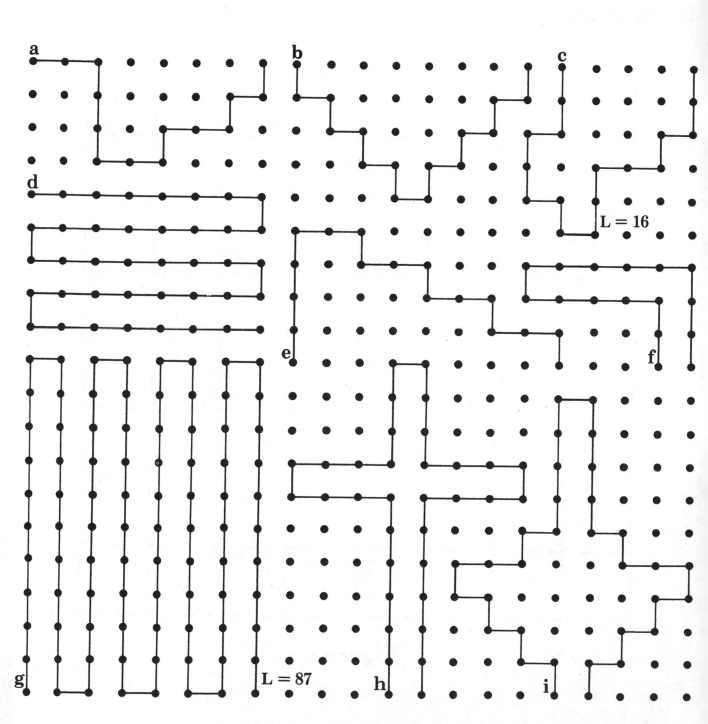

L = 16

L = 87

Lengths (L) of Edges of Squares

Name . . . .

The length of an edge of a square is the square root of the area of the square. Thus the length of an edge of the square in Figure 1 is $\sqrt{2}$ as shown in Figure 2.

Find the lengths of the edges of squares a through k by finding the areas of the squares. Some of the lengths of the edges of the squares have already been found for you as a check for your work.

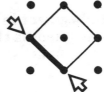

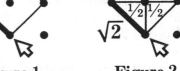

Figure 1   Figure 2

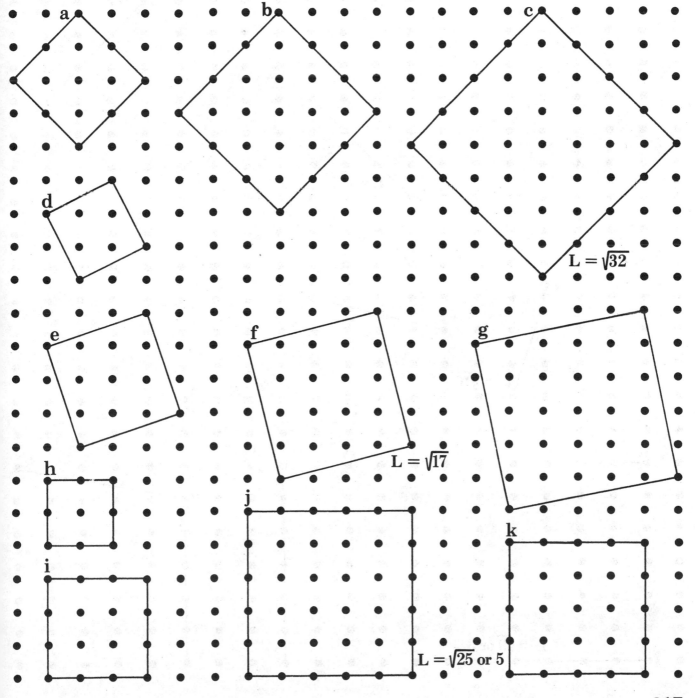

L = $\sqrt{32}$

L = $\sqrt{17}$

L = $\sqrt{25}$ or 5

MATH GAMES & ACTIVITIES. COPYRIGHT © 1984

217

Lengths (L) of Segments

Name ....

The length of the segment in Figure 1 is $\sqrt{2}$ because the segment is the edge of a square of area 2 as shown in Figure 2.

Find the lengths of segments a through k by constructing squares on the segments. Some of the lengths of the segments have already been found for you as a check for your work.

Figure 1　　　**Figure 2**

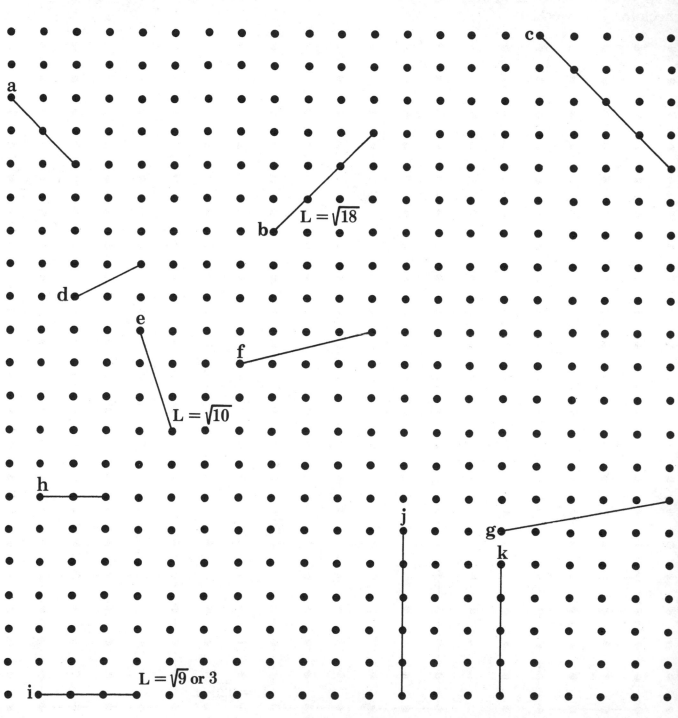

$L = \sqrt{18}$

$L = \sqrt{10}$

$L = \sqrt{9}$ or 3

MATH GAMES & ACTIVITIES. COPYRIGHT © 1984 BY 'R IN R INK

Equivalent Square Roots

Name...................................

Two number names for the length of the segment in Figure 1 is $\sqrt{8}$ and $2\sqrt{2}$ because the segment is the edge of a square of area 8 and the edge of two adjacent squares of area 2 each as shown in Figure 2.

Find two number names for the lengths of segments a through g by constructing squares on the segments. Some of the number names for the lengths of the segments have already been found for you as a check for your work.

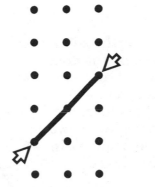

Figure 1

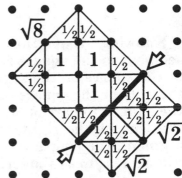

Figure 2

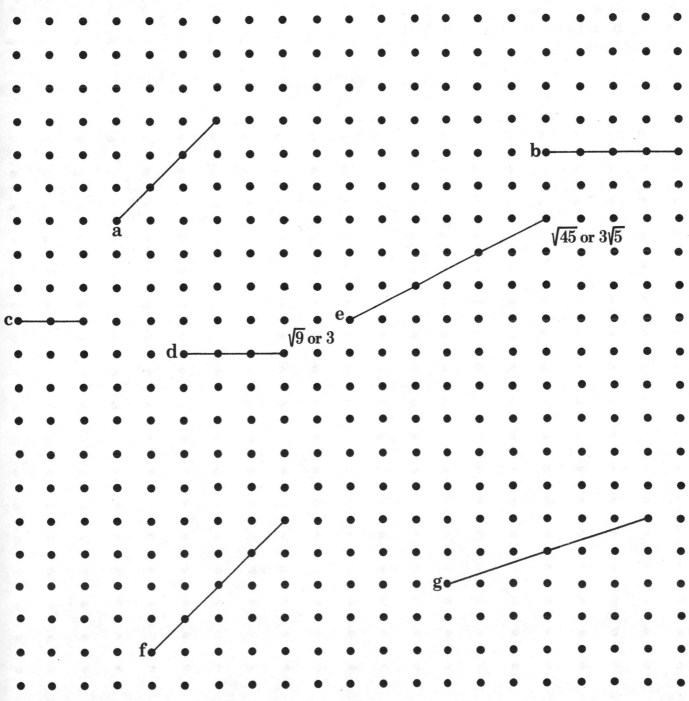

a

b

c

d $\sqrt{9}$ or 3

e $\sqrt{45}$ or $3\sqrt{5}$

f

g

Applying the Pythagorean Theorem

Name ....

Knowing that the length of a segment is the square root of the area of the square on the segment and that the area of the square on a segment is the sum of the areas of the squares on the legs of the right triangle on the segment, the length of the segment in Figure 1 is $\sqrt{13}$ as shown in Figure 2.

Find the lengths of segments a through g by constructing right triangles on the segments. Some of the lengths of the segments have already been found for you as a check for your work.

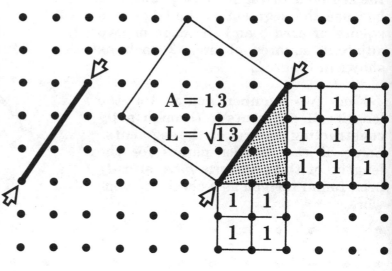

Figure 1   Figure 2

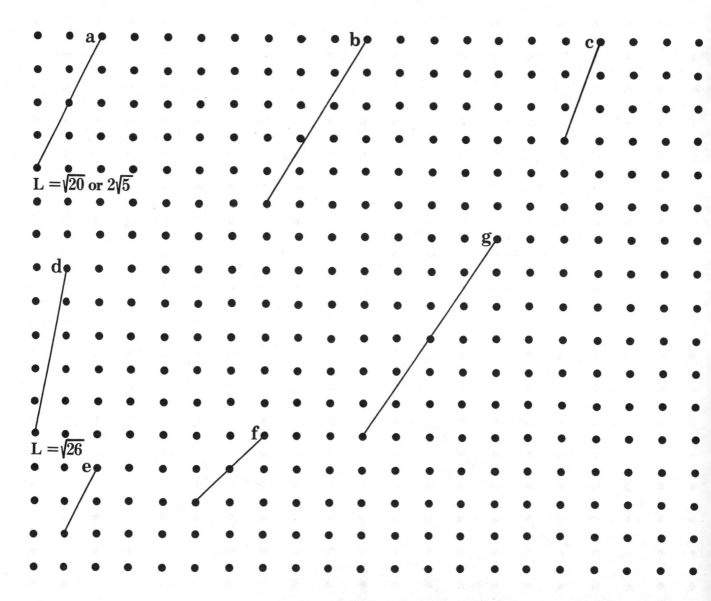

220

Perimeters of Polygons

Name.....................................

The perimeter of a polygon is the sum of the lengths of the sides of the polygon. Thus the perimeter of the polygon in Figure 1 is $5 + 2\sqrt{2} + \sqrt{5} + \sqrt{10}$ as shown in Figure 2.

Find the perimeters of polygons a through i. Some of the perimeters of the polygons have already been found for you as a check for your work.

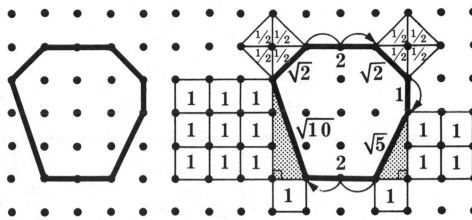

Figure 1   **Figure 2**

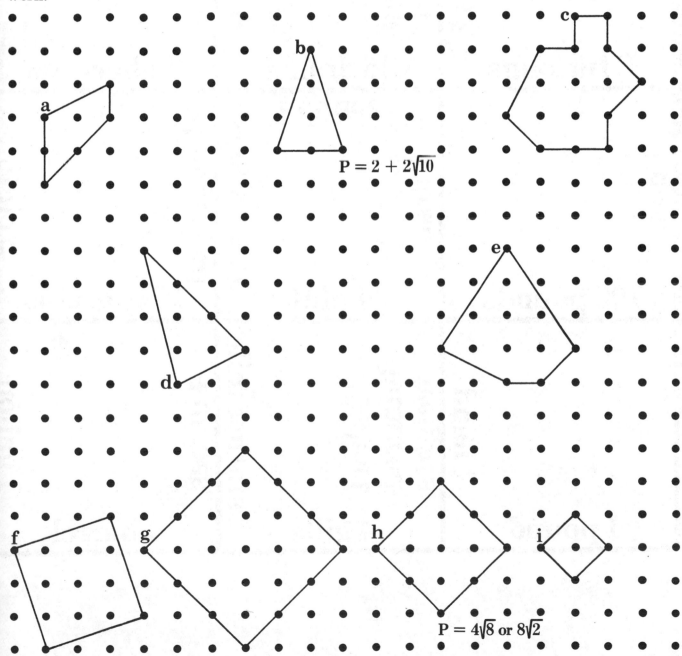

$P = 2 + 2\sqrt{10}$

$P = 4\sqrt{8}$ or $8\sqrt{2}$

MATH GAMES & ACTIVITIES. COPYRIGHT © 1984   **221**

ENGLISH SYSTEM OF MEASUREMENT

2 barrels	1 short hundred-weight	16 ounces
8 furlongs	16 drams	4 quarts
	1 ounce	
1 quart	1 dram	1 hogshead
100 pounds	1 pint	$31\frac{1}{2}$ gallons
		2 pints
		$27\frac{11}{32}$ grains
1 hand	20 short hundred-weights	4 inches
		1 statute mile
1 pound	4 gills	1 gallon
		1 barrel

Basic Units

Meter (m): a little more than a yard
Liter (L): a little more than a quart
Gram (g): about the weight of a raisin

Prefixes

Kilo- (k): one thousand (1000)
Deci- (d): one-tenth (0.1)
Centi- (c): one-hundredth (0.01)
Milli- (m): one-thousandth (0.001)

Length

One kilometer (km) = 1000 meters (m) or a little more than half a mile
One decimeter (dm) = 0.1 meters (m) or about 4 inches
One centimeter (cm) = 0.01 meters (m) or about half the width of a thumb
One millimeter (mm) = 0.001 meters (m) or about the width of the tip of a ball-point pen

Volume (Capacity)

One cubic meter (m^3) = 1000 liters (L) or about the size of a telephone booth
One cubic decimeter (dm^3) = 1 liter (L)
One cubic centimeter (cm^3) = 1 milliliter (mL) or about half the size of a thimble

Weight (Mass)

One metric ton (t) = 1000 kilograms (kg) or about the weight of a small foreign car
One kilogram (kg) = 1000 grams (g) or a little more than 2 pounds
One milligram (mg) = 0.001 grams (g) or less even than the weight of a grain of sand

Conversions

Within units: Just move the decimal point. For example,

2.5 m = 250 cm (because 1 m = 100 cm)
3 mL = 0.003 L (because 1 mL = 0.001 L)
0.047 kg = 47 g (because 1 kg = 1000 g)

Between units: Refer to the following:

Length and volume: See the listings for volume.

Volume and weight: One milliliter (mL) of water weighs 1 gram (g). Thus 1 liter (L) of water weighs 1 kilogram (kg), and 1000 liters (L) of water weigh 1 metric ton (t).

METRIC SYSTEM

METRIC SYSTEM

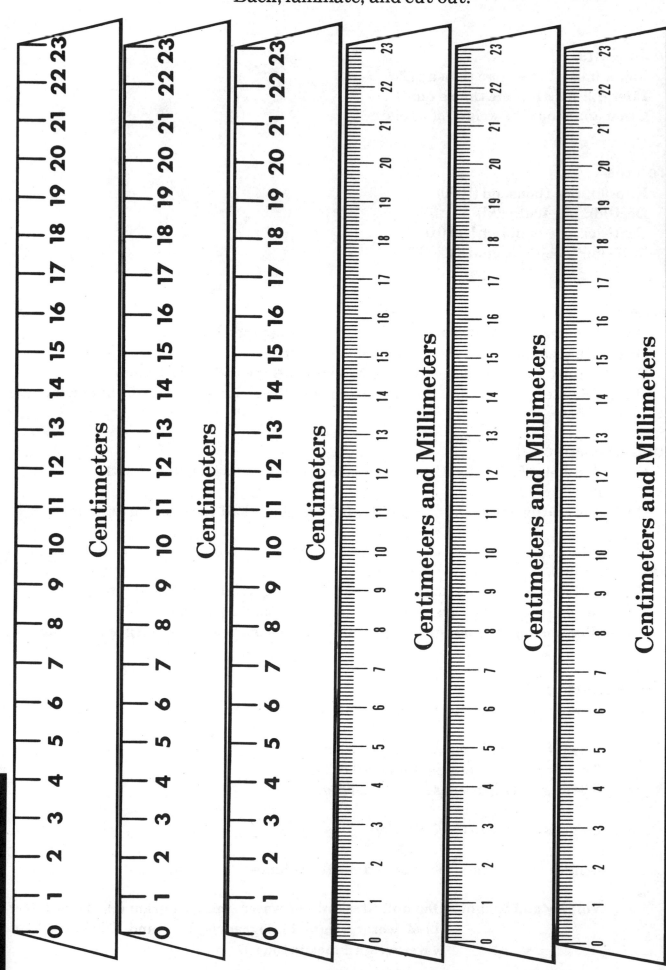

Centimeters

Centimeters

Centimeters

Centimeters and Millimeters

Centimeters and Millimeters

Centimeters and Millimeters

Metric Calipers
Back, laminate, and cut out.
Fold along dotted lines.

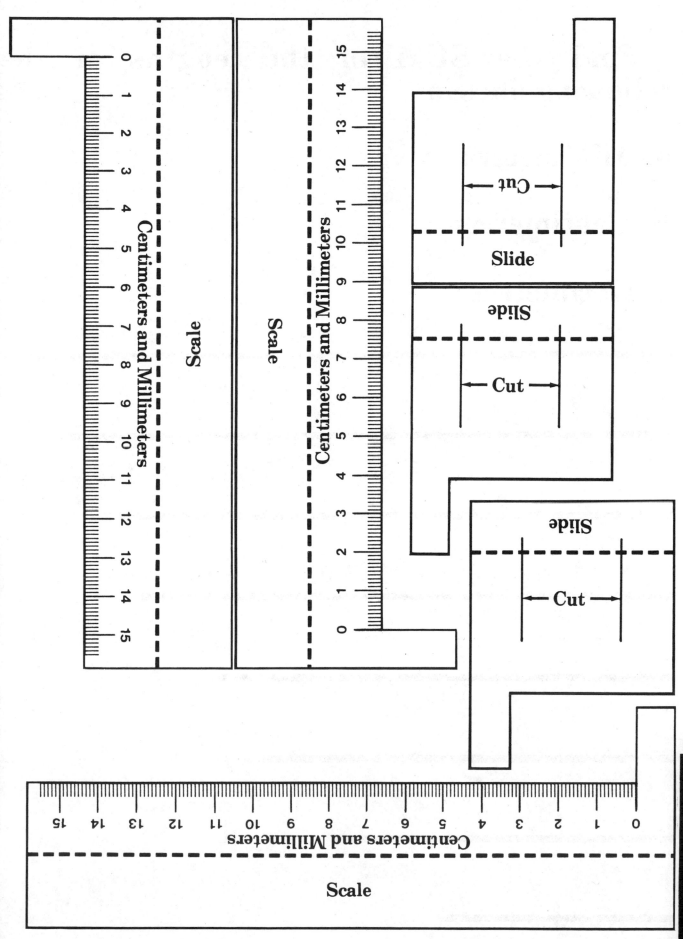

Name. . . . .

    Find the SUM of the lengths of the following lines in

a. Millimeters

b. Centimeters

c. Decimeters

_____

_____

_____

_____

_____

_____

_____

Metric Array Cards
(Prefixes)
Back, laminate, and cut along solid lines.

2.5 cm 25 m	10 mm 1000 m	500 m 0.001 g 1200 m
0.75 m 25 cm	100 cm 0.5 km 1000 mL	1.2 km 25 mm 1.2 m
1 m 75 cm 1 cm	10 cm 120 cm 100 mm	1 km 1 mg 1 L

The weight of 500 mL of water 1 kg 100 g	The weight of 100 L of water 10 kg	1 m³ The weight of 10 mL of water 1 dm³
The weight of 1 L of water 1 L · 1 g 1 cm³	10 g The weight of 100 mL of water · 1	The weight of 10 L of water 1 mL The weight of 0.001 mL of water
The weight of 1000 L of water 500 g	100 kg The weight of 1 mL of water 1 t	1000 L

Metric Prefix Concentration Cards
(Page 1 of two pages)
Back, laminate, and cut along solid lines.

METRIC PREFIX CONCENTRATION **1 mg**	**METRIC PREFIX CONCENTRATION** **0.001 g**
METRIC PREFIX CONCENTRATION **1 cm**	**METRIC PREFIX CONCENTRATION** **0.01 m**
METRIC PREFIX CONCENTRATION **1 L**	**METRIC PREFIX CONCENTRATION** **1000 mL**
METRIC PREFIX CONCENTRATION **1 m**	**METRIC PREFIX CONCENTRATION** **0.001 km**

METRIC SYSTEM

Metric Prefix Concentration Cards
(Page 2 of two pages)
Back, laminate, and cut along solid lines.

METRIC PREFIX CONCENTRATION **3.5 cm**	METRIC PREFIX CONCENTRATION **35 mm**
METRIC PREFIX CONCENTRATION **3.5 m**	METRIC PREFIX CONCENTRATION **350 cm**
METRIC PREFIX CONCENTRATION **1 kg**	METRIC PREFIX CONCENTRATION **1000 g**
METRIC PREFIX CONCENTRATION **3.5 km**	METRIC PREFIX CONCENTRATION **3500 m**

METRIC SYSTEM

Metric Conversion Concentration Cards
(Page 1 of two pages)
Back, laminate, and cut along solid lines.

METRIC CONVERSION CONCENTRATION The weight of 1 L of water	METRIC CONVERSION CONCENTRATION **1 kg**
METRIC CONVERSION CONCENTRATION **1 dm³**	METRIC CONVERSION CONCENTRATION **1 L**
METRIC CONVERSION CONCENTRATION **1 cm³**	METRIC CONVERSION CONCENTRATION **1 mL**
METRIC CONVERSION CONCENTRATION The weight of 1 mL of water	METRIC CONVERSION CONCENTRATION **1 g**

METRIC SYSTEM

Metric Conversion Concentration Cards
(Page 2 of two pages)
Back, laminate, and cut along solid lines.

METRIC CONVERSION CONCENTRATION The weight of 5 L of water	METRIC CONVERSION CONCENTRATION **5 kg**
METRIC CONVERSION CONCENTRATION The weight of 0.001 mL of water	METRIC CONVERSION CONCENTRATION **1 mg**
METRIC CONVERSION CONCENTRATION **1 m³**	METRIC CONVERSION CONCENTRATION **1000 L**
METRIC CONVERSION CONCENTRATION The weight of 1000 L of water	METRIC CONVERSION CONCENTRATION **1 t**

METRIC SYSTEM

Name................................

What am I? Connect equivalent measurements to find out.

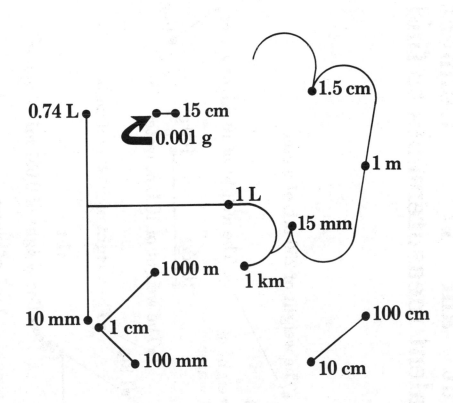

Name..................

What am I? Connect equivalent measurements to find out.

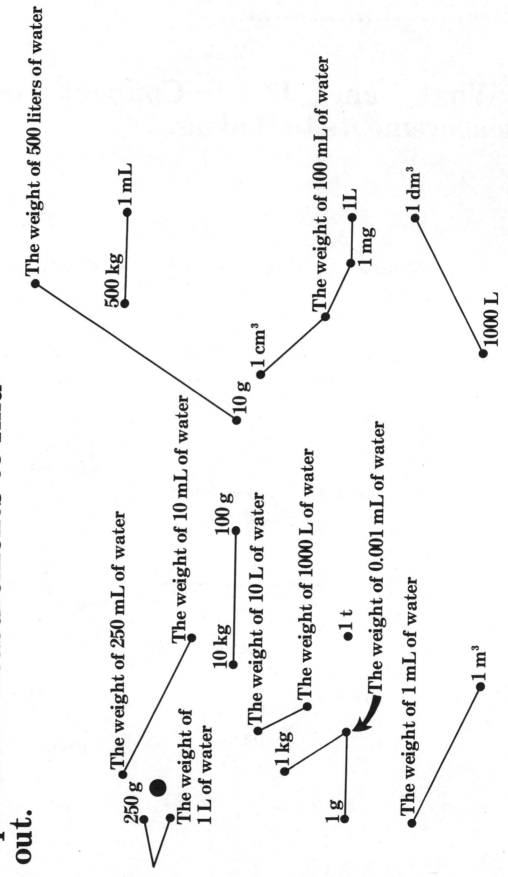

The weight of 500 liters of water — 500 kg — 1 mL

The weight of 100 mL of water — 1L — 1 mg

10 g — 1 cm³

1 dm³ — 1000 L

The weight of 250 mL of water — 250 g

The weight of 10 mL of water — 100 g — 10 kg

The weight of 1 L of water

The weight of 10 L of water — 1 kg

The weight of 1000 L of water — 1 t

The weight of 0.001 mL of water — 1 g

The weight of 1 mL of water — 1 m³

Metric Proverbs

Name...

For each sentence, fill in the first blank with the familiar term, the second blank with the metric counterpart for the term.

1. There was a crooked man and he walked a crooked _____ .
   _____

2. Peter Piper picked a _____ of pickled peppers.
   _____

3. Give them an _____ and they'll take a _____ .
   _____   _____

4. Oh, Thumbelina, what's the difference if you're very small? When your heart is full of love you're _____ tall.
   _____

5. A miss is as good as a _____ .
   _____

6. An _____ of prevention is worth a _____ of cure.
   _____   _____

7. I wouldn't touch a skunk with a _____ pole.
   _____

8. He's all wool and a _____ wide.
   _____

9. The Texan pulled a rabbit out of a _____ hat.
   _____

10. My favorite dessert is _____ cake.
    _____

11. Don't hide your light under a _____ basket.
    _____

12. He fell for it like a _____ of bricks.
    _____

13. This is a _____ stone (post) in my life.
    _____

14. I love you a _____ and a _____ .
    _____   _____

15. Penny wise and _____ foolish
    _____

Space Race Gameboard
(Consumable)

SPACE
RACE

Dodecahedron

Cube

Octahedron

Tetrahedron

Icosahedron

Space Race Cards
(Page 1 of three pages)
Back, laminate, and cut along solid lines.

SPACE RACE	SPACE RACE	SPACE RACE
Use the shortest distance in your discard pile.	Use the longest distance in your discard pile.	Use one-half your last distance.
SPACE RACE	SPACE RACE	SPACE RACE
Use twice your last distance.	Use the sum of your last two distances.	Use the difference of your last two distances.
SPACE RACE	SPACE RACE	SPACE RACE
Go directly to Tetrahedron.	Go directly to the nearest corner.	Return to the tip of the rocket's nose.
SPACE RACE	SPACE RACE	SPACE RACE
1 cm	2 cm	3 cm
SPACE RACE	SPACE RACE	SPACE RACE
4 cm	5 cm	6 cm

METRIC SYSTEM

Space Race Cards
(Page 2 of three pages)
Back, laminate, and cut along solid lines.

SPACE RACE	SPACE RACE	SPACE RACE
7 cm	**8 cm**	**9 cm**
SPACE RACE	SPACE RACE	SPACE RACE
10 cm	**11 cm**	**12 cm**
SPACE RACE	SPACE RACE	SPACE RACE
13 cm	**14 cm**	**15 cm**
SPACE RACE	SPACE RACE	SPACE RACE
1.1 cm	**1.5 cm**	**1.9 cm**
SPACE RACE	SPACE RACE	SPACE RACE
2.2 cm	**2.5 cm**	**2.8 cm**

METRIC SYSTEM

Space Race Cards
(Page 3 of three pages)
Back, laminate, and cut along solid lines.

SPACE RACE	SPACE RACE	SPACE RACE
3.3 cm	**3.5 cm**	**3.7 cm**
SPACE RACE	SPACE RACE	SPACE RACE
4.1 cm	**5.9 cm**	**6.3 cm**
SPACE RACE	SPACE RACE	SPACE RACE
7.2 cm	**8.4 cm**	**9.6 cm**
SPACE RACE	SPACE RACE	SPACE RACE
10.8 cm	**11.7 cm**	**12.6 cm**
SPACE RACE	SPACE RACE	SPACE RACE
13.4 cm	**14.5 cm**	**16.0 cm**

METRIC SYSTEM

Metric Mastery Gameboard
Left side
Color, back, and laminate.

MARVELOUS METRICS

CHANCE
CHANCE
CHANCE
CHANCE

CHANCE
CHANCE
CHANCE
CHANCE

CHANCE

Deci- = 0.1
Centi- = 0.01
Milli- = 0.001

10 mm = 1 cm

1 mg = 0.001 g

1000 m = 1 km

1 mL of water weighs 1 g

1 dm³ = 1 L

CHANCE
CHANCE
CHANCE
CHANCE

METRIC SYSTEM

240

Metric Mastery Gameboard
Right side
Color, back, and laminate.

START

FINISH

Kilo- = 1000

100 cm = 1 m

1 L of water weighs 1 kg

1000 mm = 1 m

1 cm³ = 1 mL

1 m³ = 1000 L

1000 kg = 1 t

CHANCE

CHANCE

CHANCE

CHANCE

METRIC MASTERY

METRIC MESS

Metric Mastery Question Cards
(Page 1 of six pages)
Back, laminate, and cut along solid lines.

METRIC MASTERY 1

Which is a unit of volume?

a. Milliliter
b. Centimeter
c. Kilogram
d. Span

METRIC MASTERY 2

Which is a unit of weight?

a. Milliliter
b. Centimeter
c. Kilogram
d. Span

METRIC MASTERY 3

Which is the appropriate unit of measure for the width of a football field?

a. Meter
b. Mile
c. Kilometer
d. Centimeter

METRIC MASTERY 4

Which is the appropriate unit of measure for the amount of lemonade in a jug?

a. Milliliter
b. Meter
c. Liter
d. Gram

METRIC MASTERY 5

Which is the appropriate unit of measure for the weight of a candy bar?

a. Kilogram
b. Gram
c. Milligram
d. Pound

METRIC MASTERY 6

The length of a one-dollar bill is approximately

a. 10 centimeters
b. 15 centimeters
c. 20 centimeters
d. 25 centimeters

METRIC MASTERY 7

The length of a Volkswagon bug is approximately

a. 1 meter
b. 2 meters
c. 5 meters
d. 10 meters

METRIC MASTERY 8

Which is 1 square centimeter in area?

a. ▢   b. ◯

c. ▢   d. ▢

METRIC SYSTEM

Metric Mastery Question Cards
(Page 2 of six pages)
Back, laminate, and cut along solid lines.

METRIC MASTERY   9

A meter is _____ a yard.

a. Less than
b. The same as
c. More than

METRIC MASTERY   10

A kilometer is _____ a mile.

a. Less than
b. The same as
c. More than

METRIC MASTERY   11

A liter is _____ a quart.

a. Less than
b. The same as
c. More than

METRIC MASTERY   12

A gram is _____ an ounce.

a. Less than
b. The same as
c. More than

METRIC MASTERY   13

A kilogram is _____ a pound.

a. Less than
b. The same as
c. More than

METRIC MASTERY   14

A metric ton is _____ a U.S.A. ton.

a. Less than
b. The same as
c. More than

METRIC MASTERY   15

A kilometer is how many meters?

a. 0.001
b. 1
c. 1000
d. 100,000

METRIC MASTERY   16

A milliliter is how many liters?

a. 1000
b. 1
c. 0.001
d. 0.01

METRIC SYSTEM

Metric Mastery Question Cards
(Page 3 of six pages)
Back, laminate, and cut along solid lines.

METRIC MASTERY   17

How many kilograms are 47.5 grams?

a. 475
b. 47,500
c. 0.0475
d. 4.75

METRIC MASTERY   18

The volume of 1 cubic decimeter is

a. 1 liter
b. 1 kilogram
c. 1 cubic centimeter
d. 1 gram

METRIC MASTERY   19

A milliliter of water weighs

a. 1 kilogram
b. 1 cubic centimeter
c. 1 gram
d. 0.001 meters

METRIC MASTERY   20

The volume of a person who weighs 63 kilograms is approximately

a. 63,000 liters
b. 63 liters
c. 1 cubic decimeter
d. 1 cubic meter

METRIC MASTERY   21

How many centimeters make a meter?

METRIC MASTERY   22

How many kilograms are 1000 grams?

METRIC MASTERY   23

How many millimeters make a meter?

METRIC MASTERY   24

Which is longer, a meter or a kilometer?

Metric Mastery Question Cards
(Page 4 of six pages)
Back, laminate, and cut along solid lines.

METRIC MASTERY **25**

Which holds more, a 10-milliliter container or a 10-liter container?

METRIC MASTERY **26**

Which weighs more, a gram of lead or a kilogram of feathers?

METRIC MASTERY **27**

What is the basic unit for weight in the metric system?

METRIC MASTERY **28**

What is the basic unit for length in the metric system?

METRIC MASTERY **29**

What is the basic unit for volume in the metric system?

METRIC MASTERY **30**

A cubic centimeter is how much in volume?

METRIC MASTERY **31**

A liter of water weighs how much?

METRIC MASTERY **32**

A milliliter of water weighs how much?

METRIC SYSTEM

Metric Mastery Question Cards
(Page 5 of six pages)
Back, laminate, and cut along solid lines.

METRIC SYSTEM

METRIC MASTERY 33

How big in square centimeters?

METRIC MASTERY 34

How long in meters?

METRIC MASTERY 35

How long in meters?

METRIC MASTERY 36

How long in millimeters?

METRIC MASTERY 37

How long in meters?

METRIC MASTERY 38

How long in centimeters?

METRIC MASTERY 39

How long in centimeters?

METRIC MASTERY 40

How long in millimeters?

246

Metric Mastery Question Cards
(Page 6 of six pages)
Back, laminate, and cut along solid lines.

METRIC MASTERY 41

A metric ton is how many kilograms?

METRIC MASTERY 42

How many liters are 1000 milliliters?

METRIC MASTERY 43

Which is NOT true?

a. The metric system is a reflection of decimal arithmetic.
b. The metric system is the only measuring system that interrelates measurement and computation.
c. The metric system originated in France in 1791.
d. The world is primarily non-metric.

METRIC MASTERY 44

Meter is to yard as

a. Pound is to ounce
b. Gram is to liter
c. Liter is to quart
d. Gram is to kilogram

METRIC MASTERY 45

A raisin weighs about how much?

a. 1 centimeter
b. 1 kilogram
c. 1 gram
d. 5 grams

METRIC MASTERY 46

A thumb is about how wide?

a. 2 centimeters
b. 4 centimeters
c. 2 meters
d. 2 milliliters

METRIC MASTERY 47

Which indicates 1 meter, 3 decimeters, 2 centimeters, and 5 millimeters?

a. 1.523 m
b. 1325 m
c. 1.0325 m
d. 1.325 m

METRIC MASTERY 48

Which indicates 2 meters and 3 centimeters?

a. 2.3 m
b. 2.03 m
c. 2.003 m
d. 23 m

METRIC SYSTEM

Metric Mastery Chance Cards
(Page 1 of two pages)
Back, laminate, and cut along solid lines.

METRIC MASTERY
CHANCE

You just won a free trip to Paris to attend a metric convention. Advance to **MARVELOUS METRICS.**

METRIC MASTERY
CHANCE

Your parents can't fix your bicycle because their old tools won't fit. Go back two spaces.

METRIC MASTERY
CHANCE

Sorry, but you heard the temperature was 25 degrees Celsius and put on your long underwear. Go to **METRIC MESS.**

METRIC MASTERY
CHANCE

You just traded in your yardstick for a meter stick. Advance four spaces.

METRIC MASTERY
CHANCE

You just slowed down to 80 km / h in a 50 mph zone. Advance two spaces.

METRIC MASTERY
CHANCE

You just traded a kilogram of apples for a pound of pears. Go back two spaces.

METRIC MASTERY
CHANCE

You broke your meter stick measuring Mt. Everest. Go back four spaces.

METRIC MASTERY
CHANCE

You just bought a set of metric wrenches. Advance three spaces.

METRIC SYSTEM

248

Metric Mastery Chance Cards
(Page 2 of two pages)
Back, laminate, and cut along solid lines.

METRIC MASTERY CHANCE	METRIC MASTERY CHANCE
You lost a kilogram dieting. Advance three spaces.	You just drank a liter of coffee and got the shakes. Go back a space.
METRIC MASTERY **CHANCE** Your thumb is exactly 2 centimeters wide. Advance two spaces.	**METRIC MASTERY** **CHANCE** You just tried to buy a metric screwdriver. Go back a space.
METRIC MASTERY **CHANCE** The inchworm is out of date. Go back three spaces.	**METRIC MASTERY** **CHANCE** You just ran the 100-meter dash in 12 seconds. Advance four spaces.
METRIC MASTERY **CHANCE** It just took you eight minutes to jog a kilometer. Go back a space.	**METRIC MASTERY** **CHANCE** You just bought a kilogram of ground round instead of a pound of hamburger. Advance a space.

METRIC SYSTEM

METRIC MASTERY

KEY

1.	a	25.	A 10-liter container
2.	c	26.	A kilogram of feathers
3.	a	27.	The gram
4.	a or c	28.	The meter
5.	b	29.	The liter
6.	b	30.	1 milliliter
7.	c	31.	1 kilogram (or 1000 grams)
8.	c	32.	1 gram (or 0.001 kilograms)
9.	c	33.	18 square centimeters
10.	a	34.	0.1 meters
11.	c	35.	0.085 meters
12.	a	36.	27 millimeters
13.	c	37.	0.05 meters
14.	c	38.	10 centimeters
15.	c	39.	7.3 centimeters
16.	c	40.	100 millimeters
17.	c	41.	1000
18.	a	42.	One
19.	c	43.	d
20.	b	44.	c
21.	100	45.	c
22.	One	46.	a
23.	1000	47.	d
24.	A kilometer	48.	b

Angle Wedges
Small (10⁰), medium (15⁰), and large (30⁰)
Back, laminate, and cut along solid lines.

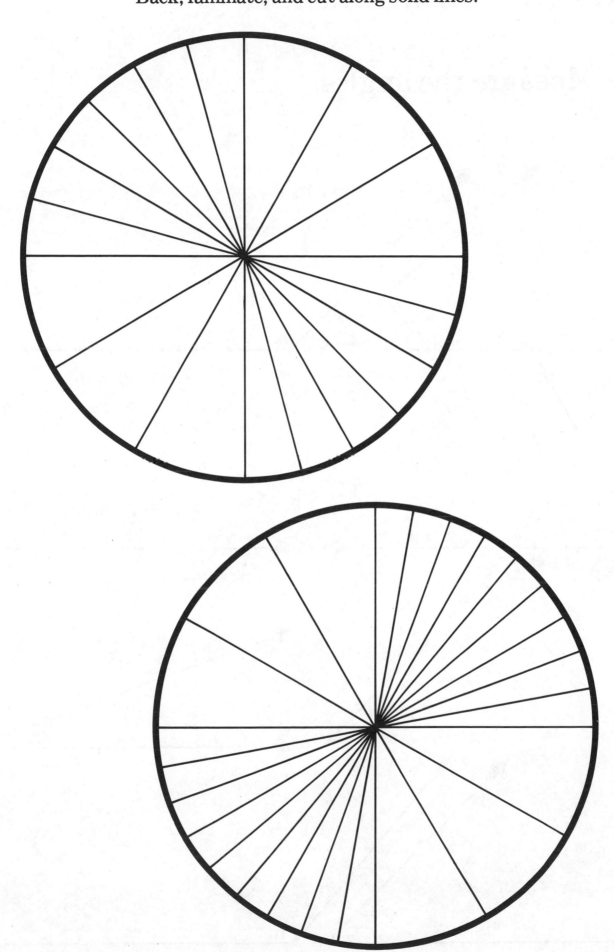

Angles

Name ....

Measure the angles.

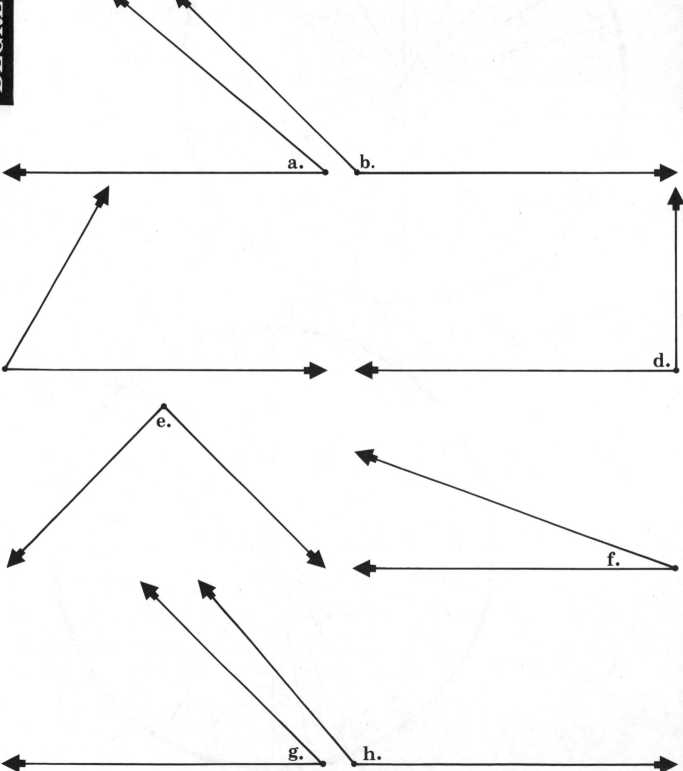

Compass Worksheet

Name. . . . .

1.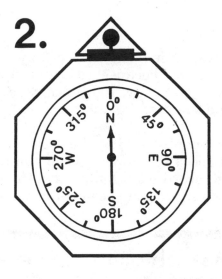

2.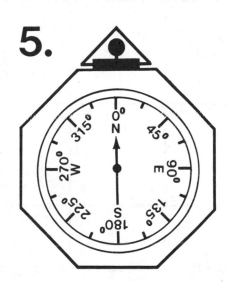

3.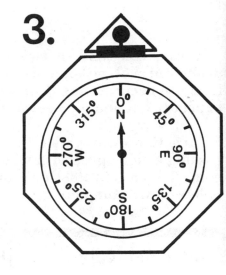

4.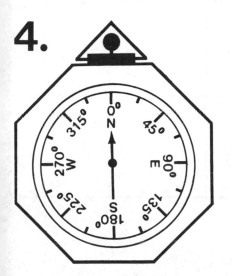

5.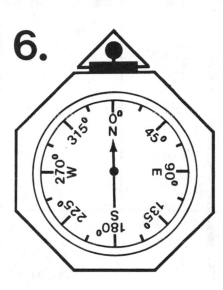

6.

7.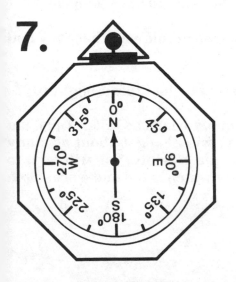

8.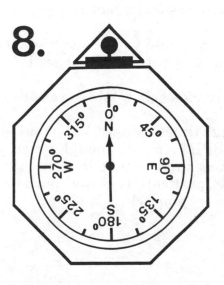

9.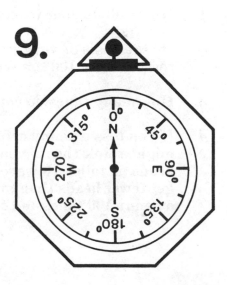

Verifying Probabilities
(Tossing one coin)

Name.......................................

A coin can land in two ways: heads up or tails up. The probability of either outcome is ½, because either is equally likely to occur. Thus if we toss a coin, say, 100 times, we would expect to get about 50 heads and 50 tails.

Investigate how well the probabilities for the outcomes of tossing a coin agree with what actually happens when you toss a coin. Toss a coin 100 times and record what happens in the table below. Then complete the table and answer the questions below.

PROBABILITY

Outcome	Tally	Fre-quency	Relative frequency	Proba-bility	Difference between relative frequency and probability
Heads up				$\frac{1}{2} = \frac{50}{100}$	
Tails up				$\frac{1}{2} = \frac{50}{100}$	
Sum	100	$\frac{100}{100} = 1$	$\frac{2}{2} = \frac{100}{100} = 1$		

1. How well do your results for tossing a coin agree with "what should have happened"?

2. On the basis of your results, would you be surprised if someone told you that they had tossed a coin 100 times and had gotten only 40 heads?

3. How many times do you think a coin would have to be tossed to "act like it ought to"?

4. If you toss a penny enough times, you will get about as many heads as tails. Thus you might think that if you SPIN a penny enough times, you will also get about as many heads as tails. However, as reality would have it, if you spin a penny, you will tend to get fewer heads than tails, particularly if you spin a penny which is old and worn. Spin a penny 100 times and see for yourself.

Verifying Probabilities
(Tossing two coins)

Name.......................................

Two coins can land in four ways: heads up, heads up (h,h); heads up, tails up (h,t); tails up, heads up (t,h); or tails up, tails up (t,t). The probability of each outcome is ¼, because each is equally likely to occur. Thus if we toss two coins, say, 100 times, we would expect to get about 25 of each outcome.

Investigate how well the probabilities for the outcomes of tossing two coins agree with what actually happens when you toss two coins. Toss a penny and a nickel together 100 times and record what happens in the table below. Then complete the table and answer the questions below.

Outcome	Tally	Fre-quency	Relative frequency	Proba-bility	Difference between relative frequency and probability
(h,h)				$\frac{1}{4} = \frac{25}{100}$	
(h,t)				$\frac{1}{4} = \frac{25}{100}$	
(t,h)				$\frac{1}{4} = \frac{25}{100}$	
(t,t)				$\frac{1}{4} = \frac{25}{100}$	
Sum	100		$\frac{100}{100} = 1$	$\frac{4}{4} = \frac{100}{100} = 1$	

1. How well do your results for tossing two coins agree with "what should have happened"?

2. Are the events two heads, a head and a tail, and two tails equally likely to occur?

3. A gambling house advertises a friendly game of chance. It and a gambler do the following: The house tosses a coin. If the coin comes up heads, the house wins $1 and gets to toss the coin again. If tails, nobody wins, and the gambler gets to toss the coin. If the coin comes up heads, the gambler wins $2. If tails, the gambler loses $1. In either case, the gambler must return the coin to the house. Is the game fair? Explain.

Verifying Probabilities
(Rolling one die)

Name...

A die can land with any of six numbers showing: a 1, 2, 3, 4, 5, or 6. The probability of each outcome is 1/6, because each is equally likely to occur. Thus if we roll a die, say, 100 times, we would expect to get about 16 or 17 of each outcome.

Investigate how well the probabilities for the outcomes of rolling a die agree with what actually happens when you roll a die. Roll a die 100 times and record what happens in the table below. Then complete the table and answer the questions below.

PROBABILITY

Outcome	Tally	Fre-quency	Relative frequency	Proba-bility	Difference between relative frequency and probability
1				$\frac{1}{6}$	
2				$\frac{1}{6}$	
3				$\frac{1}{6}$	
4				$\frac{1}{6}$	
5				$\frac{1}{6}$	
6				$\frac{1}{6}$	
Sum		100	$\frac{100}{100} = 1$	$\frac{6}{6} = 1$	

1. How well do your results for rolling a die agree with "what should have happened"?

2. On the basis of your results, would you be surprised if someone told you that they had rolled a die 100 times and had gotten a one 30 times?

3. What would you think of a die that came up with a six about one out of every three rolls?

MATH GAMES & ACTIVITIES. COPYRIGHT © 1984

Verifying Probabilities
(Rolling two dice)

Name...

Two dice can show any of 11 totals: a 2, 3, 4, 5, 6, 7, 8, 9, 10, 11, or 12. In examining the 36 ways in which these totals can be made, we see at the right that there is one way to make the 2, two ways to make the 3, ..., six ways to make the 7, ..., two ways to make the 11, and one way to make the 12. So the probability of rolling the 2 is 1 / 36, the 3, 2 / 36 = 1 / 18, ..., the 7, 6 / 36 = 1 / 6, ..., the 11, 2 / 36 = 1 / 18, and the 12, 1 / 36, because each of the ways is equally likely to occur. Thus if we roll two dice, say, 100 times, we would expect to get about 3 twos, 6 threes, ..., 17 sevens, ..., 6 elevens, and 3 twelves.

```
            2     3     4     5     6
(1,1)  (1,2)  (1,3)  (1,4)  (1,5)  (1,6)        7
(2,1)  (2,2)  (2,3)  (2,4)  (2,5)  (2,6)        8
(3,1)  (3,2)  (3,3)  (3,4)  (3,5)  (3,6)        9
(4,1)  (4,2)  (4,3)  (4,4)  (4,5)  (4,6)       10
(5,1)  (5,2)  (5,3)  (5,4)  (5,5)  (5,6)       11
(6,1)  (6,2)  (6,3)  (6,4)  (6,5)  (6,6)       12
```

Investigate how well the probabilities for the outcomes of rolling two dice agree with what actually happens when you roll two dice. Roll two dice 100 times and record what happens in the table below. Then complete the table and answer the questions below.

Outcome	Tally	Frequency	Relative frequency	Probability	Difference between relative frequency and probability
2				1 / 36	
3				2 / 36 = 1 / 18	
4				3 / 36 = 1 / 12	
5				4 / 36 = 1 / 9	
6				5 / 36	
7				6 / 36 = 1 / 6	
8				5 / 36	
9				4 / 36 = 1 / 9	
10				3 / 36 = 1 / 12	
11				2 / 36 = 1 / 18	
12				1 / 36	
Sum		100	100 / 100 = 1	36 / 36 = 1	

1. How well do your results for rolling two dice agree with "what should have happened"?

2. The probability of rolling a seven with two dice is six times that of rolling a two or 12. How well do your results for rolling two dice verify that?

3. How many times do you think two dice would have to be rolled to "act like they ought to"?

Verifying Probabilities
(Guessing on a test)

Name........ ....

A multiple-choice question with four choices can be answered in four ways: a, b, c, or d. If each choice is equally likely to be picked, the probability of answering the question correctly is ¼. Thus if we guess on, say, 50 such questions, we would expect to answer 12 or 13 of them correctly.

Investigate how well the probability of guessing the correct answer to a four-choice, multiple-choice question agrees with what actually happens when you guess on a multiple-choice test with four choices per question. Take the 50-question final exam for MA 699 QUASI MATHENOMIAL COMPLEXULUS. Since you do not have the exam, just circle the a's, b's, c's, and d's of your choice on the answer sheet below. Then check your answers using the key at the bottom of this page and record your results in the table. Then complete the table and answer the questions below.

ANSWER SHEET

1. a b c d	11. a b c d	21. a b c d	31. a b c d	41. a b c d
2. a b c d	12. a b c d	22. a b c d	32. a b c d	42. a b c d
3. a b c d	13. a b c d	23. a b c d	33. a b c d	43. a b c d
4. a b c d	14. a b c d	24. a b c d	34. a b c d	44. a b c d
5. a b c d	15. a b c d	25. a b c d	35. a b c d	45. a b c d
6. a b c d	16. a b c d	26. a b c d	36. a b c d	46. a b c d
7. a b c d	17. a b c d	27. a b c d	37. a b c d	47. a b c d
8. a b c d	18. a b c d	28. a b c d	38. a b c d	48. a b c d
9. a b c d	19. a b c d	29. a b c d	39. a b c d	49. a b c d
10. a b c d	20. a b c d	30. a b c d	40. a b c d	50. a b c d

Outcome	Tally	Fre-quency	Relative frequency	Proba-bility	Difference between relative frequency and probability
Correct				$\frac{1}{4}$	
Incorrect				$\frac{3}{4}$	
Sum		50	$\frac{50}{50} = 1$	$\frac{4}{4} = 1$	

1. What was your score on the exam?

2. Did anyone in your class score more than 50%? Less than 10%?

3. Which would you recommend for getting a high score on a multiple-choice test, guessing or studying?

4. Charley Brown uses the following strategy for taking a multiple-choice test:

> "Let's see now. In a multiple-choice test, the answer to the first question is almost always C. Then A to sort of balance the C. Then A again to trick you. Then B and D to break the pattern. They never go too long without a D. Then three B's in a row. They always have three B's in a row someplace. Then C and A . . . . If you're smart, you can pass a multiple-choice test without being smart."

Take the 50-question final exam for MA 699 QUASI MATHEMOMIAL COMPLEXULUS again using Charley Brown's strategy for taking a multiple-choice test and see if you can improve on your score.

Key: caabdbbca dbcccabdda bcaabbcdda ccbadcabcd baddbbddcac

Verifying Probabilities
(Blank)

Name..

Event _____

Outcome	Tally	Fre-quency	Relative frequency	Proba-bility	Difference between relative frequency and probability
	Sum				

PROBABILITY

PROBABILITY

Roter Roter Roter Roter Roter Roter Roter Roter Roter Roter

Roter Roter Roter Roter Roter Roter Roter Roter Roter Roter

Estimating Probabilities
(Dropping thumbtacks)

Name.......................................

Try your luck! A thumbtack can land in two ways: point up or point down. For a pretend $10, guess within five the number of thumbtacks that will land point up if you drop 100 thumbtacks. Write your guess here: _____

Point up

Point down

Check your guess by shaking 10 thumbtacks in a paper cup and dropping them 10 times. Record your results in the table below and answer the questions after the table.

Outcome	Tally	Frequency	Relative frequency
Point up			
Point down			
Sum	100	$\frac{100}{100} = 1$

1. Did you "win" $10?

2. How well do your results for the thumbtack experiment agree with your classmates' results?

3. How many thumbtacks do you think would land point up if you dropped 1000 thumbtacks?

4. If someone told you that they had dropped a thumbtack in a chair, would you take a chance on the thumbtack having landed point down and sit in the chair?

Estimating Probabilities
(Tossing a paper cup)

Name...

Try your luck! A paper cup can land in three ways: large end down, small end down, or side down. For a pretend kiss, guess within two the number of times a paper cup will land large end down if you toss it 50 times. Write your guess here: _____

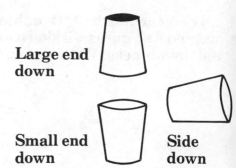

Large end down

Small end down

Side down

Check your guess by tossing a paper cup 50 times. Record your results in the table below and answer the questions after the table.

Outcome	Tally	Frequency	Relative frequency
Large end down			
Small end down			
Side down			
Sum		50	$\frac{50}{50} = 1$

1. Did you "win" a kiss?

2. How well do your results for the paper cup experiment agree with your classmates' results?

3. How many times do you think a paper cup would land large end down if you tossed it 1000 times?

4. How do you think a cork would land if you tossed it once?

MATH GAMES & ACTIVITIES. COPYRIGHT © 1984

Estimating Probabilities
(Breaking a code)

Name. . . . .

Try your luck! There are 26 letters in the English alphabet. For a pretend pretzel, guess which one of them is used most often in the English language. Write your guess here:

_____

Check your guess by selecting a paragraph from a book written in English and counting the number of times each letter of the alphabet occurs in the paragraph. Record your results in the table at the right and answer the questions below.

1. Did you "win" a pretzel?

2. Cryptographers, that is, code breakers, have determined that the five most used letters in the English alphabet are e, a, o, i, and d IN THAT ORDER. How well do your results for the letter-counting experiment agree with their findings?

3. On the basis of your results, how many e's would you expect to find in a short story using 50,000 letters?

Outcome	Tally	Frequency	Relative frequency
a			
b			
c			
d			
e			
f			
g			
h			
i			
j			
k			
l			
m			
n			
o			
p			
q			
r			
s			
t			
u			
v			
w			
x			
y			
z			
Sum			

PROBABILITY

4. The following is a code left by Captain Kidd in "The Gold Bug" by Edgar Allan Poe. It directs the translator to a buried treasure. Break the code by substituting e, the letter used most often in the English language, for 8, the symbol used most often in the code.

5 3 # # $ 3 0 5)) 6 * ; 4 8 2 6) 4 # .) 4 #) ; 8 0 6 *

; 4 8 $ 8 @ 6 0)) 8 5 ; & # (; : # * 8 $ 8 3 (8 8) 5 *

$; 4 6 (; 8 8 * 9 6 * ? ; 8) * # (; 4 8 5) ; 5 * $ 2 :

* # (; 4 9 5 6 * 2 (5 * - 4) 8 @ 8 * ; 4 0 6 9 2 8 5) ;

) 6 $ 8) 4 # # ; & (# 9 ; 4 8 0 8 & ; 8 : 8 # & ; 4 8 $ 8

5 ; 4) 4 8 5 $ 5 2 8 8 8 0 6 * 8 & (# 9 ; 4 8 ; (8 8 ; 4 (

? 3 4 ; 4 8) 4 # ; & 6 & ; : & 8 8 ; # ? ;

Estimating Probabilities
(Laughing at cartoons)

Name...

Try your luck! When shown a cartoon, people can smile or not smile. For a pretend pet frog, guess within one the number of people that will smile at Cartoon 1 if you show it to 10 people. Write your guess here: _____

Check your guess by showing the cartoon to 10 people. Record your results in the table below and answer the questions after the table.

Cartoon 1

Outcome	Tally	Frequency	Relative frequency
Smile			
No smile			
	Sum	10	$\frac{10}{10} = 1$

1. Did you "win" a pet frog?

2. On the basis of your results for the cartoon experiment, how many people out of 100 do you think would smile at Cartoon 1? Cartoon 2?

Cartoon 2

MATH GAMES & ACTIVITIES. COPYRIGHT © 1984

Estimating Probabilities
(Checking parking meters)

Name. . . . .

Try your luck! A parking meter can show either time or a violation. For a pretend avocado, guess within five the number of parking meters that will show a violation if you view 100 parking meters. Write your guess here: _____

Check your guess by viewing 100 parking meters. Record your results in the table below and answer the questions after the table.

Outcome	Tally	Frequency	Relative frequency
Time			
Violation			
Sum		100	$\frac{100}{100} = 1$

1. Did you "win" an avocado?

2. On the basis of your results for the parking meter experiment, how many parking meters out of 1000 do you think would show a violation?

3. If a city spends $30,000 on 1000 parking meters and collects $2 each time they show a violation, how long do you think it will have to wait to get its money back? Justify your answer.

Estimating Probabilities
(Blank)

Name.......................................

Event _____

PROBABILITY

Outcome	Tally	Frequency	Relative frequency
	Sum		

Elementary Statistics
(The mean, median, and mode of test results)

This is a data-collection, data-analysis activity. All your results are to be collected and analyzed on separate pieces of paper. Do NOT write, or allow anyone else to write, on this paper.

To begin, take the following 10-item arithmetic test and check your answers with the key at the bottom of this page. Then give the test to 10 people and determine the mean, median, and mode for their scores. In conclusion, compare your score for the test to the mean, median, and mode for the other scores for the test and describe your reaction to the comparison.

When finished, hand everything in.

1. $\begin{array}{r} 437 \\ +592 \\ \hline \end{array}$

2. $\begin{array}{r} 306 \\ -159 \\ \hline \end{array}$

3. $\frac{2}{3} + \frac{4}{5} = ?$

4. $\frac{1}{2} \div \frac{7}{12} = ?$

5. $43.06 - 1.9 = ?$

6. $\begin{array}{r} 4.25 \\ \times .103 \\ \hline \end{array}$

7. $\frac{4}{5} = ?\%$

8. 35% of $20 = ?$

9. A plane carrying 312 passengers leaves Sydney and lands in Honolulu bound for Los Angeles. In Honolulu, 178 of the passengers get off, and 49 new passengers get on. How many passengers are bound for Los Angeles?

10. If a worker earned $8 an hour for six hours one day and $7 an hour for eight hours another day, how much did the worker earn all total?

1. 1029 2. 147 3. $1\frac{7}{15}$ 4. $\frac{6}{7}$ 5. 41.16 6. .43775 7. 80% 8. 7 9. 183 10. $104

Elementary Statistics
(The mean, median, and mode of the results of a values survey)

This is a data-collection, data-analysis activity. All your results are to be collected and analyzed on separate pieces of paper. Do NOT write, or allow anyone else to write, on this paper.

To begin, take the following 10-item values survey. Then give the survey to 10 people and, using your "score" as the key, determine the mean, median, and mode for their scores. (If you agree or strongly agree with a statement, make "strongly agree" a five, "agree" a four, and so on down to "strongly disagree" a one. If the reverse, make "strongly disagree" a five, "disagree" a four, and so on down to "strongly agree" a one. If undecided, get "decided.") In conclusion, compare your score for the survey to the mean, median, and mode for the other scores for the survey and describe your reaction to the comparison.

When finished, hand everything in.

Directions:

React to each of the following statements by answering "strongly agree," "agree," "undecided," "disagree," or "strongly disagree."

1. Money is like a sixth sense. Without it, you can't enjoy the other five.

2. The better you get to know someone, the less you will tend to like them.

3. Being friendly acts on people just like water acts on porcelain. It wears away at even the slightest resistance. Witness the bathroom sink.

4. If you own something, you should be allowed to do whatever you want with it.

5. Anything a person does is all right so long as it does not hurt another person.

6. One doesn't have to be as polite with friends or family as with strangers.

7. Watching TV is a good substitute for reading a book.

8. Saying "I'm sorry" can often heal a broken relationship.

9. Telling a lie is OK in certain situations.

10. If a person tells you they will do something, they should do it or at least tell you they have changed their mind about doing it.

Count the Dots

Name...............................

How many dots for a triangle made of dots with 100 dots on an edge? Find out by counting dots. D = number of dots. Some of them have already been counted for you.

One dot on an edge

D = ___

Two dots on an edge

D = ___

Three dots on an edge

D = _6_

Four dots on an edge

D = ___

Five dots on an edge

D = ___

Six dots on an edge

D = ___

Seven dots on an edge

D = ___

FUNCTIONS

MATH GAMES & ACTIVITIES. COPYRIGHT © 1984

269

Name.............................

What's the most number of regions for 100 lines on a rectangle? **Find out by counting regions. R = number of regions. Some of them have already been counted for you.**

One line on a rectangle

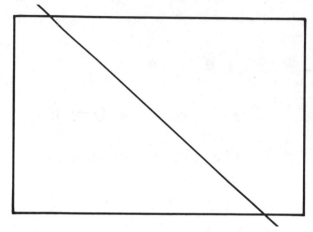

R = ____

Two lines on a rectangle

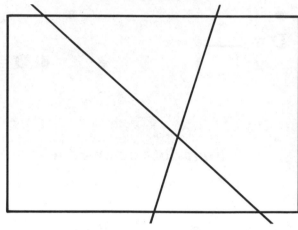

R = ____

Three lines on a rectangle

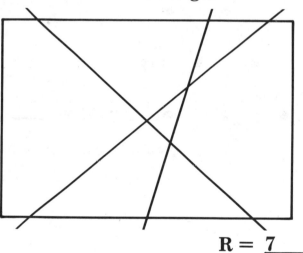

R = _7_

Four lines on a rectangle

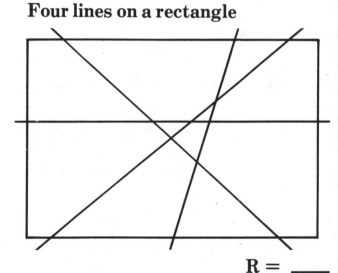

R = ____

Five lines on a rectangle

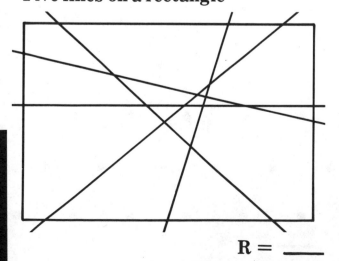

R = ____

Six lines on a rectangle

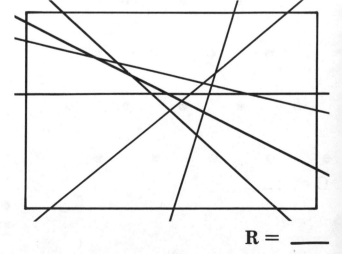

R = ____

Count the Diagonals

Name.........................

How many diagonals for a polygon with 100 sides? Find out by counting diagonals. D = number of diagonals. Some of them have already been counted for you.

Polygon with three sides

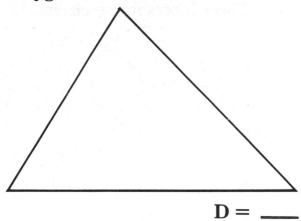

D = ____

Polygon with four sides

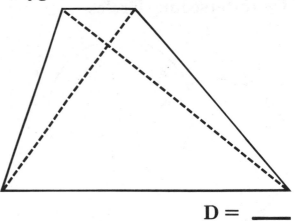

D = ____

Polygon with five sides

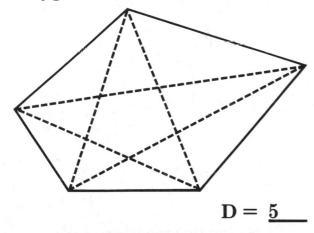

D = _5_

Polygon with six sides

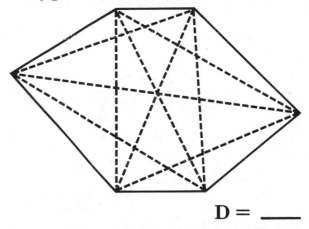

D = ____

Polygon with seven sides

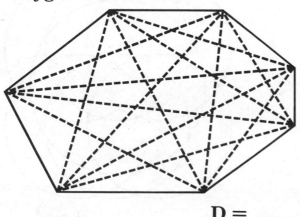

D = ____

Polygon with eight sides

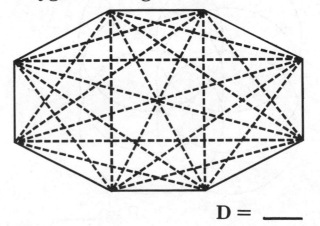

D = ____

FUNCTIONS

Count the Intersection Points

Name. . . . .

What's the maximum number of intersection points for 100 intersecting circles? Find out by counting intersection points. P = number of intersection points. Some of them have already been counted for you.

Two intersecting circles

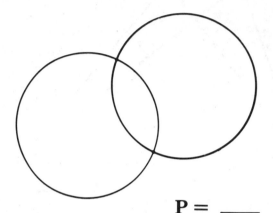

P = ____

Three intersecting circles

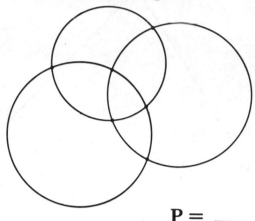

P = ____

Four intersecting circles

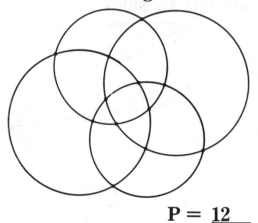

P = __12__

Five intersecting circles

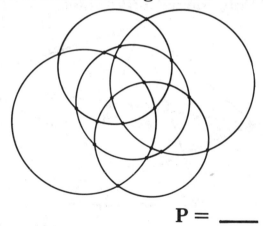

P = ____

Six intersecting circles

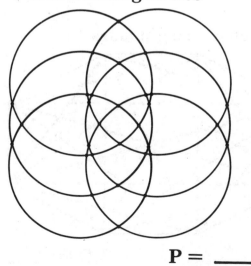

P = ____

Seven intersecting circles

P = ____

FUNCTIONS

Tower Puzzle

Name...

Solve the tower puzzle pictured below. The object is to move the tower of rings a ring at a time from one peg to another without placing a larger ring on a smaller ring.

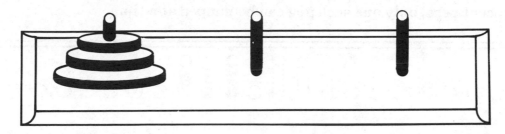

To begin, solve the puzzle for only 1 ring. Then for 2 rings, 3 rings (as pictured), and so on. Each time, strive for the least number of moves possible and record the number of moves in the table below. N = number of rings. Part of the table has already been filled in as a check for your work.

As soon as you can complete the table without having to actually solve the puzzle, do so. Then answer the questions following the table.

N	2^N	Number of moves
1		
2		
3	8	7
4		
5		
6		
7		
8		
9		
10		

1. What would you think if someone said they took 4100 moves to move a 12-ring tower?

2. What's the rule for the least number of moves to move a tower made of N rings?

3. How long would it take to move a 30-ring tower if each move took one second?

FUNCTIONS

Leapfrog

Name.......................................

Solve the leapfrog puzzle pictured below. The object is to reverse the position of the pegs about the center hole by jumping the pegs a peg at a time to adjacent holes or over adjacent pegs to holes adjacent to those pegs. Backward jumps are not permitted. In the case of jumping adjacent pegs, only one such peg can be jumped at a time.

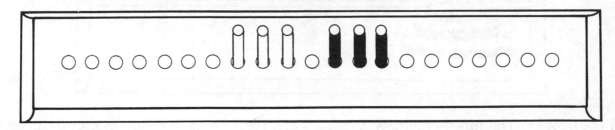

To begin, solve the puzzle for only 1 peg on either side of the center hole. Then for 2 pegs, 3 pegs (as pictured), and so on. Each time, strive for the least number of moves possible and record the number of moves in the table below. N = number of pegs on either side of the center hole. Part of the table has already been filled in as a check for your work.

As soon as you can complete the table without having to actually solve the puzzle, do so. Then answer the questions following the table.

N	N²	Number of moves
1		
2		
3	9	15
4		
5		
6		
7		
8		
9		
10		

1. Can 12 pegs on either side of the center hole be reversed in 170 jumps? Explain.

2. What's the least number of jumps it would take to reverse 15 pegs on either side of the center hole?

3. What's the rule for the least number of jumps to reverse N pegs on either side of the center hole?

MATH GAMES & ACTIVITIES. COPYRIGHT © 1984

FUNCTIONS

APPENDIX

Overview

The appendix, in conjunction with **Motley Crab Adder, The Scruffy Twin Subtractors, Sir Crab Multiplier,** and **The Impeccable Twin Dividers,** is a program for giving meaning to arithmetic word problems. The appendix itself is a collection of lesson plans and action / problem banks for 30 mini lessons: three for each of the 10 ways of categorizing arithmetic word problems given in the appendix. And **Motley Crab Adder** "and mates" taken collectively are a conceptual framework by which students might remember and make sense of the lessons.

In viewing the lessons in the appendix, this cautionary: The objective of the lessons is **not** to teach the 10 ways of categorizing arithmetic word problems given there. Rather, it is to reduce the various ways of categorizing arithmetic word problems to first combining or separating problems, and second, to JUST combining or separating problems or to combining or separating "neatly" (by or into twos, threes, fours, . . .) problems. In this way, arithmetic word problems can be understood with the simple two-step, "What's-happening?-How's-it-happening?" heuristic explained on page 080 in the front matter. The alternative to this approach is to teach all 10 ways of categorizing arithmetic word problems -- a mind boggling confrontation for most learners.

ADDITION
AS
COMBINING

Objectives:

To teach addition as the action of combining. To draw attention to addition as combining in the real world. And to note the combining implicit in arithmetic word problems soluble by addition.

Materials:

Twenty to 25 Unifix cubes (or counters) per student.

Procedure:

Begin with some introductory remarks about the above objectives as to what is to follow. Then proceed with the lessons and activities given below. Tie them together with whatever verbiage you think is appropriate.

COMBINING*

Combining with Unifix Cubes

Lesson:

If I say, "Show me a two," I mean show me this. (See Figure 1.) If I say, "Show me a three," I mean show me this. (See Figure 2.) And if I say, "Show me what **Motley Crab Adder** would do with them," I mean show me this. (See Figure 3.) Furthermore, if I say, "Describe the action," I want you to say, "JUST combining (putting together), or 'adding.'"

Figure 1. A two

*The bringing together of things alike in some way

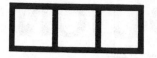

Figure 2. A three

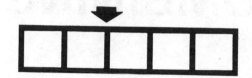

Figure 3. The two being combined
with the three

Activity:

Using a "show me" format, ask students to demonstrate four or five combining exercises like the foregoing with the Unifix cubes and to describe the action for each one.

Combining in the Real World

Lesson:

If I say, "Show me **Motley Crab Adder** raking grass," I mean show me something like this. (Mime raking grass.) Then if I say, "Describe the action," I want you to say, "JUST combining, or 'adding.'"

Activity:

Using a "show me" format, ask students to mime **Motley Crab Adder** for four or five actions from the **Action Bank for Addition/Combining** on pages 294-295 and to describe each action.

Combining in Arithmetic Word Problems

Lesson:

If I say, "Show me what **Motley Crab Adder** would be doing in the following problem," I mean show me something like this. (Mime acquiring a tent, a stove, and a lantern.)

> A family is getting ready to go camping. They buy a tent for $120, a stove for $20, and a lantern for $15. How much did they spend?

Then if I say, "Describe the action," I want you to say, "JUST combining, or 'adding.'"

Activity:

Using a "show me" format, ask students to mime what **Motley Crab Adder** would be doing in four or five problems from the **Problem Bank for Addition/Combining** on pages 303-305 and to describe the action for each one.

278

Note: To consolidate all the foregoing on addition and reinforce the notion of addition as combining, follow with **Addition (Combining) Dominoes.**

SUBTRACTION AS SEPARATING

Objectives:

To teach subtraction as separating from three viewpoints: "taking away," "finding differences," and "counting on." To draw attention to subtraction as separating in the real world. And to note the separating implicit in arithmetic word problems soluble by subtraction.

Materials:

Twenty to 25 Unifix cubes (or counters) per student.

Procedure:

Begin with some introductory remarks about the above objectives as to what is to follow. Then proceed to the lessons and activities given below. Tie them together with whatever verbiage you think is appropriate.

TAKING AWAY*

Taking Away with Unifix Cubes

Lesson:

If I say, "Show me a five," I mean show me this. (See Figure 4.) And if I say, "Show me what **The Scruffy Twin Subtractors** would do with it if they wanted a two," I mean show me this. (See Figure 5.) Furthermore, if I say, "Describe the action," I want you to say, "JUST separating, or 'subtracting.'"

---

*The separating of a whole, either given or implied, into two parts

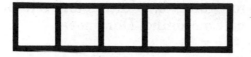

Figure 4. A five

Figure 5. A two being separated
from the five

Activity:

Using a "show me" format, ask students to demonstrate four or five exercises on taking away like the foregoing with the Unifix cubes and to describe the action for each one.

Taking Away in the Real World

Lesson:

If I say, "Show me **The Scruffy Twin Subtractors** trimming the fat off a steak," I mean show me something like this. (Mime trimming the fat off a steak.) Then if I say, "Describe the action," I want you to say, "JUST separating, or 'subtracting.'"

Activity:

Using a "show me" format, ask students to mime **The Scruffy Twin Subtractors** for four or five actions from the **Action Bank for Subtraction/Taking Away** on pages 295-297 and to describe each action.

Taking Away in Arithmetic Word Problems

Lesson:

If I say, "Show me what **The Scruffy Twin Subtractors** would be doing in the following problem," I mean show me something like this. (Mime taking away some of the mercury in a thermometer.)

Pretend it is winter and the temperature outside is 19°C.
Pretend as well that the temperature is supposed to drop 7°C overnight. What will be the temperature in the morning?

Then if I say, "Describe the action," I want you to say, "JUST separating, or 'subtracting.'"

Activity:

Using a "show me" format, ask students to mime what **The Scruffy Twin Subtractors** would be doing in four or five problems from the **Problem Bank for Subtraction / Taking Away** on page 305 and to describe the action for each one.

FINDING DIFFERENCES*

Finding Differences with Unifix Cubes

Lesson:

New rule: If I say, "Show me a five," I mean show me this. (See Figure 4, again.) If I say, "Show me a two," I mean show me this. (See Figure 6.) And if I say, "Show me what **The Scruffy Twin Subtractors** would do with them if they wanted to compare them," I mean show me this. (See Figure 7.) Furthermore, if I say, "Describe the action," I want you to say, "JUST separating, or 'subtracting.'"

Figure 6. A two

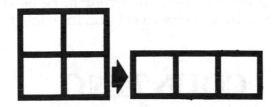

Figure 7   The two next to the five with a three, or "what's left over," being separated from the five

Activity:

Using a "show me" format, ask students to demonstrate four or five exercises on finding differences like the foregoing with the Unifix cubes and to describe the action for each one.

Finding Differences in the Real World

Lesson:

If I say, "Show me **The Scruffy Twin Subtractors** comparing a short stack of pancakes to a tall stack of pancakes," I mean show me something like this. (Mime comparing a short

*The comparing of a given to another given, the latter of which is often just implied.

281

stack of pancakes to a tall stack of pancakes.) Then if I say, "Describe the action," I want you to say, "JUST separating, or 'subtracting.'"

Activity:

Using a "show me" format, ask students to mime **The Scruffy Twin Subtractors** for four or five actions from the **Action Bank for Subtraction / Finding Differences** on page 297 and to describe each action.

Finding Differences in Arithmetic Word Problems

Lesson:

If I say, "Show me what **The Scruffy Twin Subtractors** would be doing in the following problem," I mean show me something like this. (Mime comparing two stacks of coins.)

A newspaper boy paid 75 cents a week per customer for newspapers and collected $1.20 a week from each customer. How much did he earn per week per customer?

Then if I say, "Describe the action," I want you to say, "JUST separating, or 'subtracting.'"

Activity:

Using a "show me" format, ask students to mime what **The Scruffy Twin Subtractors** would be doing in four or five problems from the **Problem Bank for Subtraction / Finding Differences** on pages 306-307 and to describe the action for each one.

COUNTING ON*

Counting On with Unifix Cubes

Lesson:

New rule: If I say, "Show me a two," I mean show me this. (See Figure 6, again.) If I say, "Show me a five," I mean show me this. (See Figure 4, again.) And if I say, "Show me what **The Scruffy Twin Subtractors** would do with them if they wanted to make the two a five," I mean show me this. (See Figure 8.) Furthermore, if I say, "Describe the action," I want you to say, "JUST separating, or 'subtracting.'"

*The building up of a given to equal another given, the latter of which is often just implied

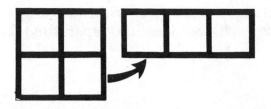

Figure 8.   The two next to the five
with   a   three   being
separated from the five
and moved to the two

Activity:

Using a "Show me" format, ask students to demonstrate four or five counting on exercises like the foregoing with the Unifix cubes and to describe the action for each one.

Counting On in the Real World

Lesson:

If I say, "Show me **The Scruffy Twin Subtractors** making change after a purchase," I mean show me something like this. (Mime tearing off and handing over, say, a 3-dollar "piece" of a 10-dollar bill.) Then if I say, "Describe the action," I want you to say, "JUST separating, or 'subtracting.'"

Activity:

Using a "show me" format, ask students to mime **The Scruffy Twin Subtractors** for four or five actions from the **Action Bank for Subtraction / Counting On** on page 298 and to describe each action.

Counting On in Arithmetic Word Problems

Lesson:

If I say, "Show me what **The Scruffy Twin Subtractors** would be doing in the following problem," I mean show me something like this. (Mime putting 35 dollars onto a stack of 70 dollars to get a stack of 105 dollars.)

> Pretend you want a bicycle which costs $105 and your parents
> said they would give you $70 toward the purchase of it if you
> would earn the money for the rest of it. How much will you have
> to earn?

Then if I say, "Describe the action," I want you to say, "JUST separating, or 'subtracting.'"

Activity:

Using a "show me" format, ask students to mime what **The Scruffy Twin Subtractors** would be doing in four or five problems from the **Problem Bank for Subtraction / Counting On** on pages 307-308 and to describe the action for each one.

283

Note: To consolidate all the foregoing on subtraction and reinforce the notion of subtraction as separating, follow with **Subtraction (Separating) Rummy.**

MULTIPLICATION AS COMBINING NEATLY

Objectives:

To teach multiplication as combining "neatly" (by twos, threes, fours, and so on) from three viewpoints: "repeated addition," "grouping," and "combinations." To draw attention to multiplication as combining neatly in the real world. And to note the combining neatly implicit in arithmetic word problems soluble by multiplication.

Materials:

Twenty to 25 Unifix cubes (or counters) per student.

Procedure:

Begin with some introductory remarks about the above objectives as to what is to follow. Then proceed with the lessons and activities given below. Tie them together with whatever verbiage you think is appropriate.

REPEATED ADDITION*

Repeated Addition with Unifix Cubes

Lesson:

If I say, "Show me a three," I mean show me this. (See Figure 9.) And if I say, "Show me what **Sir Crab Multiplier** might do with four threes," I mean show me this. (See figures 10 through 12.) Furthermore, if I say, "Describe the action," I want you to say, "Combining neatly, or 'multiplying.'"

*The arriving at a whole in exact increments **an increment at a time**

Figure 9. A three

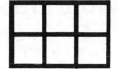

Figure 10. A second three being combined with the three

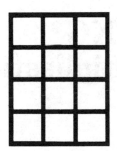

Figure 11. A third three being combined with the three

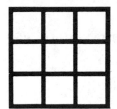

Figure 12. A fourth three being combined with the three

Activity:

Using a "show me" format, ask students to demonstrate four or five exercises on repeated addition like the foregoing with Unifix cubes and to describe the action for each one. Insist that in demonstrating them that they do so in the an-increment-at-a-time way illustrated.

Repeated Addition in the Real World

Lesson:

If I say, "Show me **Sir Crab Multiplier** making a beaded belt," I mean show me something like this. (Mime making a beaded belt a row at a time.) Then if I say, "Describe the action," I want you to say, "Combining neatly, or multiplying.'"

285

Activity:

Using a "show me" format, ask students to mime **Sir Crab Multiplier** for four or five actions from the **Action Bank for Multiplication/Repeated Addition** on pages 298-299 and to describe the action for each one.

Repeated Addition in Arithmetic Word Problems

Lesson:

If I say, "Show me what **Sir Crab Multiplier** would be doing in the following problem," I mean show me something like this. (Mime burying 100 kangaroos every day, day after day.)

How many dead kangaroos every year if 100 of them are shot every day?

Then if I say, "Describe the action," I want you to say, "Combining neatly, or 'multiplying.'"

Activity:

Using a "show me" format, ask students to mime what **Sir Crab Multiplier** would be doing in four or five problems from the **Problem Bank for Multiplication / Repeated Addition** on pages 308-309 and to describe the action for each one.

GROUPING*
(In terms of multiplication)

Grouping with Unifix Cubes

Lesson:

New rule: If I say, "Show me a three," I mean show me this. (See Figure 9, again.) And if I say, "Show me what else **Sir Crab Multiplier** might do with four threes," I mean show me this. (See Figure 12, again.) Furthermore, if I say, "Describe the action," I want you to say "Combining neatly, or 'multiplying.'"

Activity:

Using a "show me" format, ask students to demonstrate four or five grouping exercises like the foregoing with the Unifix cubes and to describe the action for each one. Insist that in demonstrating them that they do so in the simultaneous way illustrated.

Grouping in the Real World

Lesson:

If I say, "Show me **Sir Crab Multiplier** building a log cabin," I mean show me

*The arriving at a whole in exact increments in a simultaneous way

286

something like this. (Mime building a log cabin with just a snap of the fingers.) Then if I say, "Describe the action," I want you to say, "Combining neatly, or 'multiplying.'"

Activity:

Using a "show me" format, ask students to mime **Sir Crab Multiplier** for four or five actions from the **Action Bank for Multiplication / Grouping** on pages 299-300 and to describe each action.

Grouping in Arithmetic Word Problems

Lesson:

If I say, "Show me what **Sir Crab Multiplier** would be doing in the following problem," I mean show me something like this. (Mime counting 12 chairs to a row and then noting that there are six such rows.)

How many chairs in six rows of 12 chairs each?

Then if I say, "Describe the action," I want you to say, "Combining neatly, or 'multiplying.'"

Activity:

Using a "show me" format, ask students to mime what **Sir Crab Multiplier** would be doing in four or five problems from the **Problem Bank for Multiplication / Grouping** on pages 310-311 and to describe the action for each one.

COMBINATIONS*

Combinations with Unifix Cubes

Lesson:

New rule: If I say, "Show me a three," I mean show me this. (See Figure 9, again.) And if I say, "Show me what **Sir Crab Multiplier** would do with four for each one of three," I mean show me this. (See Figure 13.) Furthermore, if I say, "Describe the action," I want you to say, "Combining neatly, or 'multiplying.'"

*The following of an event by another event or sequence of events

Figure 13. Three fours -- a four for each one of three -- being combined

Activity:

Using a "show me" format, ask students to demonstrate four or five exercises on combinations like the foregoing with the Unifix cubes and to describe the action for each one.

Combinations in the Real World

Lesson:

If I say, "Show me **Sir Crab Multiplier** fiddling with putting books on a shelf," I mean show me something like this. (Mime putting books on a shelf and rearranging the books in as many ways as possible.) Then if I say, "Describe the action," I want you to say, "Combining neatly, or 'multiplying.'"

Activity:

Using a "show me" format, ask students to mime **Sir Crab Multiplier** for four or five actions from the **Action Bank for Multiplication / Combinations** on page 300 and to describe each action.

Combinations in Arithmetic Word Problems

Lesson:

If I say, "Show me what **Sir Crab Multiplier** would be doing in the following problem," I mean show me something like this. (Mime going from town A to town B, and for each way, going from town B to town C in four ways.)

> If there are three ways to get from town A to town B and four ways to get from town B to town C, how many ways are there to get from town A to town C?

Then if I say, "Describe the action," I want you to say, "Combining neatly, or 'multiplying.'"

Activity:

Using a "show me" format, ask students to mime what **Sir Crab Multiplier** would be doing in four or five problems from the **Problem Bank for Multiplication / Combinations** on page 312 and to describe the action for each one.

Note: To consolidate all the foregoing on multiplication and reinforce the notion of multiplication as combining neatly, follow with **Multiplication (Combining Neatly) Dominoes.**

DIVISION AS SEPARATING NEATLY

Objectives:

To teach division as separating "neatly" (into twos, threes, fours, and so on) from three viewpoints: "repeated subtraction," "grouping," and "sharing." To draw attention to division as separating neatly in the real world. And to note the separating neatly implicit in arithmetic word problems soluble by division.

Materials:

Twenty to 25 Unifix cubes (or counters) per student.

Procedure:

Begin with some introductory remarks about the above objectives as to what is to follow. Then proceed with the lessons and activities given below. Tie them together with whatever verbiage you think is appropriate.

REPEATED SUBTRACTION*

Repeated Subtraction with Unifix Cubes

Lesson:

If I say, "Show me a nine," I mean show me this. (See Figure 14.) And if I say, "Show

*The exhausting of a whole by exact increments **an increment at a time**

me what **The Impeccable Twin Dividers** might do with it if they wanted twos," I mean show me this. (See Figures 15 through 18.) Furthermore, if I say, "Describe the action," I want you to say, "Separating neatly, or 'dividing.'"

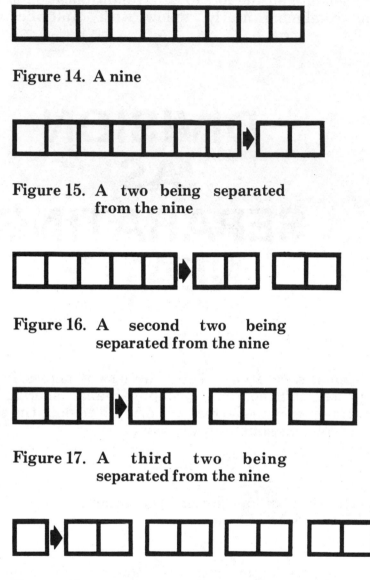

Figure 14. A nine

Figure 15. A two being separated from the nine

Figure 16. A second two being separated from the nine

Figure 17. A third two being separated from the nine

Figure 18. A fourth two being separated from the nine

Activity:

Using a "show me" format, ask students to demonstrate four or five exercises on repeated subtraction like the foregoing with the Unifix cubes and to describe the action for each one. Insist that in demonstrating them that they do so in the an-increment-at-a-time way illustrated.

Repeated Subtraction in the Real World

Lesson:

If I say, "Show me **The Impeccable Twin Dividers** emptying a carton of milk into glasses," I mean show me something like this. (Mime pouring all of a carton of milk into glasses.) Then if I say, "Describe the action," I want you to say, "Separating neatly, or 'dividing.'"

Activity:

Using a "show me" format, ask students to mime **The Impeccable Twin Dividers** for four or five actions from the **Action Bank for Division/Repeated Subtraction** on pages 301-302 and to describe each action.

Repeated Subtraction in Arithmetic Word Problems

Lesson:

If I say, "Show me what **The Impeccable Twin Dividers** would be doing in the following problem," I mean show me something like this. (Mime driving 600 kilometers, then another 600 kilometers, then another 600 kilometers, and so on until all 3000 kilometers have been driven.)

> If your family drives 600 kilometers a day, how many days will it take it to drive 3000 kilometers?

Then if I say, "Describe the action," I want you to say, "Separating neatly, or 'dividing.'"

Activity:

Using a "show me" format, ask students to mime what **The Impeccable Twin Dividers** would be doing in four or five problems from the **Problem Bank for Division / Repeated Subtraction** on pages 312-313 and to describe the action for each one.

GROUPING*
(In terms of division)

Grouping with Unifix Cubes

Lesson:

If I say, "Show me a nine," I mean show me this. (See Figure 14, again.) And if I say, "Show me what else **The Impeccable Twin Dividers** might do with it if they wanted twos," I mean show me this. (See Figure 18, again.) Furthermore, if I say, "Describe the action," I want you to say, "Separating neatly, or 'dividing.'"

Activity:

Using a "show me" format, ask students to demonstrate four or five of the foregoing with the Unifix cubes and to describe the action for each one. Insist that in demonstrating them that they do so in the simultaneous way illustrated.

*The exhausting of a whole by exact increments in a simultaneous way

Grouping in the Real World

Lesson:

If I say, "Show me **The Impeccable Twin Dividers** putting chairs in rows," I mean show me something like this. (Mime a huge stack of chairs suddenly being put in rows.) Then if I say, "Describe the action," I want you to say, "Separating neatly, or 'dividing.'"

Activity:

Using a "show me" format, ask students to mime **The Impeccable Twin Dividers** for four or five actions from the **Action Bank for Division / Grouping** on page 302 and to describe each action.

Grouping in Arithmetic Word Problems

Lesson:

If I say, "Show me what **The Impeccable Twin Dividers** would be doing in the following problem," I mean show me something like this. (Mime thinking with satisfaction of 1000 eggs being separated into groups of 12 with just a snap of the fingers.)

> One thousand eggs. Twelve eggs to a carton. How many cartons of eggs?

Then if I say, "Describe the action," I want you to say, "Separating neatly, or 'dividing.'"

Activity:

Using a "show me" format, ask students to mime what **The Impeccable Twin Dividers** would be doing in four or five problems from the **Problem Bank for Division / Grouping** on pages 313-314 and to describe the action for each one.

SHARING*

Sharing with Unifix Cubes

Lesson:

If I say, "Show me a 12," I mean show me this. (See Figure 19.) And if I say, "Show me what **The Impeccable Twin Dividers** would do with it if they had four friends," I mean show me this. (See Figure 20.) Furthermore, if I say, "Describe the action," I want you to say, "Separating neatly, or 'dividing.'"

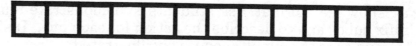

Figure 19. A twelve

*The distributing of a whole equitably

Figure 20. The twelve separated
between four friends

Activity:

Using a "show me" format, ask students to demonstrate four or five of the foregoing with the Unifix cubes and to describe the action for each one.

Sharing in the Real World

Lesson:

If I say, "Show me **The Impeccable Twin Dividers** cutting a pie," I mean show me something like this. (Mime cutting a pie equitably into, say, six pieces.) Then if I say, "Describe the action," I want you to say, "Separating neatly, or 'dividing.'"

Activity:

Using a "show me" format, ask students to mime **The Impeccable Twin Dividers** for four or five actions from the **Action Bank for Division / Sharing** on page 303 and to describe each action.

Sharing in Arithmetic Word Problems

Lesson:

If I say, "Show me what **The Impeccable Twin Dividers** would be doing in the following problem," I mean show me something like this. (Mime distributing 50 meters of fencing equitably between 10 fence rails.)

How far apart are the fence rails in a 10-rail, 50 meter fence?

Then if I say, "Describe the action," I want you to say, "Separating neatly, or 'dividing.'"

Activity:

Using a "show me" format, ask students to mime what **The Impeccable Twin Dividers** would be doing in four or five problems from the **Problem Bank for Division / Sharing** on pages 314-315 and to describe the action for each one.

Note: To consolidate all the foregoing on division and reinforce the notion of division as separating neatly, follow with **Division (Separating Neatly) Rummy**.

ACTION BANK
FOR
ADDITION/COMBINING

1. Raking grass or leaves

2. Collecting rocks, stamps, butterflies, or the like

3. Building something like a house or a model airplane

4. Saving money in a piggy bank

5. Putting toys in a toy box

6. Counting calories

7. Putting clothes in a dryer or a washing machine

8. Gluing something together like a doll or a broken dish

9. Putting letters in a mail box

10. Putting groceries in a shopping basket

11. Making a deposit to a checking or a savings account

12. Building a rock wall

13. Putting food on a plate

14. Putting clothes in a wardrobe

15. Putting dishes in a dishwasher

16. Decorating a Christmas tree

17. Sweeping a floor

18. Putting on make-up

19. Assembling something like a kite or a train set

20. Putting photographs in a picture album

21. Packing a lunch

22. Making a sandwich

23. Putting a puzzle together

24. Packing a suitcase

25. Putting one's hair in a bun

26. Following a recipe

27. Painting a picture

28. Loading up the trunk of a car

29. Building a bonfire

30. Hanging clothes

31. Playing 52-card pick up

32. Writing a letter

33. Making tea or coffee

34. Making a skirt or a blouse

35. Getting dressed

36. Growing a beard

37. Making a bed

38. Pinning pictures to a pin-up board

39. Collecting autographs

40. Making a collage

41. Making a sandcastle

42. Catching fish in a net

43. Mixing paint, cement, bread dough, or the like

44. Making soup, stew, pizza, or the like

ACTION BANK
FOR
SUBTRACTION/TAKING AWAY

1, Trimming fat off a steak

2. Whittling a stick

3. Getting a haircut

4. Sanding a table top

5. Pruning something like a tree or a rose bush

6. Digging a hole

7. Robbing a piggy bank

8. Letting some air out of a tire

9. Mowing the lawn

10. Making shorts from a pair of pants

11. Trimming a hedge

12. Pitting a cherry

13. Taking the ornaments off a Christmas tree

14. Cutting the end off a board

15. Taking a piece of pie or cake

16. Taking a bite out of something like a pear or an apple

17. Splitting a piece of wood

18. Abbreviating a word

19. Sculpting a block of marble

20. Drinking part of a glass of something like water or soda

21. Taking up the hem of a dress

22. Taking in the waist on a pair of pants

23. Spending part of a nickel, dime, or quarter

24. Parting one's hair

25. Peeling a banana, orange, potato, or the like

26. Skinning one's knee

27. Spending part of a dollar

28. Tearing pages from a pad

29. Scaling a fish

30. Shaking salt from a salt shaker

31. Separating the white from the yolk of an egg

32. Sawing a women in half

33. Taking an appendix out

34. Stealing a hubcap

35. Having a tooth pulled

36. Shaving

37. Ripping a page out of a telephone book

38. Splitting an atom

39. Weeding a garden

40. Clipping or filing one's toenails or fingernails

41. Shelling something like a shrimp or a peanut

42. Cashing a check

43. Making a withdrawal from a savings account

44. Slashing prices

ACTION BANK
FOR
SUBTRACTION/FINDING DIFFERENCES

1. Comparing ages, heights, weights, or the like

2. Determining the winner of a race

3. Feeling fat but wishing skinny

4. Feeling out of shape but wishing fit

ACTION BANK
FOR
SUBTRACTION/COUNTING ON

1. Completing a job

2. Filling a near empty gas tank with gas

3. Walking, riding, or flying the balance of a distance

4. Giving change after a purchase

5. Reading the rest of a book

6. Writing the rest of a letter

7. Doing the rest of an assignment

8. Letting out the waist on a pair of pants

9. Letting down a hem

10. Paying the rest of a bill

ACTION BANK
FOR
MULTIPLICATION/REPEATED ADDITION

1. Making a rug or a beaded belt

2. Hoarding rolls of pennies, nickels, dimes, or quarters a roll at a time

3. Counting the legs of, say, ants or chairs an ant or a chair at a time

4. Exchanging nickels, dimes, or quarters for pennies a coin at a time

5. Counting by ones, twos, threes, or so on

6. Pumping up a tire

7. Running upstairs three steps at a time

8. Blowing up a balloon

9. Buying roses by the dozen

10. Laying floor or roof tiles

11. Planting so many seeds to a hill or a row, a hill or a row at a time

12. Bringing in the milk a bottle at a time

13. Buying shoes or earrings a pair at a time

14. Stacking lumber

15. Converting years to days, days to hours, hours to minutes, or minutes to seconds a year, day, hour, or minute at a time

16. Exchanging dollars for pennies, nickels, dimes, or quarters a dollar at a time

17. Collecting animals for Noah's ark

18. Marrying people

19. Buying things that come in sets like tires or flashlight batteries a set at a time

20. Soaking up water with a sponge

21. Converting kilometers to meters, meters to centimeters, or centimeters to millimeters a kilometer, meter, or centimeter at a time

22. Picking four leaf clovers

23. Polishing fingernails a hand at a time

24. Hanging wallpaper

25. Knitting something like a scarf or an afghan

26. Writing "I love math" 50 times

ACTION BANK
FOR
MULTIPLICATION/GROUPING

1. Buying rolls of pennies, nickels, dimes, or quarters

2. Buying things that come in arrays like eggs or stamps one or more arrays worth at a time

3. Exchanging dollars for pennies, nickels, dimes, or quarters

4. Converting kilometers to meters, meters to centimeters, or centimeters to millimeters

5. Building an array type structure like a brick wall or a log cabin with a snap of the fingers

6. Converting years to days, days to hours, hours to minutes, or minutes to seconds

7. Buying things that come grouped like cigarettes or chocolates

8. Counting things that come grouped like cars in a car park or trees in an orchard

9. Freezing water in an ice cube tray

10. Baking things that are arranged in arrays like biscuits or cupcakes

11. Bringing in the milk

12. Buying things that come in pairs

13. Stocking a store with things that come in sets like tires or sparkplugs

ACTION BANK
FOR
MULTIPLICATION/COMBINATIONS

1. Arranging books on a shelf in as many ways as possible

2. Going from town A to town B to town C in as many ways as possible

3. Making as many shirt / pant or blouse / skirt combinations as possible

4. Making as many license plate numbers as possible

5. Making as many telephone numbers as possible

6. Making as many first name / last name combinations as possible

ACTION BANK
FOR
DIVISION/REPEATED SUBTRACTION

1. Emptying the contents of a large container into small containers of equal size

2. Eating an ear of corn

3. Folding socks

4. Putting a pile of pennies, nickels, dimes, or quarters into rolls

5. Tearing down a brick wall a row at a time

6. Moving a pile of dirt with a wheelbarrow

7. Taking six-packs from a case or cases from a truck

8. Counting down by ones, twos, threes, or so on

9. Taking handfuls of pennies, nickels, dimes, or quarters from a piggy bank a handful at a time

10. Taking donuts off a rack by the dozen

11. Gulping water from a canteen

12. Bailing out a boat

13. Taking wood from a woodpile an armload at a time

14. Harvesting, say, corn or wheat by the bushel

15. Unraveling knitting

16. Taking tissues from a tissue box 1, 2, 3, or more tissues at a time

17. Taking handfuls of things from a container like nuts from a bowl or chocolates from a box

18. Eating something like pudding or cereal a spoonful at a time

19. Taking peoples' shoes off

20. Mowing a lawn in strips

21. Cleaning venetian blinds

22. Converting seconds to minutes 60 seconds at a time, minutes to hours 60 minutes at a time, hours to days 24 hours at a time, or days to years 365 days at a time

23. Converting millimeters to centimeters 10 millimeters at a time, centimeters to meters 100 centimeters at a time, or meters to kilometers 1000 meters at a time

24. Exchanging coins of one denomination for coins of a larger denomination so many coins at a time (e.g., five pennies for a nickel five pennies at a time)

25. Taking pairs of things from where they belong like shoes from a closet or earrings from a jewelry box a pair at a time

26. Distributing something in a uniform way like soup with a ladle or ice cream with a scoop

27. Using up a tin of chopped nuts on ice cream cones or a tin of decorator beads on cup cakes

28. Taking pills from a pill bottle in keeping with a prescription

ACTION BANK
FOR
DIVISION/GROUPING

1. A whole bunch of people putting things in order like chairs in rows or popcorn in bags

2. Spending all of an amount of money on a relatively inexpensive item (e.g., five dollars on bags of peanuts)

3. Converting seconds to minutes, minutes to hours, hours to days, or days to years all at once

4. Converting millimeters to centimeters, centimeters to meters, or meters to kilometers all at once

5. Exchanging coins of one denomination for coins of a larger denomination all at once

6. Selling a stock of things that come in arrays like eggs or stamps one or more arrays worth at a time

7. Selling a stock of things that come in pairs like shoes or earrings

8. Picking teams

9. Two or more hairdressers plaiting a head of hair

10. Transporting car, bus, or plane loads of people

ACTION BANK
FOR
DIVISION/SHARING

1. Cutting a pie or a cake

2. Slicing a pizza or a loaf of bread

3. Sharing something with friends

4. Splitting wood

5. Putting away things like dishes or silverware that tend to go in special categories

6. Assigning equitable work loads

7. Carving a roast or a turkey

8. Putting hair in pig tails

9. Dealing out a deck of cards

PROBLEM BANK
FOR
ADDITION/COMBINING

1. A family is getting ready to go camping. They buy a tent for $120, a stove for $20, and a lantern for $15. How much did they spend on camping?

2. A crow raids a camp. It eats a box of cookies that cost 80 cents and a bag of potato chips that cost 45 cents. How much monies worth of nibbles did the crow eat?

3. A boy is figuring his expenses for the week: 30 cents for a chocolate bar, 75 cents for a pet goldfish, 45 cents for three packs of gum, and $1.20 for the movies. How much are his expenses for the week?

4. A booth at a school bazaar took in the following: $4 for an alarm clock, 20 cents for a teddy bear, 35 cents for a box of crayons, and $3 for a picture frame. How much did the booth take in?

5. A person just spent 45 cents in gas to drive to a store to buy a watch that was on sale for $10. How much did the person actually spend on the watch?

6. Pretend you are having dinner with your family at a hamburger place and you order a hamburger for 55 cents, a large order of french fries for 45 cents, and a vanilla malt for 50 cents. How much will you spend on dinner?

7. Pretend your family just bought a puppy, that you are playing with the puppy, and that it tears your new jeans costing $14 and chews a hole in the end of one of your shoes, the pair of which cost $8. How much will it cost to replace your jeans and shoes?

8. Pretend your family is trying to sell its house and that on Monday 23 people came to look at it, on Tuesday, 17, and on Wednesday, 35. How many people altogether came to look at it?

9. A lifeguard is reading a book. Yesterday, the lifeguard read to page 76. Today, the lifeguard read the next 49 pages. On what page will the life guard start reading tomorrow?

10. A lifeguard rescued three people one day, five people another day, and two people a third day. How many people altogether did the lifeguard rescue?

11. A rodeo lasted three days. The number of people attending the first day was 9576, the second day, 4980, and the third day, 14,302. How many people attended the rodeo?

12. Some people in a land cruiser were traveling through the bush and stopping at crossings. At one crossing they counted 257 sheep, at another crossing, 365 sheep, and at a third crossing, 417 sheep. How many sheep did they count altogether?

13. A cookie recipe for 30 dozen cookies calls for the following: 1 kilogram of butter, 5 kilograms of flour, 2 kilograms of white sugar, 4 boxes of raisins, 1 small bottle of vanilla, and 2 dozen eggs. If the butter cost $4.25, the flour, $2.49, the sugar, $4.79, the raisins, $1.20, the vanilla, 79 cents, and the eggs, $2.39, how much will the cookies cost?

14. If Sarno is eight years old, how old will he be in five years?

15. How many dots on a dominoe with three dots on one end and six dots on the other end?

16. What is the total for two dice with a three showing on one and a four showing on the other?

17. A fisherman caught five fish on Saturday and seven fish on Sunday. How many fish altogether did the fisherman catch?

18. Pretend your class is putting on a play. If eight of you act, 12 of you sing, and four of you take tickets, how many of you will be helping with the play?

19. If it were 2:35 PM, what time would it be in 15 minutes?

20. If a husband and wife have two sons and three daughters, how many children do they have?

21. In setting up for an experiment, a mad scientist spent one hour cleaning apparatus, three hours building a stand, and four hours assembling things. How long did the mad scientist work on setting up for the experiment?

22. If 23 people asked you the time yesterday, and 47 people asked you the time today, how many people altogether asked you the time?

23. What is the total value of a nickel and a dime?

24. A checking account with $27 in it, a $400 deposit to the account: How much in the account after the deposit?

25. One large hamburger at 850 calories, one large chocolate malt at 830 calories: How many calories altogether?

26. Pretend you are throwing darts and you throw a 20, a 30, and a 50. What is your score?

27. How high off the floor is a 2-meter man standing on a 1-meter table?

28. If someone was 140 centimeters tall and grew 3 centimeters, how tall would that person be now?

29. If someone weighed 70 kilograms and gained 3 kilograms, how much would that person weigh now?

PROBLEM BANK
FOR
SUBTRACTION/TAKING AWAY

1. Pretend it is winter and the temperature outside is 19°C. Pretend as well that the temperature is supposed to drop 7°C overnight. What will be the temperature in the morning?

2. If you had five nickels and spent three of them, how many of them would you have left?

3. How much change from a $5 bill for a $3.45 purchase?

4. How much money would be left in a checking account with $1350 to begin with after writing a $125 check?

5. If someone weighed 48 kilograms to begin with and lost 2 kilograms dieting, how much would that person weigh now?

6. If 2 meters were cut from a 3-meter board, how much of the board is left?

7. If you had seven balloons, and three of them popped, how many balloons would you have left?

8. If it is 3:30 now, what time was it 15 minutes ago?

9. How much money would be left in a savings account with $35,000 to begin with after an $8000 withdrawal?

PROBLEM BANK
FOR
SUBTRACTION / FINDING DIFFERENCES

1. A newspaper boy paid 75 cents a week per customer for newspapers and collected $1.20 a week from each customer. How much did he earn per week per customer?

2. If the temperature of the water in a swimming pool is 24°C in the summer and 12°C in the winter, how much warmer is the water in the swimming pool in the summer than in the winter?

3. The Sears Tower has 110 floors, the Canadian Imperial Bank 57 floors. How much taller than the Canadian Imperial Bank is the Sears Tower?

4. Two boa constrictors: One is 3 meters long, the other 2 meters long. How much longer is the long one?

5. Some people are trying to raise money with a quiz night. They spend $160 for prizes and make $490 in admissions. How much money did they raise?

6. Suppose that the usual cost for developing a roll of 24 prints is $5.95, but that to draw attention to a new service, a developer is offering to do the job for $3.98. How much a savings is that?

7. The floor of a play room measures 15 square meters. A rug for the floor measures 12 square meters. How much smaller is the rug than the floor?

8. A roller rink with 156 skaters -- 81 of them girls, 75 of them boys: How many more girls than boys?

9. If you can pedal a bicycle downhill at a speed of 19 kilometers per hour and uphill at a speed of 7 kilometers per hour, how much faster can you pedal downhill than uphill?

10. Pretend that two weeks ago your dad weighed 83 kilograms and that now he weighs 78 kilograms. How much weight did he lose?

11. Suppose a rocket weighed 3,868,500 kilograms at blast off and 530,200 kilograms at touch down. How much fuel did the rocket burn from blast off to touch down?

12. If you hopped on one foot 127 times before falling, and a friend of yours hopped on one foot 85 times before falling, how many more times than your friend did you hop on one foot before falling?

13. If Fas is 17 years old, and Slo is 12 years old, how much older is Fas than Slo?

14. If Hy is 210 centimeters tall, and Lough is 160 centimeters tall, how much taller is Hy than Lough?

15. If a gravestone reads "Died 1912," how long ago did someone die?

16. Regular price: $15. Sale price: $10. How much a savings?

17. If you went to a park with 20 slices of bread to feed to the pigeons and returned home with only seven slices of bread, how many slices of bread did you feed to the pigeons?

18. If 49 people like it, and 12 people do not like it, how many more people like it than do not like it?

19. Pretend you are skipping rocks across a river and the first rock you skip skips seven times and the second rock you skip skips three times. How many more times did the first rock skip than the second rock skip?

20. Canaries: $45 at one store, $38 at another store. How much less from one store to the other?

21. If a friend of yours skipped rope 64 times before missing, and you skipped rope 17 times before missing, how many more times than you did your friend skip rope before missing?

PROBLEM BANK
FOR
SUBTRACTION/COUNTING ON

1. Pretend you want a bicycle which costs $105 and your parents said they would give you $70 toward the purchase of it if you would earn the money for the rest of it. How much will you have to earn?

2. The Empire State Building is 102 floors high. If you walked to the twenty-seventh floor, how many floors would you be from the top?

3. The first skyscraper was built in Chicago in 1884. It stood until 1931. How many years did it stand?

4. Pretend you have a broken arm on which you have had a cast for two weeks. Pretend as well that your arm itches like mad, but the cast has to stay on six weeks all total. How many more weeks is that?

5. Suppose you used to have to practice the piano 30 minutes every day, but now you have to practice it 45 minutes every day. How many more minutes a day is that?

6. Pretend you have a puppy which usually costs you 45 cents a day in dog food, but today costs you 95 cents because you bought it a hamburger for its birthday. How much more than usual did you spend on your puppy today?

7. If you just took the tenth picture of a 24-exposure roll of film, how many more pictures would you have to take?

8. The first automobile race in the world was in France in 1894. How many years ago was that?

9. Pretend you just put together 132 pieces of a 500-piece jigsaw puzzle. How many pieces are left to put together?

10. If the sixth round of a 15-round boxing match just ended, how many rounds would be left in the match?

11. How many years from now until the year 2000?

12. If you read the first 25 pages of a 178-page book, how many pages would you still have to read?

13. If you traveled 438 kilometers of a 748-kilometer trip, how far away would you be from your destination?

PROBLEM BANK
FOR
MULTIPLICATION/REPEATED ADDITION

1. How many dead kangaroos every year if 100 of them are shot every day?

2. If the round-trip distance from your home to school were 3 miles, how far would you travel from home to school and back in five days?

3. If El Gordo spent 90 cents on a sundae and ate it and did this five times, how much did he spend on sundaes?

4. If you were training for a marathon and ran 12 kilometers every night, how many kilometers would you run in five nights?

5. If a baseball game were rained out and 12,375 tickets for the game had to be refunded at $4.50 each, how much money would have to be refunded?

6. If the gate keeper at a national park collects $2 from each car that passes through the park, how much money would the gate keeper collect from 12 cars?

7. If a lifeguard earns $4.50 an hour, how much does the lifeguard earn a day (eight hours)?

8. If a Venus's-flytrap eats about 15 flies a day, about how many flies does it eat a year?

9. If a tree grows about 2 feet a year, about how many feet will it grow in five years?

10. If about 25,000 people from overseas visit Australia every week, about how many people from overseas visit it every year (52 weeks)?

11. If Tazzi ran the 100-meter dash five times, how far did Tazzi run altogether?

12. If a worker gets a 25-cent-an-hour raise, how much extra does the worker get a week (40 hours)?

13. If a parrot says "hello" about 25 times a day, about how many times a month (30 days) does it say hello?

14. If you sleep about eight hours a day, about how many hours do you sleep a year (365 days)?

15. If Dozer, a python, sleeps about 20 hours a day, about how many hours does Dozer sleep a week?

16. If Duke, a male Siamese fighting fish, is eager to fight 120 times a day, how many times a week is he eager to fight?

17. If you owned a motorcycle that got 60 miles to the gallon, how far could you drive the motorcycle on 10 gallons of gas?

18. If W. Logged surfs about six hours a day, about how many hours does W. Logged surf a week?

19. If an average sized man under heavy stress consumes about 2000 liters of air per hour, about how many liters of air would such a man under heavy stress consume in three hours?

20. If you and some friends were washing cars and you washed 25 cars for $1.25 each, how much did you earn?

21. How much are three fours? Twenty-seven sixes? One hundred twenty-nine tens?

22. A family of four is camping. They use paper plates for meals three times a day. How many paper plates will they use in four days?

23. If it costs $1.75 a night to rent a pair of skates, how much will it cost to rent a pair of skates for six nights?

24. A person at a rummage sale sold 14 39-cent books. How much money did the person take in?

25. If a logging truck can haul seven logs in one trip, how many logs can it haul in 35 trips?

26. Pretend you are working for $8.95 an hour. How much will you earn in a week (40 hours)?

27. Pretend you own a Saint Bernard that eats 7 kilograms of dog food a day. How many kilograms of dog food will your Saint Bernard eat in a month (30 days)?

28. If a frog can jump 30 centimeters in one jump, how far can it jump in 10 jumps?

29. If once around a block is 500 meters, how far is five times around the block?

30. How far is 10 times around a 2-mile track?

31. If a sister is four times as old as her three-year-old brother, how old is the sister?

PROBLEM BANK
FOR
MULTIPLICATION/GROUPING

1. How many chairs in six rows of 12 chairs each?

2. How many apple trees in 24 rows of 30 trees each?

3. How many tires (including the spare) on 35 automobiles?

4. How many boxes of cereal in 15 cases of 24 boxes each?

5. How many bricks in a wall 75 bricks wide and 12 bricks tall?

6. How much carpeting in a piece of carpet 6 meters wide and 9 meters long?

7. How many pennies in 20 rolls of 50 pennies each?

8. How many nickels in 15 rolls of 40 nickels each?

9. How many shopping baskets in three rows of 17 shopping baskets each?

10. How many paving stones in a sidewalk three stones wide and 1465 stones long?

11. How many strawberry plants in 20 rows of 120 plants each?

12. How many tiles in a floor 16 tiles wide and 25 tiles long?

13. How many shingles in a roof 28 shingles long and 17 shingles wide?

14. How many pictures in nine rolls of 12-exposure film?

15. If a person on the moon can lift six times that which they could lift on earth, how much could a person on the moon lift if they could lift 150 pounds on earth?

16. If a person delivering papers earned $1.50 per customer per month, how much would the person earn a month for 40 customers?

17. How many legs on 40 sheep?

18. How much would three hamburgers cost if they cost 55 cents each?

19. How many batteries would you have to buy for 20 two-battery flashlights?

20. How many windows in a 35-floor building with 20 windows to the floor?

21. If some people in a parade are riding four people to the carriage, how many people are riding in 35 carriages?

22. If some fancy goldfish are on sale for 45 cents each, how much would six of them cost?

23. Pretend you are playing a card game where you get five points for every seven you get. How many points would you get for three sevens?

24. How many dots on a double-six dominoe?

25. What is the total for two dice with a four showing on each one?

26. If some macrame cord comes 50 meters to the roll, how many meters of cord would there be in six rolls of the cord?

27. How many soda bottles in a case if a case contains four rows of six bottles each?

28. How many eggs in a carton if a carton contains two rows of six eggs each?

29. How many sections in a chocolate bar if the bar contains four rows of 15 sections each?

30. About how many words on a page 35 lines long with about 12 words to the line?

31. How many slices of bread in five loaves of 22 slices each?

32. If some nails cost 75 cents a pound, how much would five pounds of the nails cost?

33. A pan of brownies was cut into six rows with four brownies to the row. How many brownies were in the pan?

34. How many shoes would 25 people have on their feet?

35. If a brand of chewing gum costs 20 cents a pack, how much would eight packs of the gum cost?

36. If a male gorilla can lift three times his own weight, how much could a male gorilla weighing 420 kilograms lift?

37. Eight 20-centimeter bricks laid end to end: How long altogether?

38. Ten millimeters in 1 centimeter: How many millimeters in 25 centimeters?

39. One hundred centimeters in 1 meter: How many centimeters in 6 meters?

40. One thousand meters in 1 kilometer: How many meters in 12 kilometers?

41. How many legs on 40 ants?

42. How many legs on 30 chairs?

43. If a box of raisins contains about 50 raisins, about how many raisins would 10 such boxes contain?

44. What is the value of seven dimes?

45. How many pennies in three quarters?

PROBLEM BANK
FOR
MULTIPLICATION/COMBINATIONS

1. If there are three ways to get from town A to town B and four ways to get from town B to town C, how many ways are there to get from town A to town C?

2. How many outfits can you make with five shirts and three pairs of pants?

3. How many ways to put three books on a shelf?

4. Using the digits 0, 1, 2, 3, 4, 5, 6, 7, 8, and 9, how many two-digit numerals?

5. How many different names with Zak, Rug, and Arn for first names and Blgh, Crsh, Rsst, and Jrdn for last names?

PROBLEM BANK
FOR
DIVISION/REPEATED SUBTRACTION

1. How many steps to climb 30 meters if each step is 0.25 meters high?

2. At $1.50 per admission, how many admissions to make $5000?

3. Five dollars for sodas, 25 cents per soda: How many sodas?

4. One commercial every three minutes: How many commercials in one hour (60 minutes) ?

5. Twelve dollars for pizza, $1.50 per pizza: How many pizzas?

6. If one step takes you half a meter, how many steps will take you 500 meters?

7. If your family drives 600 miles a day, how many days will it take it to drive 3000 miles?

8. Twenty-five windows washed a day: How many days to wash 1050 windows?

9. One patient every 20 minutes: How many patients every hour (60 minutes)?

10. Eight hundred meters of macrame cord needed, 20 meters of macrame cord to the roll: How many rolls of macrame cord?

11. If each time you pedal a bicycle you go 2 meters, how many times will you have to pedal it to go a kilometer (1000 meters)?

12. If you drive 80 kilometers per hour, how long will it take you to drive 5000 kilometers?

13. At $2 a sale, how many sales to make $50?

14. Twenty dollars to spend on shirts at $5 a shirt: How many shirts?

15. An average sized man under heavy stress breathes approximately 2000 liters of air per hour. How many hours could such a person under heavy stress breathe in a room containing 14,000 liters of air?

16. Forty kilometer race, 5 kilometers per lap: How many laps?

17. Three thousand kilometer journey, 500 kilometers a day: How many days?

PROBLEM BANK
FOR
DIVISION/GROUPING

1. One hundred fifty coins, 50 coins to a roll: How many rolls of coins?

2. Two hundred coins, 40 coins to a roll: How many rolls of coins?

3. Fifty cents per admission, $140 in admissions: How many admissions?

4. Forty-eight eyes: How many creatures?

5. One hundred cow legs: How many cows?

6. Sixty minutes: How many 15-minute intervals?

7. One dollar in nickels: How many nickels?

8. One thousand eight (1008) eggs, 12 eggs to a carton: How many cartons of eggs?

9. One hundred twenty bottles of soda, 24 bottles to a case: How many cases of soda?

10. Seven hundred centimeters, 100 centimeters to a meter: How many meters?

11. Four thousand meters, 1000 meters to a kilometer: How many kilometers?

12. Fifty millimeters, 10 millimeters to a centimeter: How many centimeters?

13. How many candles weighing 35 grams each could you make with 2 kilograms (2000 grams) of wax?

14. Ten flashlight batteries: How many two-battery flashlights filled with batteries?

15. Fifty popsicles, 10 popsicles to a bundle: How many bundles of popsicles?

16. Thirty-six bottles, six bottles to a carton: How many cartons of bottles?

17. Eight hundred pennies: How many dollars?

18. How many meters (100 centimeters) in 850 centimeters?

PROBLEM BANK
FOR
DIVISION/SHARING

1. How long are the fence rails in a 10-rail, 50-meter fence?

2. How far apart are the rungs in a 7-rung, 4-meter ladder?

3. How far apart are the fence posts in an 11-post, 100-meter fence?

4. Thirty brownies, five people: How many brownies per person?

5. Eighty dollars, four people: How many dollars per person?

6. Six hundred pancakes, 120 children: How many pancakes per child?

7. Ten minutes to shake hands with 210 people: How many people per minute?

8. Seventy-five kilometers on 12 liters of petrol: How many kilometers per liter of petrol?

9. Ten classrooms, 250 children: How many children per classroom?

10. Twelve dollars per hour (60 minutes): How much per minute?

11. Eighteen dollars needed, six people to share the cost: How much per person?

12. Three bags of potato chips for $2.40: How much per bag?

13. Seventy-five dollars a week in groceries for a family of four: How much per person?

14. Three hundred kilograms of sand to carry, five people to carry it: How many kilograms of sand per person?

15. If it costs $6.95 to have a roll of 24-exposure film developed and printed, how much does it cost per exposure?

16. If you paid $12 for a shirt and got to wear it 10 times before it wore out, how much did you pay per wearing?

17. If four persons shared the cost of renting a sailboat for $24, how much did each person have to pay?

18. One thousand dollars, four partners: How much per partner?

19. A large pizza containing 2412 calories, four people to eat the pizza: How many calories per person?

20. Twenty-four apples, six children: How many apples per child?

21. Twelve sandwiches, six people: How many sandwiches per person?

INDEX*

*The page numbers in the index refer to the page numbers of the duplicating designs.

Bibliography

"Activities with DMP Geometric Pieces," Rand McNally & Company.

Arnsdorf, E.E. "A game for reviewing basic facts of arithmetic," **The Arithmetic Teacher**, 19: 589-590, 1972.

Bolster, L.C. "Centimeter and millimeter measurements," **The Mathematics Teacher**, 67: 623-626, 1974.

Brown, C.R. "Math rummy," **The Arithmetic Teacher**, 20: 44-45, 1973.

Dumas, E. and C.W. Schminke. **Math Activities for Child Involvement**, Allyn and Bacon, Inc., 1977.

Frey, S.J. "Creative classroom: Link that chain," **Teacher**, 1979.

Friesen, C.D. "Check your calculator computations," **The Arithmetic Teacher**, 23: 660, 1976.

Hunt, A. "Metric proverbs," **Science Teacher**, 1974.

Jacobs, I. "If the hands can do it the head can follow," **The Arithmetic Teacher**, 19: 571-577, 1972.

Jencks, S.M. and D.M. Peck. "'Thought starters' for the circular geoboard," **The Mathematics Teacher**, 67: 228-233, 1974.

Knaupp, J. and G. Knamiller. **Open Math**, Arizona State University, 1974.

Krause, M.C. "Wind Rose, the beautiful circle," **The Arithmetic Teacher**, 20: 375-379, 1973.

Lee, C. and M. Hoban. **Probability, An Approach to Basic Mathematics**, Harper's College Press, 1975.

Maletsky, E.M. "Designs with tessellations," **The Mathematics Teacher**, 67: 335-338, 1974.

Metric Guide for Educational Materials, American National Metric Council, 1977.

Nelson, R.S. "Variations on rummy," **The Arithmetic Teacher,** 25: 40-41, 1978.

Oakland County Mathematics Project Staff, **Reflections and Rotations,** Midland, Michigan: The McKay Press, 1970.

Taking Chances, Midland, Michigan: The McKay Press, Inc., 1971.

O'Daffer, P.G. and S.R. Clemens. **Laboratory Investigations in Geometry,** Addison-Wesley Publishing Company, Inc., 1976.

Palmer, R. **Springboards: Ideas for Mathematics,** Thomas Nelson Australia Pty. Ltd., 1979.

Schussheim, J.Y. "Calculator talk," **Teacher,** Mar., 1978.

Seehafer, C. "Creative classroom: It's your move -- in metrics!" **Teacher,** Sept., 1978.

Shoecraft, P.J. **Basic Mathematics: A Blueprint for Success,** Addison-Wesley Publishing Company, Inc., 1979.

"Fifteen billion hamburgers is a lot of multiplication and division," **The Arithmetic Teacher,** 22: 612-613, 1975.

Szczepanski, R. "Predictor Polynomials," **The Mathematics Teacher,** 65: 267-271, 1972.